AUTHORITATIVE GUIDE TO
LIONEL'S POSTWAR
OPERATING CARS

Joseph P. Algozzini & Emanuel F. Piazza

Edited by:
Roger Carp & John W. Schmid

PROJECT ROAR™
PUBLISHING

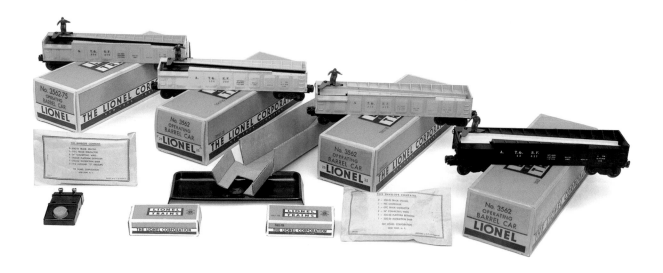

Published by Project Roar Publishing

P.O. Box 599
Winfield, IL 60190
630-653-ROAR (7627)

Visit our website or email us for additional product and ordering information.
www.projectroar.com
orders@projectroar.com

Publisher's Cataloging-In-Publication Data
(Prepared by The Donohue Group, Inc.)

Algozzini, Joe.
    Authoritative guide to Lionel's postwar operating cars / Joseph P. Algozzini and Emanuel F. Piazza ; edited by Roger Carp and John W. Schmid.

    p. : ill. ; cm. -- (Lionel postwar encyclopedia series)
    Includes index.
    ISBN: 1-933600-00-4 (pbk.)
    ISBN: 1-933600-01-2 (hardcover)

1. Lionel Corporation. 2. Railroads--Models--United States--Encyclopedias. 3. Locomotives--Models--United States--Encyclopedias. 4. Locomotives--Models--United States--Collectors and collecting. I. Piazza, Emanuel F. II. Carp, Roger. III. Schmid, John W. IV. Title.

TF197 .A44 2005
625.1/9

Design and Layout: Kristi Ludwig
Image Management: Mardi Callahan
Production Management: Helene Tsigistras

Printed in Canada
Lionel® is the registered trademark of Lionel L.L.C., Chesterfield, Michigan.
Photos (pages 44, 60, 63, 68-70, 72, 74, 79, 87, 91, 98, 106, 130-131, 133-135) used with permission of *Classic Toy Trains* magazine.

TABLE OF CONTENTS

Acknowledgements

As with all of my previous writings, I've received plenty of help from many individuals over the years as I compiled information contained in this volume. **Thank you one and all**!

I would especially like to thank Bob Jacobson, who has been as helpful as any collector I've ever known. His understanding of the trains as manufactured by the original Lionel Corporation is outstanding.

To make this volume even more outstanding, I've had the help of James Sattler, whose understanding and research of the Lionel Corporation, from 1901 through 1969 has no equal.

Very special thank-yous go to Bob Pasztor, Mike Toth, Joe Henley of Valparaiso Pet and Hobby, Joe Astorg and the late Howard Klumpp. I am also grateful to the staff of Lionel Trains Inc., who assisted me when I visited the Lionel archives and photographed many key pieces there. In particular, I want to thank Lenny Dean at Lionel; he always has time to answer my questions.

As always, a special thanks to Sid Brown, Ed Dougherty, Ed Holderle, Barry Keener, Ernie Reising, John Truckenbrod and Joe Zambon, who let me inspect items in their collections whenever I have asked and loaned key pieces to photograph.

Thanks to Bob Ford, for his help in establishing rarity. Similarly, Ed Lugowski made drawings that illustrate the subtle yet important changes that occurred.

Special thanks to Don Corrigan, Craig Chidester, Raymond J. Fetzner, George Lumas, Dan Mega, Tom Pagano, Paul Peters, Adair Roberts, Richie Shanfeld, Bob Swanson and John White for their contributions.

Others contributing in various ways to this project over the past few years include Paul Ambrose, Bruce Balsley, Alan Bondjoukdjian Jr., Frank Cutler, Don Fiore, Ron Hollander, Len Hopkins, Carl and Chuck Hurschik, Ed Kapuscinski, Joseph Lechner, Ed and Eddie Mills, Ed Mullin, Mel Nicholas, John Nowaczyk, Mary Osterman, Frank Piazza, Alan Smith, Alan Stewart, Greg Stout, Todd Wagner, Steve "Coach" Wroblewski, and the late Don Herman.

Also, I want to express my gratitude to five other individuals. First, to Don McClure and the late Ken Hein; back in the early 1970s, they helped me make many of the "Perfect Private Party Purchases" that I used as reference throughout this volume.

To Roger Carp, senior editor at *Classic Toy Trains* magazine, whose knowledge and dedication to the toy train hobby is appreciated. He tirelessly provided guidance and editorial assistance and made this volume exciting and easy to read.

To George and John Schmid of Project Roar Publishing; without them, I would not have been able to complete this volume. They truly are dedicated to preserving the history of Lionel.

Finally, I want to thank my parents, Joseph and Antoinette Algozzini, for their understanding and patience over the years.

Publisher's Dedication

To my wife, Laura and children Collin, Zachary and Alexandria, thank you for all your love and support, especially the last few months of this project…..and to answer your question, "**yes, the book is done!**"

To my mother and father, thank you for all the support and for fostering my love of toy trains. Thanks for making this Lionel "adventure" and Project Roar Publishing a reality.

Introduction

Welcome to Project Roar Publishing's first volume in the Lionel Postwar Encyclopedia Series. This new book covers the many operating cars manufactured by the original Lionel Corporation between 1945 and 1969.

Never before has so much information about these exciting and memorable cars been supported by a high degree of independent research as well as actual Lionel documentation related to the production of these items. This enormous task is possible because the main author, Joseph P. Algozzini, has collected operating cars in such a way that, together with his extensive knowledge of the Lionel Archives, other printed Lionel documentation, and help from a select group of dedicated collectors, his research has become an easier task.

His method of collecting and observing includes:

1. Sole purchaser and owner of mint operating cars offered for sale by hobby shops and other retailers between 1965 and 1975. These perfect examples shed light on how Lionel originally sold and packaged the items and provide an unmarred item for inspection and dating.

2. Perfect Private Party Purchases of original Lionel equipment obtained from either its original owners or hobby shops or dealers who acquired original equipment from their original owners. The main author is, therefore, sure that this equipment has not been modified or "swapped out."

3. Operating cars as offered for sale at auctions, flea markets, and other venues that help achieve a chronological order of production.

4. Observations of hundreds of toy train collections and the inspection of their operating cars.

5. Access to and inspection of the operating cars contained in the Lionel Archives. These observations provide exact dating of features and variations straight from Lionel.

6. Access to Lionel factory and internal documentation providing the authoritative records direct from the manufacturer.

7. Collaboration with well-known Lionel collector and author Manny Piazza, along with publishers and collectors George and John Schmid. Together, they provided the missing information necessary to finalize this breakthrough volume.

This first volume includes a complete chronology of Lionel's postwar operating cars and information on production, rarity, and pricing. It is the first reference guide to include complete information on every item, including its original box, insert/liner, packed envelope, instruction sheet, and any other peripherals that came with it. This comprehensive level of research has never been presented in such detail and clarity.

By "original" we mean items manufactured, assembled, and packaged by Lionel between 1945 and 1969 through company distribution methods.

Sources of Authoritative Information

Project Roar Publishing is dedicated to preserving the history of hobby collectables. Our publications stem from "fact based research" of actual production documents combined with expert observations. True to this mission, the foundation of this publication is internal Lionel documentation as well as years of expert observations from leading postwar historians. Thousands of actual postwar Lionel documents were reviewed and numerous interviews with former Lionel employees were conducted.

This research provides the authoritative word straight from postwar Lionel. The authors have weaved this information seamlessly into the text and also provide "green" pop-up boxes containing specific interesting facts. These pop-ups make reference to numerous documents, each of which is summarized here.

Lionel Blueprints

Each part manufactured by Lionel included a blueprint drawing. Changes to the blueprints were recorded along with a dated description. For this volume, blueprints provide complete manufacturing information of every part, the changes made, as well as when the change occurred.

Components Parts Index

Component Parts Indexes are paired with blueprints to provide the complete list of parts and subassemblies used to manufacturer a complete item or finished good. They also provide the master index of each fully assembled item's individual blueprints. For this volume, Component Parts Indexes provide a complete list of every part and subassembly, the materials used and dates of any changes.

Production Control Files

Every Lionel finished good included a "packet" of documents, which when taken as a whole was the bill of materials for the fully assembled (boxed or unboxed) finished good. These files list every part, subassembly and processes required to make the finished

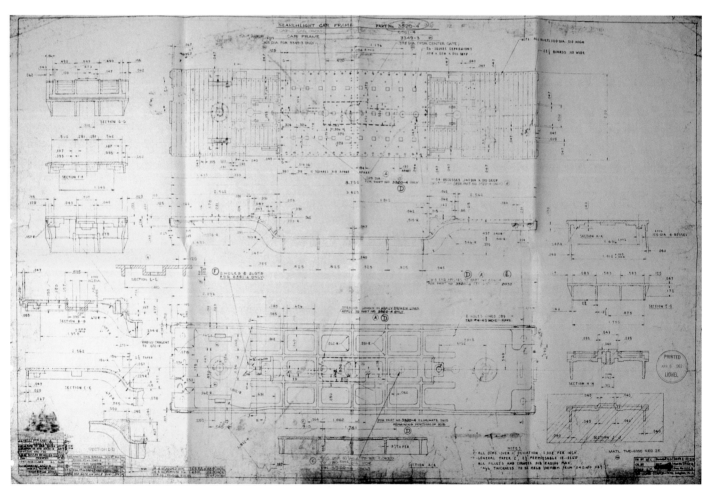

The 3520-4 blueprint details when changes were made to the frame as well as all the dimensions and materials used. Of interest, the other parts that shared this blueprint were the 6561-4 and 3349-3.

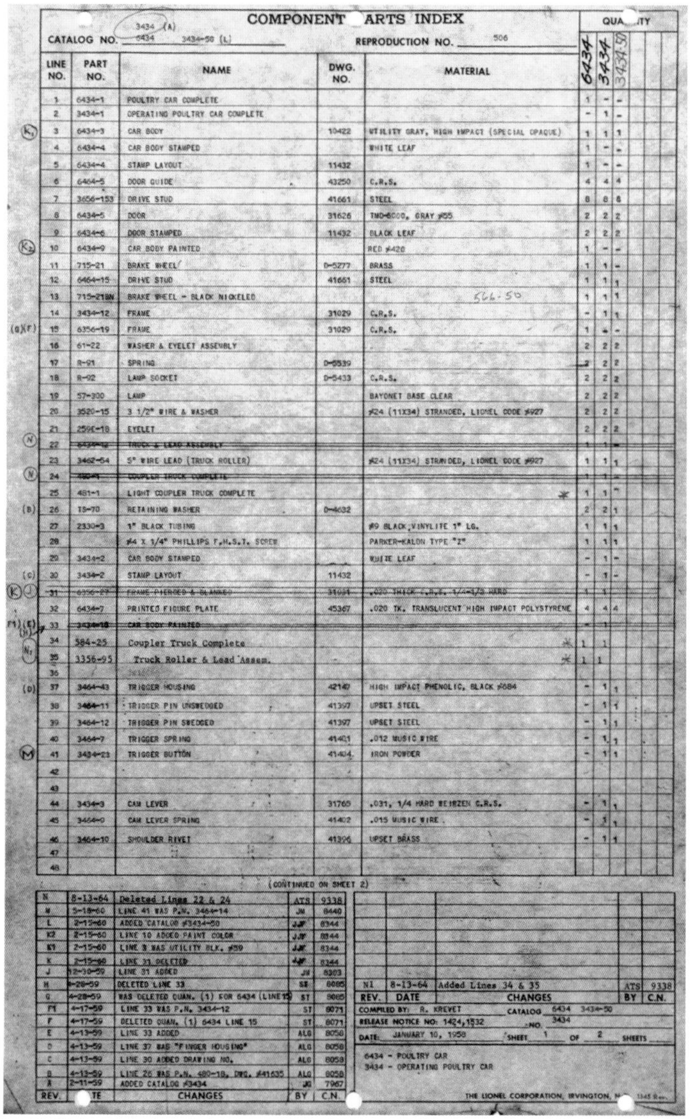

Component Parts Index (top left document)

COMPONENT PARTS INDEX
CATALOG NO. 3434 (A) 6434 3434-50 (L) REPRODUCTION NO. 506

LINE NO.	PART NO.	NAME	DWG. NO.	MATERIAL	6434	3434	3434-50
1	6434-1	POULTRY CAR COMPLETE			1	-	-
2	3434-1	OPERATING POULTRY CAR COMPLETE			-	1	1
3	6434-3	CAR BODY	10422	UTILITY GRAY, HIGH IMPACT (SPECIAL OPAQUE)	1	1	1
4	6434-4	CAR BODY STAMPED		WHITE LEAF	1	-	-
5	6434-4	STAMP LAYOUT	11432		1	-	-
6	6464-5	DOOR GUIDE	43250	C.R.S.	4	4	4
7	3056-153	DRIVE STUD	41661	STEEL	8	8	8
8	6434-5	DOOR	31626	TWO-6000, GRAY #55	2	2	2
9	6434-6	DOOR STAMPED	11432	BLACK LEAF	2	2	2
10	6434-9	CAR BODY PAINTED		RED #420	1	-	-
11	715-21	BRAKE WHEEL	0-5277	BRASS	1	1	1
12	6464-15	DRIVE STUD	41661	STEEL	1	1	1
13	715-21BN	BRAKE WHEEL - BLACK NICKELED			1	1	1
14	3434-12	FRAME	31029	C.R.S.	-	1	1
15	6356-19	FRAME	31029	C.R.S.	1	1	1
16	61-22	WASHER & EYELET ASSEMBLY			2	2	2
17	R-21	SPRING	0-5539		2	2	2
18	R-02	LAMP SOCKET	0-5433	C.R.S.	2	2	2
19	57-200	LAMP		BAYONET BASE CLEAR	2	2	2
20	3520-15	3 1/2" WIRE & WASHER		#24 (11X34) STRANDED, LIONEL CODE #027	2	2	2
21	250K-19	EYELET			2	2	2
23	3456-54	5" WIRE LEAD (TRUCK ROLLER)		#24 (11X34) STRANDED, LIONEL CODE #027	1	1	1
25	451-1	LIGHT COUPLER TRUCK COMPLETE			1	1	
26	19-70	RETAINING WASHER	0-4632		2	2	1
27	2330-3	1" BLACK TUBING		#9 BLACK VINYLITE 1" LG.	1	1	1
28		#4 X 1/4" PHILLIPS P.H.S.T. SCREW		PARKER-KALON TYPE "Z"	1	1	1
29	3434-2	CAR BODY STAMPED		WHITE LEAF	-	1	1
30	3434-2	STAMP LAYOUT	11432		-	1	
31	6356-37	FRAME - PIERCED & BLANKED	31029	.020 THICK C.R.S. 1/4-3/2 HARD	1	1	1
32	6434-7	PRINTED FIGURE PLATE	45367	.020 TK. TRANSLUCENT HIGH IMPACT POLYSTYRENE	4	4	4
34	584-25	Coupler Truck Complete			1	1	
35	3356-95	Truck Roller & Lead Assem.			1	1	
38	3464-43	TRIGGER HOUSING	42147	HIGH IMPACT PHENOLIC, BLACK #684	-	1	1
39	3464-11	TRIGGER PIN UNSWEDGED	41397	UPSET STEEL	-	1	1
40	3464-12	TRIGGER PIN SWEDGED	41397	UPSET STEEL	-	1	1
41	3464-1	TRIGGER SPRING	41401	.012 MUSIC WIRE	-	1	1
42	3464-C2	TRIGGER BUTTON	41404	IRON POWDER	-	1	1
44	3464-3	CAM LEVER	31765	.031, 1/4 HARD HEIZEN C.R.S.	-	1	1
45	3464-0	CAM LEVER SPRING	41402	.015 MUSIC WIRE	-	1	1
46	3464-10	SPINDLER RIVET	41396	UPSET BRASS	-	1	1

(CONTINUED ON SHEET 2)

THE LIONEL CORPORATION, IRVINGTON, N.J.

The Component Parts Index for a 3434 was shared with the 6434 and 3434-50. It lists all the parts and subassemblies for each of these cars as well as the materials used. Note the "DWG NO" column provides an index for all the blueprints.

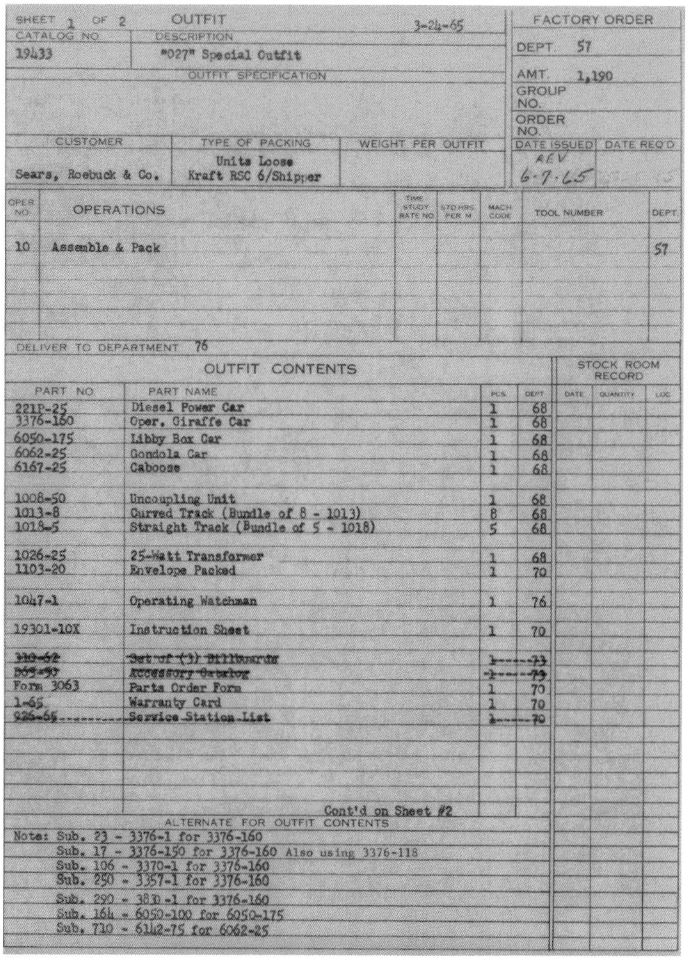

Factory Order (top right document)

SHEET 1 OF 2 OUTFIT 3-24-65 FACTORY ORDER
CATALOG NO. 19433 DESCRIPTION "027" Special Outfit DEPT. 57
AMT. 1,190
CUSTOMER: Sears, Roebuck & Co. TYPE OF PACKING: Units Loose, Kraft RSC 6/Shipper
REV 6-7-65

OPER. NO.	OPERATIONS	DEPT.
10	Assemble & Pack	57

DELIVER TO DEPARTMENT 76

OUTFIT CONTENTS

PART NO.	PART NAME	PCS	DEPT	STOCK ROOM RECORD
221P-25	Diesel Power Car	1	68	
3376-160	Oper. Giraffe Car	1	68	
6050-175	Libby Box Car	1	68	
6062-25	Gondola Car	1	68	
6167-25	Caboose	1	68	
1008-50	Uncoupling Unit	1	68	
1013-8	Curved Track (Bundle of 8 - 1013)	8	68	
1018-5	Straight Track (Bundle of 5 - 1018)	5	68	
1026-25	25-Watt Transformer	1	68	
1103-20	Envelope Packed	1	70	
1047-1	Operating Watchman	1	76	
19301-10X	Instruction Sheet	1	70	
310-62	Set of (3) Billboards	1	73	
955-97	Accessory Order	1	73	
Form 3063	Parts Order Form	1	70	
1-65	Warranty Card	1	70	
926-65	Service Station List	1	70	

Cont'd on Sheet #2

ALTERNATE FOR OUTFIT CONTENTS

Note: Sub. 23 - 3376-1 for 3376-160
Sub. 17 - 3376-150 for 3376-160 Also using 3376-118
Sub. 106 - 3370-1 for 3376-160
Sub. 250 - 3357-1 for 3376-160
Sub. 290 - 3830-1 for 3376-160
Sub. 164 - 6050-100 for 6050-175
Sub. 710 - 6112-75 for 6062-25

The Factory Order for Sears set 19433 details the set bill of materials, the quantity of sets, the packing (not shown) and the substitutions. This set was used to deplete the inventory of many operating cars.

---

good. Also included was the boxing and packing information. Per former Lionel employees, these were known as "Operating Packets." Lionel's production control department created and managed these documents. For this volume, Production Control Files provide a complete list of materials used to manufacture items, changes to the manufacturing processes, a list of the molds and tools used, as well as a complete list of every peripheral a component boxed item included.

Factory Orders

When an item was ready to be manufactured, Lionel would issue a "Factory Order" by making a copy of its Production Control File (Operating Packet) and releasing it to the manufacturing floor. This order provided the quantity needed and date required. For this volume, Factory Orders provide a complete list of every item included in the set, as well as the original item quantities and item substitutions.

The Part Card for the 3459-4 frame outlines the material and operations required to manufacturer. Note the handwritten changes over time.

The Engineering Specifications for the 3357-1 Cop & Hobo Car provides a summary of the car, its operation, packaging information and any other special requirements.

A Change Affecting Future Production for the 6812 details how each car was to be manufactured. Note the instructions to deplete the inventory of yellow parts (platforms and bases).

Lionel Engineering Specifications

Every item included a textual description created early in the items development process. An Engineering Specification document lists the item and its features. For this volume, these provide an overview of Lionel's intended production.

Lionel Changes Affecting Future Production

Lionel would attach memos to the Production Control Files indicating changes that would affect a future production run. Most often, these changes were due to inventory issues that required a substitution of a part or subassembly. For this volume Changes Affecting Future Production documents help identify and date many variations.

Production Planning Records

A Production Planning Record, which is part of a Production Control File, provides orders and shipments from third party vendors. For this volume, Production Planning Records are used to identify quantities of parts ordered, especially instruction sheets.

Lionel Part Card

Lionel Part Cards are the individual pages from early postwar Production Control Files. Each page summarizes a part or subassembly as well as its manufacturing process. For this volume, Part Cards are used to identify materials, processes, tooling and changes to each part and subassembly.

Other Documents Not Mentioned in Pop-ups

Many other documents were used, but not specifically mentioned in a "green" pop-up. Some examples include 1957, 1958, 1961, and 1965 Lionel production records as well as thousands of other memoranda, reports, drawings, artwork, production records, orders and correspondence. Taken as a whole, these documents provide a comprehensive description of every operating car included in this volume. The authors and Project Roar Publishing bring all this information together in this concise "authoritative" volume.

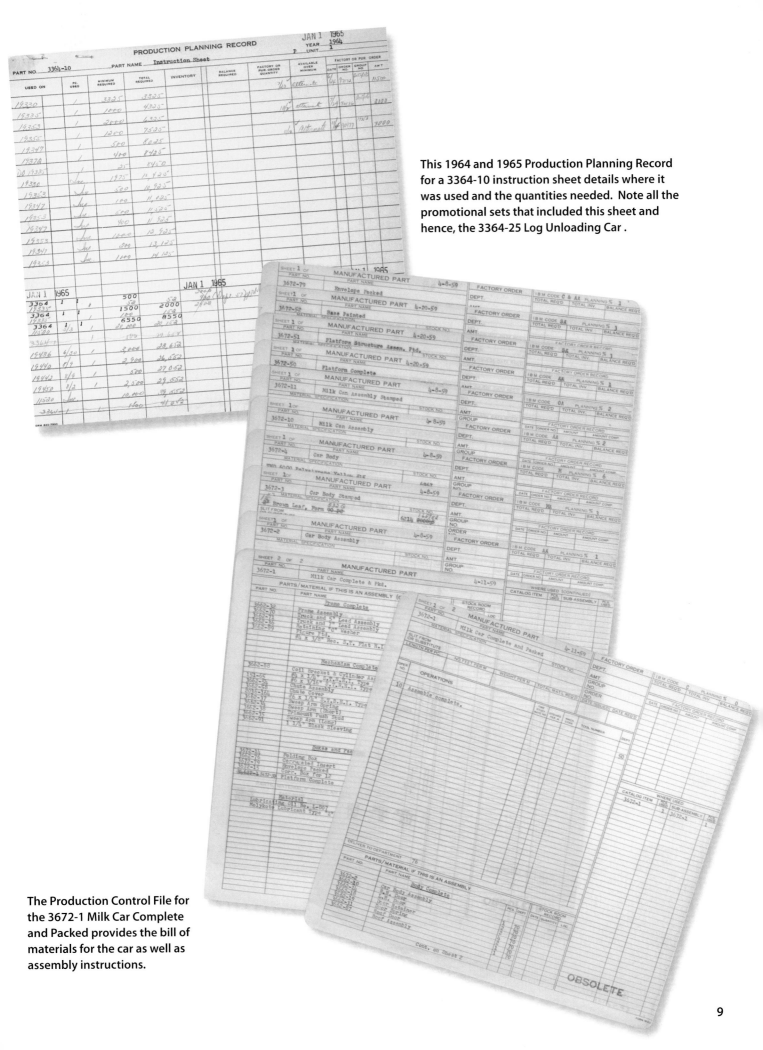

This 1964 and 1965 Production Planning Record for a 3364-10 instruction sheet details where it was used and the quantities needed. Note all the promotional sets that included this sheet and hence, the 3364-25 Log Unloading Car .

The Production Control File for the 3672-1 Milk Car Complete and Packed provides the bill of materials for the car as well as assembly instructions.

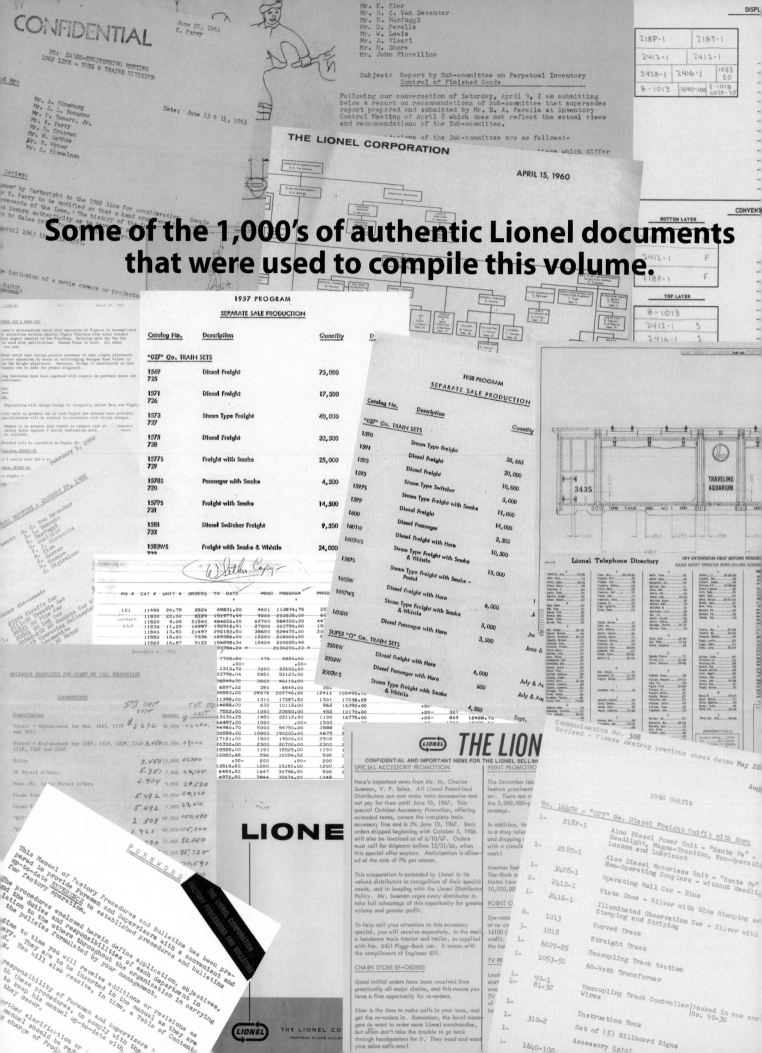

Some of the 1,000's of authentic Lionel documents that were used to compile this volume.

Definitions

The terms and definitions used in this volume come from Lionel documentation. As such, their meaning and usage may differ slightly from what is customary in the toy train hobby.

What is an Operating Car?

Deciding which cars to include in this volume was a challenge. For example, the operating log and dump cars, together with the horse and cattle cars and their corrals were easy choices. So, too, were the operating box cars, barrel cars, and searchlight cars. They all provide action, animation, and operation by way of a special track section, a roller pickup or movement of the car.

Other models did not easily conform to a common understanding of an operating car. The 6822 Night Crew Searchlight Car does not revolve or operate like its earlier cousins. However, we felt it needed to be covered to complete the chronology. Also, the 6434 Poultry Car isn't really an operating car. However, its production directly affected the 3356 Horse Car. So we decided that it should be included to properly address those modifications.

Operating cars usually came with instruction sheets that explained the operation of a car. So if a car came with an instruction sheet, it was likely classified as an operating car and is included in this volume.

Space and Military operating cars fall into the Space and Military category, which will be covered in depth in a future volume as part of Project Roar Publishing's Lionel Postwar Encyclopedia Series.

Yearly Transition

Every year at Lionel should be considered a transition year. Transition means that Lionel often had leftover merchandise or parts from the previous year. This often flowed directly into the following year's production.

For example, Lionel manufactured the 6812 Track Maintenance cars in 1959 with bases and platforms in various combinations of yellow plastic. In 1960, the base came in black and the platform in gray or vice versa. Transition means that yellow versions can show up in 1960, but black and gray ones cannot show up in 1959. Information of this nature is derived from the *Lionel Service Manual*, internal Lionel documentation, consumer catalogs, advertisements, and inspection of many 6812s included in unmarred outfits, including pieces in the company's archives.

Another point to be addressed is the notion of what was the "Highest Probability" in regard to how an item was produced or packaged. What, in other words, was Lionel's "Intended Production?"

For example, Lionel introduced the 3494-550 Monon and 3494-625 Soo Line operating box cars in 1957 and carried over the 3494-275 State of Maine operating box car from 1956. Each car included a vinylite figure with painted face and hands. But which figure?

Lionel had available figures of two different sizes. Photos in other reference guides often show one box car with the small figure and another with the large one. However, since all three operating box cars were produced in 1957, wouldn't Lionel have used the same size figure?

Instead of relying on previously published secondary information to "figure" a way out of this dilemma, the authors conducted their own research. First, Perfect Private Party Purchases always included the small figure with painted face and hands. Second and more importantly, the *Production Samples* of *all* three boxcars in the *Lionel Archives* also included the same small figure. From this new and extensive research, we believe that the *Intended Production* for those three operating box cars included the small figure with painted face and hands.

Of course, some readers may argue that anything was possible at Lionel (a point on which we would agree). However, if you have the chance to buy a Monon or a Soo Line model without a rubberized figure, would you choose to install the small figure (for the reasons outlined above) or the large figure (purchased, perhaps, from an uninformed seller)?

Throughout this volume, we have been very careful when using the words "Early" or "Late" in regard to Lionel's production. Did Lionel use a "First-In, First Out," or "Last-In, First-Out" method of packaging? It likely varied for different items. So, unless we have reason to believe a particular variation came first, or the probability existed that it came first, then the *emphasis* in this volume is they were both made during the same year.

In short, we have devoted much time and conducted exhaustive research to make sure that what is presented is correct and accountable.

Item Peripherals

This volume uses the term "peripherals" to encompass all the ancillary items that came with an operating car. These include the original item box, inserts, liners, packed envelope, instruction sheet, figures and anything else that would have come as part of the item when originally purchased. These peripherals are described in each item listing.

Use of Suffixes

A suffix is the indicator that Lionel added after an individual item's base number. Preceded by a dash, a suffix might consist of a number, a letter, or a combination of the two. Lionel used suffixes on operating cars and other items to distinguish differences in road name, color, decoration, trucks and couplers, loads, wheel configurations, traction aids (a rubber tire or weight). Suffixes also denoted the inclusion or exclusion of items in a box, along with an altogether different item.

This volume provides complete suffix information and sheds light on many previously unknown suffixes. Lionel generally denoted complete items in their box with all peripherals with "-1"; the item alone was designated by "-25". This distinction between boxed and unboxed items became commonplace around 1955 with the advent of unboxed items placed in outfits. If "-1" or "-25" was already assigned to an item, other suffixes were used. Thus, the 3376 Operating Giraffe Car actually came four different ways:

Part Number	Description
3376-1	Boxed Blue Operating Giraffe Car
3376-25	Unboxed Blue Operating Giraffe Car
3376-150	Unboxed Green Operating Giraffe Car
3376-160	Boxed Green Operating Giraffe Car

Outfit versus Set

During the postwar era, Lionel interchangeably used the words "outfit" and "set" to describe the contents packaged together and offered for sale. Most often, "set" was used in catalog descriptions and "outfit" appeared in internal documentation. Throughout this volume, we will use outfit and set interchangeably, and our explanation should eliminate any reader confusion.

How to Use This Volume

As both collectors and authors, we are often approached by postwar Lionel enthusiasts who are confused by previously published information. They wonder why information in one source differs from or even contradicts what is found in another source.

Confusion may result when different terms are used to describe the same item. For example, a model may be called "Tuscan", "maroon", or "red", depending on the source.

Or one guide refers to the 3444 as the "Cop And Hobo Car", whereas another uses that name for the 3357. Meanwhile, a third source calls the 3357 the "Hydraulic Platform Maintenance Car." Again, which is the correct Lionel terminology?

A Semblance of Order

What postwar Lionel enthusiasts (collectors and operators) need is material that provides a "semblance of order" regarding the many facts and other information contained within that publication.

Project Roar Publishing will offer that material and the necessary semblance of order. The information presented in this first volume will correct and update material in all other guides printed to date. In other words, it will provide the reader with the most authoritative look ever published on this subject.

Each of the operating cars manufactured by Lionel between 1945 and 1969 has its own entry. The cars have been placed in one of the following eight chapters based on the type of car and its operation: box cars, gondolas, lumber cars, dump cars, lights + cameras = action, rolling stock with accessories, novelty and cranks, and prototypes, mock-ups and factory errors.

Within the chapters you'll find individual entries. Each contains a comprehensive description of the operating car, with a complete chronology as well as interesting facts and anecdotes.

Throughout this volume, we use the item name and description that the original Lionel Corporation assigned it and then had printed or stamped on the outside of its original box. As an example, recall the 3357. The box is labeled "3357 Cop and Hobo Car." When such information is not available, we will follow an item's listing in a Lionel catalog or internal documentation.

In many cases, the items will be referred to by either its base number without a suffix (for example 3357) or its Lionel assigned name ("Cop and Hobo Car"). When we make specific references to a boxed or unboxed version of a car, we use the appropriate Lionel assigned suffix. In the case of the 3357, that is "-1" for boxed or "-25" for unboxed.

Color Variances

The description used for the colors of paints and plastics is subjective, mainly because those colors can change over time - both naturally and artificially. Therefore, the colors presented in this volume are those colors that Lionel originally assigned to its products. However, if a color wasn't assigned, then we used the colors accepted by well-known postwar Lionel hobbyists, who eagerly shared their opinions. We also received help from a commercial artist.

Boxes

A listing for each operating car box is covered in each entry as well as in Appendix B. Important box information dealing with chronology is included in the text and the author's comments. Also included is information about the cardboard inserts (help stabilize the item in the box) and liners (fully wrap and protect item) that secured those cars within their boxes.

Envelopes and Packets

This volume includes a chronology of the packed envelopes that were included with certain cars. This is important because until this volume, it was extremely difficult to understand which envelope went with which version of certain operating cars. As such, many cars today have an envelope that was incorrectly matched to the car. A complete listing of these envelopes is also included in Appendix D.

Instruction Sheets

Instruction sheets were included with many of the operating cars. Some were placed within the packed envelope; some were packaged inside the car's box; and still others were placed loose inside the set box. Each listing explains these details as does Appendix D.

Trucks and Couplers

Trucks and couplers play an important role in helping to date items. A yearly summary of each truck and coupler variation is included in Appendix C as well as in each item listing.

Other Peripherals

Many times other items were placed in an item's component box. These items included barrels, boxes, milk cans, and figures. Peripherals are described in an item's listing and referred to when differentiating variations and versions by year.

Pop-ups

Information straight from internal Lionel documentation is highlighted in "green" pop-up boxes just as the text shown here. A description on what these pop-ups include is covered in the Sources of Authoritative Information section.

Pricing Condition and Rarity

Every entry includes a table summarizing the operating cars price and rarity. See the section on Pricing, Condition, Rarity and Demand.

Author's Comments

Every entry concludes with interesting anecdotes based on the authors' experiences of collecting and researching Lionel operating cars. Insights into why Lionel did what it did, thus resulting in collectible variations is provided, along with opinions on which cars are the rarest. Production insights are based on the author's access to internal Lionel production figures, documentation, and Lionel Archive observations.

Pricing, Condition, Rarity and Demand

Operating cars are exciting to read about, but the real fun is collecting them. Traditionally, there has been scant pricing information supporting the purchase of *complete* (with all peripherals) component boxed items. This volume provides comprehensive pricing guidance for these transactions as well as for valuation of existing collections.

This volume is unique in that it is the first to be developed using actual quantities from authoritative Lionel internal records and other related sources. These production quantities will be used to determine overall item rarity, bringing a new level of objectivity when it comes to setting a price in the marketplace.

The perceived market price for any item can be expressed as an equation of condition, rarity, demand and other related factors. These variables are all correlated in that each one affects all the others, specifically:

> **Price = Condition (Grading) : Rarity (Current Supply) : Demand : Other Factors**

This formula is used as a baseline in determining the price of each of the operating cars listed in this volume. The remainder of this section provides an overview and breakdown of this formula.

Determining Item Condition Grading Standards

The first variable in the formula, "condition (grading)", is determined by a rollup of the condition of the operating car, its individual box, instruction sheet, packed envelope as well as any inserts or liners. A 10-point grading scale is established, with 10 representing the highest classification. This scale is easily understandable; when an item moves up the scale, the better is its condition.

Our goal at Project Roar Publishing is to provide comprehensive pricing information. As such, pricing for both *unboxed* and *boxed* items is provided. This is one of the first reference guides to provide this level of detail, which is what collectors have told us they are seeking.

How to Read the Table

The following table summarizes the condition grading of each operating car and its peripherals. For each individual *unboxed* operating car, the "Items" column provides its grading descriptions, as defined by the Train Collectors Association (TCA). For a *boxed* item, the next column provides grading for the box. The last three columns summarize the peripheral grading. For example, a complete component boxed operating car would include the item, its box and all the peripherals in similar condition.

DETERMINING A COMPONENT BOXED ITEM'S CONDITION

A component boxed item is the combination of an item, its box, instruction sheet, packed envelope and inserts.

GRADING SCALE	ITEMS*	ITEM BOXES	INSTRUCTION SHEETS	PACKED ENVELOPE	INSERTS AND LINERS
C10	Mint – Brand new, all original, unused, and unblemished.	Brand new, square with all flaps present and never opened or only opened once or twice, flaps stiff to open, perforation (Orange Perforated) present and unpunched. No creases. Color appears as if it just came out of master shipping carton, bright, no fading or darkening. No box rubs, tears, holes, dents or punctures. No marks, price tags, or writing. No water damage. All liners, inserts, and outer sleeve included.	Brand new with square edges, bold and sharp printing. If a folded sheet, has never been opened. No marks, creases, folds or tears.	Envelope sealed, never opened. Condition of envelope mirrors instruction sheets. Contents all present and mirror condition of items.	
C9	Like New – Complete, no rust, no missing original parts. May show effects of being on display and/or age. May have been test run.	Same as C10, except flaps show signs of opening but still stiff. One small mark. Possible price tag. Inserts required.	Same as C10, except shows some sign of handling, i.e. if folded, can tell item has been opened. Corners sharp and square.	Sealed and never opened. Envelope same as instruction sheet. Contents all present same as items.	
C8	Excellent – Minor scratches and paint nicks, no rust, no missing original parts. No distortion of component parts.	Same as C9 with nice color, but not as crisp as C9 due to minimal fading. Small box rub and minimal dents, but no holes, tears or punctures. Minimal marks. No water damage. Inserts or liners optional. Perforation shows wear but not split.	May have small crease or fold. One corner may not be perfectly square. Printing may have some slight fading.	Could be opened, but all contents present. Condition same as instruction sheet and items.	
C7	Very Good – Minor scratches and paint nicks, minor spots of surface rust, free of dents. May have minor parts replaced.	Cardboard is slightly rounded at one corner, not completely square. One small crease possible. All flaps there, but are beginning to get floppy (not stiff). May be reinforced with tape. Color shows signs of minimal fading or darkening. Minimal box rubs, dents, but no punctures, holes or tears. Minimal marks. No water damage. Perforation beginning to separate. No inserts or liners.	Shows signs of wear and use. Corner(s) slightly off square, minor folds, or dog ears, present. May have some small pencil marks present.	Has been opened. Major contents present. Condition same as instruction sheet and items.	See "Item Boxes" condition ratings.
C6	Good – Some sign of play wear with scratches and minor paint loss. Small dents, minor surface rust, minor parts may be missing or replaced.	Same as C7, but more than one side losing squareness. One or more small creases. Can be missing one or more interior flaps. Exterior end flaps present but may be reinforced with tape. Moderate rubs, dents, and a few puncture marks. Writing or other marks present. Perforation separated but present.	Same as C7, but may have small tear(s) that were fixed with transparent tape. Some dirt present.	Opened, missing most contents. Condition same as instruction sheet and items.	
C5	Fair – Scratched, moderate paint loss, dented, missing parts, surface rust. Evidence of heavy use.	Rounded corners with creases, may be missing interior flaps or one or more exterior flaps. Remaining flaps floppy or starting to detach or are reinforced with tape. Fading very noticeable. Many box rubs and dents. Flaps may have small tears. Many markings. Perforation separated and missing.	Has been used. If folded sheet, fold is floppy and may need repair. Marks present in pen or pencil. Has tears or rips that were fixed.	Envelope only. Condition same as instruction sheet.	
C4	Poor – Requires major body repair. Heavily scratched, major rust and missing parts. Restoration candidate.	Same as C5, but at least one flap remains.	Major tears, parts of pages missing, paper is disintegrating in sections.	Envelope only. Condition same as instruction sheet.	
C3	Restoration required.	All flaps missing, not square, major rubs, marks, dents, creases, punctures, water damage or holes.	Pages missing if multiple-page sheet. Rips, tears, and partial pages remain.	Envelope only. Condition same as instruction sheet.	
C2	Parts value only.	Just a piece of the box remains.	Just part of the instruction sheet remains.	Envelope only. Condition same as instruction sheet.	
C1	Junk	Junk	Junk	Envelope only. Condition same as instruction sheet.	

*Item grading descriptions as defined by the Train Collectors Association (TCA).

Item Rarity (Current Supply)

The second variable in determining an operating car's price is the rarity of the item, its box and its peripherals. Rarity is defined as how frequently an item appears in the public, or how hard it is to find. Simply put, rarity can be thought of as the current supply of an item.

To date, the internal Lionel documentation used as reference for this volume provides the most accurate picture of the original supply of operating cars. The authors have spent years analyzing these and other documents in order to obtain a comprehensive understanding of Lionel's production quantities. Typical production runs of regular items were at least 2,500 for a minimal run; common items could reach 100,000 or more over many years. Limited production runs could be as low as twenty-five items. Prototypes, mock-ups and paint samples were usually produced in quantities of six or less.

Unfortunately, all the items produced by Lionel have not survived. Even with the knowledge of original production quantities, it is difficult to identify what still remains. Still, the authors have spent years in the hobby marketplace and so have a firm knowledge of how often an operating car appears for sale. They also know, regarding some of the rarer items, how many there are and where they currently can be found. Taking this expertise and applying it to the original quantities leads to informed estimates of the current supply of every operating car listed in this volume. This process is called "factoring", simply put:

Rarity (Current Supply) = Original Supply x Factor

How Rarity (Current Supply) is Determined

Lionel trains were toys, and operating cars provided the most play value; hence, they saw the most action. Many of these cars had fragile mechanisms that did not always stand up to this use. As such, factoring of the original supply occurs because many items did not survive. The original supply number is lowered (factored) based on the experiences and observations of the authors.

Factoring of the original supply also occurs for operating cars' peripherals. Operating cars often contained removable parts, and many of these did not survive complete or remain original. Many of these fragile peripherals were destroyed or lost, including milk cans, barrels, logs, coal, packed envelopes and other loads. For example, many 6812 Track Maintenance Cars do not have their original figures or have broken original parts. Also, the packed envelope that came with the 3454 Operating Merchandise Car is more difficult to find than the car itself. An operating car may have survived, but a complete component boxed item with all its peripherals and packaging is sometimes impossible to find.

Individual boxes can skew the rarity of a boxed operating car. Some boxed items were produced in lower quantities or spanned a transition in box styles. For example, the 3484-25 Late Classic box from 1956 is more difficult to find than its Middle Classic predecessor. This may be because 1956 was the final year of a three-year run and the 3484-25 may have been produced in smaller quantities. Either way, the Late Classic box demands a premium over the Middle Classic box.

Individual item boxes did not hold up as well as the trains they protected. Many boxes were initially discarded or severely damaged by rough treatment. Others were improperly stored and took on water, heat, cold, fading, insect, rodent, or pet damage. Individual boxes were frequently marked or marred by the retailer or owner. As boxes were opened, they were damaged and so lost their value. Consequently, a boxed item is more difficult to find than the same item unboxed.

In this volume, rarity ratings are provided for both the individual operating car and the operating car boxed with its peripherals. Rarity is assigned based on the following current supply (factored original supply) quantities:

Item Rarity	Current Supply	Example
R10	1 to 250	Black-Lettered 3484-25 Santa Fe Operating Box Car
R9	251 to 1,000	Red-Lettered 3562-25 Operating Barrel Car
R8	1,001 to 5,000	3494-550 Monon Operating Box Car
R7	5,001 to 15,000	3428 Operating Mail Car
R6	15,001 to 30,000	3562-75 Orange Operating Barrel Car
R5	30,001 to 45,000	3370 Sheriff And Outlaw Car
R4	45,001 to 65,000	3386 Regular Production Giraffe Car
R3	65,001 to 100,000	3364 Log Unloading Car
R2	100,001 to 150,000	3462 Operating Milk Car (1947 - 1948 Regular Production Version)
R1	150,001 or more	6167 Caboose

As a final note on rarity, any regular production item cannot really be considered an R10. Regular production runs were typically at least 2,500 items. R10 items are most often prototypes, mock-ups, paint samples, factory errors, or low-run variations of regular production items. The 1-250 range of R10 allows for all these variations to be properly categorized. Any items with extremely low quantities are covered in Author's Comments or Chapter 8 (Prototypes, Mock-Ups and Factory Errors).

Demand

Demand is the other side of rarity. It does not matter how rare or in what condition the operating car is in, if there is no demand, price will be reflected accordingly. The opposite is also true. An item in demand, such as a 6805 Atomic Energy Disposal Car in C9 condition, continues to sell well even though the quantities produced were fairly high.

Other Factors

Besides condition, rarity and demand, a few intangible factors can lead to temporary price fluctuations of operating cars, such as:

Short-Term Supply

Short-term supply fluctuations can influence pricing. Even if an item is rare with high demand, if two of them appear at the same train show or multiple auctions at the same time, prices may be temporarily affected. Also, if a higher than listed price is paid for an item, this may coax collectors who owned such an item for years to sell them in hopes of making profits.

Regional Supply

Due to the Internet, this is not as much of a factor as it used to be, but certain items still sell better in different regions. Specifically, a regionalized road name will likely sell well in its local region.

Eagerness to Sell

Some sellers may be willing to sell at a reduced price just to move the items whereas, others will hold on to an item for months, even years, until they get their price. Others may have short-term financial needs that drive them to sell quickly.

Eagerness to Buy

Collectors, especially those searching for a rare piece, may be willing to pay whatever it takes to acquire that item. Egos may lead to bidding wars at auctions, which can drive prices to unprecedented levels.

Salesperson Savvy

How well an item is advertised or promoted also impacts price. Good auctioneers can work a room and drive up prices. Well-listed and photographed items from a reputable seller tend to sell better on the Internet. Finally, good old-fashioned salesmanship and relationships lead to better sales.

Access to Information

In a perfect market where all information is known, an operating car will likely sell for the same price everywhere. However, information is not ubiquitous and buyers and sellers will pay a premium or discount for an operating car because they are unaware of issues, such as an operating car's completeness or the quantity produced. Volumes such as this will help create and enhance the market for operating cars because this information is now available.

Access to Distribution

Easy worldwide distribution of train items is a few clicks away. Operating cars that would never have found their way into the collector community are now available through online auctions and other Internet sale channels.

Prices in this Volume

The prices for items listed in this volume are determined by applying the pricing formula to each operating car:

$$Price = Condition\ (Grading) : Rarity\ (Current\ Supply) : Demand : Other\ Factors$$

The resulting prices are the selling prices known by the authors and publisher. These prices come from train shows across America, gleaned from major auction houses, and items sold on eBay and other Internet sources. Asking prices for items listed for sale on individual websites and in toy train club publications are also used for the pricing criteria.

How Prices are Displayed

Pricing and rarity are summarized in a table at the end of each operating car's listing. The table for a 3357 is shown below:

3357		C7	C8	C9	Rarity
Regular Production	-25	10	15	30	R5
Type IIb	-1	40	90	180	R7
Teal Blue	-25	35	75	100	
Type IIb	-1	65	150	275	
Regular Production	-25	25	40	60	R8
Type III	-1	55	115	225	
Teal Blue	-25	50	75	100	
Type III	-1	80	150	250	

For *unboxed* operating cars, C7, C8 and C9 pricing is provided. This includes only the car without any of the associated peripherals. In the pricing table, these numbers have a white background.

For *boxed* items, C7, C8 and C9 pricing is also provided:

- C7 pricing includes the item and its box, both in C7 condition. This is color-coded orange.
- C8 pricing includes the item, item box, instruction sheet and packed envelope, all in C8 condition. This is color-coded yellow.
- C9 pricing includes the item, item box, instruction sheet, packed envelope, inserts and liners and any other peripherals, all in C9 condition. This is color-coded green.

Specifically for a 3357-1 (boxed 3357), the following peripherals are included with the pricing.

A 3357 Includes	C7	C8	C9
3357 Cop and Hobo Car	Yes	Yes	Yes
3357-24 Orange Picture Box	Yes	Yes	Yes
3357-27 or 3357-23 Accessory Box with all contents, including a 3357-28 packed envelope.	No	Yes	Yes
3357-8 Instruction Sheet	No	Yes	Yes
Inserts	No	No	Yes*

*Note: While the 3357 did not include inserts, these would be required (if a car came with them) to achieve a C9 rating.

Individuals will sometimes pay a premium for the same box when it's paired with a rarer variation. For example, a 3435 Aquarium Car with only "Tank 1 and Tank 2" designations can demand an additional $300 when paired with its Orange Perforated box; however, the more common 3435 Aquarium Car with yellow rubber-stamped lettering will demand only $100 for the same Orange Perforated box. The pricing tables for each item will summarize any of these occurrences.

Also, in many cases a box may not be as rare as its associated operating car, but when paired with the car, both will reflect the car's higher rarity. The 3357 is a good example. A regular production Type IIb, 3357-25 is a R5; however, when paired with its box (which has a R7 rating) the combination is a R7. This reflects the overall component boxed rarity. But when the same box is paired with a Teal blue variation (car is a R8 rating), the combination is a R8 (even though the box alone is a R7). In this case, the car determines the overall rarity.

C10 pricing is not included in this volume, as these items are most often in limited quantities and collectors frequently pay whatever it takes to obtain them.

Selling Your Trains

Train dealers, brokers and individuals who resell trains are in the business to make a profit. For that reason, if you sell your trains to one of these individuals, you can expect to receive less than the prices listed in this volume. Depending on the profit they are seeking, and all of the other variables listed in this section, you may obtain 50 to 80 percent of the prices in this volume.

If you are selling your trains directly to an individual who does not intend to resell them (they are being added to a collection), the actual prices in this volume apply. Once again, all prices in this volume are only guidelines based on observations of current market conditions. Your experiences may vary.

Lionel Operating Cars: An Overview and an Appreciation
By Roger Carp

I. INTRODUCTION

How fitting that a venture as exciting and path-breaking as Project Roar Publishing should begin with the first comprehensive look at the operating cars that Lionel cataloged in the post-World War II decades. For these O gauge freight cars continue to stand out, just as the books published by Project Roar will. No other postwar toy train maker – or any manufacturer in the history of the model railroading hobby – brought out as many different, original, and entertaining operating cars as did Lionel. No other toy trains blended elements of realism and make believe more consistently than did these cars. The operating cars described and analyzed here are as enjoyable and noteworthy as they were when Lionel introduced them.

And as diverse. For the range of Lionel's operating cars is nothing short of astounding. Engineers relied on an assortment of mechanisms – solenoids, gears, electromagnets, cogwheels, and more – to animate virtually every kind of freight car in the line. Searchlights rotated on flat cars, figures sprang forward on refrigerator cars, crates were ejected from box cars, cattle shuffled through stock cars, and barrels were dumped from gondolas.

That was just the beginning! Fish swam, satellites roared into orbit, brakemen ducked, mailbags flew, and police officers chased tramps on Lionel's operating cars. Nothing seemed beyond the imagination and ability of the designers, electrical wizards, and model makers who worked under the direction of Joseph Bonanno, the company's hard-driving chief engineer.

Lionel's chief engineer, Joseph Bonanno (middle) with two of his top associates after the war: John Salles (left), who managed the Electrical Test Department, and John DiGirolamo (right), who managed the Electrical Research and Development Department.

Frank Pettit, Anthony Rocco, and Dorland Crosman – to name just three of Bonanno's top men – developed operating cars that simulated activities associated with railroads (delivering freight) as well as models whose animation was so fanciful that it had more in common with television than transportation (a sheriff firing away at an outlaw). Some of Lionel's cars worked in conjunction with an accessory (coal and log dump cars). A few models needed something extra, say a loading platform or a tell-tale, to operate fully. Many other postwar operating cars, of course, did not require ancillary items of any sort and proved to be just as popular then and now.

So fully do the operating cars exemplify all that was outstanding about Lionel in the postwar period that it comes as no surprise that the firm hardly faced any real competition in this area. Other toy train makers brought out excellent replicas of powerful steam engines and sleek diesels. Similarly, a number of businesses developed freight loaders, signals, bridges, light towers, and stations that strived to rival what Lionel offered.

But no other manufacturer of toy trains approached Lionel in showing the public as many diverse and original operating cars. In fact, due to patent issues and expenses, no one else tried in the O gauge market until Kusan briefly plunged ahead in the late 1950s. Otherwise, nothing!

Lionel's operating cars, even more than its other great trains,

Joseph Bonnano's personal diary entry from April 20, 1939, outlining "requirements for couplers RF control system." This was well ahead of the 4109WS Electronic Control Set issued in 1946.

beautifully mixed realism and imagination. These items reflected the prevailing corporate philosophy at Lionel that the toy trains which would best appeal to the public, enchanting kids and grown-ups alike, should look like actual trains yet go farther in providing animation, color, interaction, and pleasure.

Operating cars offered youngsters opportunities for healthy play, by themselves and with peers. These models generally helped them improve fine motor skills and hand-eye coordination. Informally, they taught children about the realms of railroading, industry, commerce, and agriculture – useful knowledge for boys expected to enter the adult world of business. All the while, kids were having fun. They marveled at what could be done on the transportation networks they were building on the floor of their bedroom or a Ping-Pong table in the basement.

The philosophy underlying the development of novel, exciting operating cars did more than increase sales. It guaranteed that model after model would capture the public's attention and eventually be lauded as classics by the collectors and operators who make these trains their passion. Items known far and wide as "the milk car", "giraffe car", "brakeman car", and "aquarium car" elicit wonderful memories and never fail to delight adult hobbyists. Youngsters half a century ago were startled and then amused by the animation. Now older and smarter, they understand how Lionel's operating cars worked. Still, if these men and women are lucky, the awe they once felt in handling models imbued with magical powers has never vanished.

II. PRELIMINARY STEPS AND ULTIMATE SUCCESS: 1925-42

To appreciate the reasons that Lionel developed operating cars during the postwar period – and to understand the origins of some of those very models – we need to first turn our attention to the prewar era. During the 1920s, Joshua Lionel Cowen, who founded the firm in 1900, expanded the roster of Standard and O gauge cars in hopes of building sales. He had learned from European and American rivals in the toy train field that financial success depended on giving customers additional products to buy once they had acquired their first train set. Track and accessories led the way, but Cowen was determined to offer cars that provided more action.

The first cars that offered youngsters more to do joined the Standard gauge line in 1926. A crane, equipped with pulleys and cranks, was installed on a modified flat car to become model no. 219. After guiding the car into place, a child could maneuver the boom and the hook by turning knobs and levers on the car. Then he could load freight into gondolas and onto flat cars. The possibilities were endless, and the fun of a Standard gauge train was significantly enhanced.

Also in 1926, Lionel cataloged the no. 216, an updated coal car with hoppers that manually opened, and the no. 218 operating dump car. The latter featured a trough that, with the turn of a lever on the side, tilted forward to dump its contents. Imagination, so vital to enjoying Lionel trains and accessories, gained even more freedom to soar. Thanks to the additions of the 218 and 219 "operating" cars, children had more that they could actually "do" with an electric train, in spite of the fact that their fingers remained the source of every bit of the action.

Lionel's founder, Joshua Lionel Cowen.

Despite – or perhaps because – of the sagging sales Lionel reported at the depths of the Great Depression, it pushed forward with efforts to make its Standard gauge roster more diverse and thrilling. Another kind of operating car – the floodlight car – entered the line in 1931.

Credit for the nos. 220 and slightly shorter 520 floodlight cars goes to Frank Pettit, then supervising the inventory of trains sold and repaired at Lionel's headquarters in New York City. Pettit, who went on to develop dozens of other items before leaving the firm in 1959, grasped the commercial benefits of using electricity to power one or even two floodlights on a moving freight car. So, as narrated in Christopher B. Ritchie's book, *It Comes From Within: The Frank Pettit Story* (published in 1999), he cobbled together models that were manufactured for the Standard and O gauge lines in the same year (the O gauge car became no. 820).

Once a boy owned a crane car, a dump car, and a floodlight car, he eagerly tackled a host of new jobs on his miniature railroad. He could dump any kind of freight with the twist of a knob. He could pick up and drop little toys, ranging from die-cast metal soldiers to sheet-metal trucks and automobiles, not to mention other Lionel cars. Moreover, work could go on day or night, with the beams shining from his floodlight car providing ample illumination.

Ironically, the junior engineers dreaming of owning one of these operating cars had to wait seven years before Lionel announced something extra for them. Not until 1938 did it bring out additional operating cars. But those models and the ones introduced in 1939 represented a significant step forward and laid

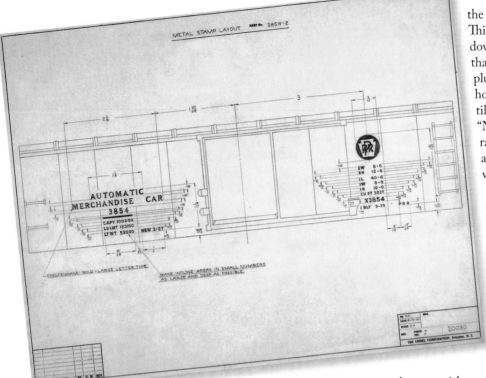

The metal stamp layout for the 3854 was dated 4-17-46 and provided details on the car's artwork.

the groundwork for all the operating cars that came after.

These electrically powered newcomers exemplified Lionel's commitment to realism as much as did the scale Hudson or the semi-scale freight cars added to the line in 1940. True, those early operating cars were far from exact replicas of actual freight cars. And the action they produced was not always smooth or dependable. Nonetheless, these O gauge cars let modelers imitate more activities and therefore feel as though they were supervising railroad empires.

The remote-controlled models that revolutionized toy train history date from the end of the prewar era. Twin versions of an operating dump car came out in 1938 (nos. 3659 and 3859). Their cousins – the nos. 3651 and 3811 lumber cars, 3652 operating gondola, and 3814 merchandise car – burst on the scene a year later.

All four types of cars, as chronicled in *It Comes From Within*, emerged from the mind of Frank Pettit. Having just refined the automatic coupler, he raced to see what else his remote-controlled activation device could do. It didn't take long to apply it to the unloading of various kinds of "freight" from O gauge cars. They did so at the whim and decision of whoever had his hands on the transformer and the buttons on a remote controller. The operator decided when and where to unload the barrels or coal. "Now for the first time", declared the Lionel consumer catalog for 1939, "you can actually make your freight train serve a purpose." More than ever, a Lionel train captured in miniature the activities and thrills of a modern railroad.

The operation of each of these cars was simple enough to be learned by school-aged children. Positioning the car at the center of a special piece of track (where an electromagnet was installed) constituted the first step. Next, the youngster pressed a button on

the remote controller connected to that track. This activated the electromagnet, which pulled down a plunger on the bottom of the car's frame that was energized by a solenoid there. The plunger was connected to the model's tray or hopper, and so it caused that moveable part to tilt. Like magic, the model dumped its cargo. "No make-believe to it – it's as real as real railroading!" the text in the catalog stated. If a boy felt like a god in control of the world, well, Lionel wouldn't have quibbled.

Lionel originally intended for operating cars to empty their contents into trays or onto bare floor. In 1940, however, it announced two remote-controlled accessories that could be used with the dump and lumber cars. Coal could be poured into the loading bin of a new no. 97 coal elevator or released from a no. 98 coal storage bunker into a waiting dump car. Dowels rolled off into the storage area of a new no. 164 log loader. Not for the last time would Lionel combine an operating car with an accessory to increase a layout's activity and multiply corporate earnings.

The fourth type of prewar operating car, known as a merchandise car, was slightly more complicated. It also relied on a remote-controlled electromagnet to energize its solenoid. However, the mechanism inside a special boxcar would, on being activated, caused plastic cubes, intended to simulate packing crates, to be ejected out of the side door that opened automatically. The cubes went flying out, much to the surprise of the kids operating and watching the car.

Lionel knew it had added significantly to its line with these four cars. It publicized the quartet in its catalogs and issues of *Model Builder*, the magazine Lionel put out before and after World War II to promote the hobby of model railroading. These cars served as outfit components, and lumber and dump cars were sold as companions to their relevant accessories.

Members of Lionel's sales staff, like members of its engineering department, looked to the future with excitement and optimism. They wondered what other kinds of operating cars might be added to the product line to demonstrate still more to the toy world that Lionel was the true leader in the field. Realism and enjoyment blended so beautifully in these operating cars that more of them were essential ingredients in the company's future prospects, even after government restrictions curtailed production of toy trains while the global war raged into 1945.

III. EMPHASIS ON REALISM: 1946-52

The seven years after World War II saw Lionel catalog several O gauge operating cars, only a handful of which broke new ground. Not until 1949 did operating cars become a top priority at the company. Until then, developing new locomotives, notably the Berkshire and Turbine steamers, the GG1 electric, and the F3 diesel, took precedence for the engineering department, along with such new features as realistic knuckle couplers and a smoke mechanism.

Overall, most of the operating cars offered between 1946 and 1952 were updated versions of items developed in the 1930s and marketed through 1942. The prevailing philosophy of creating trains that looked more like realistic models and less like playthings dictated changes in the appearance of each operating car. Thus, much of what occurred with this important segment of the line should be viewed as a continuation of what Lionel had been doing before the war.

Making prewar models look more realistic typically involved changes in the design of key parts as well as the decoration of the frame and body. Rarely did an operating car undergo "major surgery" that left it much longer or bigger. The sole exception was a new merchandise car (no. 3854) that used a scale boxcar shell created before the war. Otherwise, designers were content to substitute die-cast metal parts for sheet-metal ones to make the revised models heavier. The same goal had already influenced the development of remote-controlled die-cast metal knuckle couplers and solid, highly detailed wheelsets. These parts became standard on operating cars, as they did on the freight and passenger cars Lionel cataloged after World War II.

In addition to tougher frames and more detailed bodies, the revised operating cars looked more realistic because their colors changed so radically. Admittedly, none of the prewar versions could blind someone with their spectacular paint schemes. Still, the yellow body of the 3652 operating gondola, the shiny nickel stakes and brake wheel on the 3811 lumber car, and the red hopper on the 3859 dump car caught a viewer's eye. The form as well as the decoration of these operating models exuded elegance and charm.

And that was the problem, at least as far as Lionel's executives were concerned after the war. They wanted realistic models because they thought that was what the returning soldiers and sailors wanted. As a result, the warm hues and glossy tones that characterized so many prewar O gauge freight cars were banished from the palettes and paint spray booths at the Lionel factory.

The updated log car, assigned no. 3451, was black, right down to the steps and stakes. So was the most common variation of the new dump car (no. 3459). All but identical was the version of the dump car (no. 5459) that Lionel placed in its technologically advanced no. 4109WS Electronic Control Set. With either dump car, white lettering on the side of each car's frame sufficed for decoration. A similarly dark, somewhat drab scheme characterized the 3854 merchandise car, although it did benefit having a Pennsylvania Railroad keystone herald.

The flat, dark colors used on most of the operating cars cataloged between 1946 and 1948 enabled Lionel to take what in many instances were carryovers from the late prewar years and make them seem different. The mechanisms used on the lumber car and dump cars took advantage of an improved solenoid and plunger activated by sliding shoes on the model's trucks and the electromagnet inlaid in a special section of track (no. RCS for O gauge and no. 1019 for O27) wired to a remote controller. As with their prewar brethren, the updated dump and log cars promoted interaction with an operator. So did the radio-controlled 5459 dump car.

Lionel used 3459 operating dump cars to collect change to support relief efforts after World War II. Joshua Lionel Cowen (middle) joins Secretary of State George Marshall (left) and Attorney General Tom Clark (right) at a public display set up in New York City in 1946.

How a hobbyist in 1946 (or today) viewed the new remote-controlled dump and log cars depended on perspective. If bowled over by their stark colors and upgraded mechanisms, he might judge them as impressive steps forward. But if he disliked the dark paint and neglected the hidden technology, he might complain that these changes hardly masked the fact that Lionel had nothing new. Truthfully, when weighed against their not-so-distant ancestors, the postwar cars had received only superficial changes to make them appear different and more authentic.

That's too bad because good reasons existed to make the log and dump cars more colorful. Each worked with an accessory (carried over from the prewar era) that featured warm colors. Painting the body of the 3459 dump car in yellow or red to match sections of the 97 coal elevator would have improved its appearance. (Paint samples in both colors exist, so someone at Lionel might have proposed revamping the 3459.) The same might have been done for the 3451 log car, because red and yellow, not to mention a light green, were used on its companion 164 log loader. About the closest Lionel came to linking one of its early postwar operating cars to an accessory was painting the hopper on the 3559 dump car red (as its prewar forerunners were).

The only concession that Lionel made to visual appeal was to use silver paint on two of its early postwar operating cars. The new dump car initially came this way (illustrated in the consumer catalog for 1946 with Baltimore & Ohio markings, although no such version was mass-produced). Soon, however, black predominated. Lasting longer was the silver-painted small merchandise car. The no. 3454 kept its bright hue during the two years it was cataloged. With its blue heat-stamped lettering, the 3454 would have looked terrific with a matching 3459 dump car. Still, a flat silver paled alongside the vivid tones used before World War II.

Lionel offered a modified log car and a dump car whose elongated look hearkened back to the Standard gauge manually operating model. It also cataloged two types of merchandise cars, one that presumably finished up old boxcar shells and another that used shells created for the new no. 2454 box car. The same wish to get rid of leftover inventory would explain why a second style of dump car was cataloged from 1946 to 1948. Many of the parts on the 3559, including the red hopper and the Bakelite mechanism housing, were designed for the old 3659.

Missing from the roster of early postwar operating cars were two prewar stalwarts: the floodlight car and the operating gondola. Simply returning the 2620 floodlight and 3652 gondola cars to the line with only minimal changes (knuckle couplers, for example) would not have appealed to the powers-that-be in the mid-1940s. Both shiny sheet-metal cars would have looked old-fashioned in the presence of the new rolling stock, with its dark colors and solid feel. Having said that, it is nevertheless surprising that Lionel chose not to catalog a searchlight car until 1949 because that exciting model had been a steady seller and predictable entry for so many years.

The reasons for not revising the operating gondola are also puzzling. Yes, the 3652 would have looked out of place in the postwar line. Perhaps there was talk of building an operating version of the new no. 2452 gondola. Equipping this plastic model with the requisite mechanism and a bed that tilted up to empty a load might have been too complicated and expensive. But imagine a slightly longer sheet-metal car that carried, not barrels, but metal scraps that it dumped to be picked up by a no. 182 triple-action magnet crane. And imagine that the car had a silver-painted body to match the accessory's structure. Too bad Lionel didn't give it a shot.

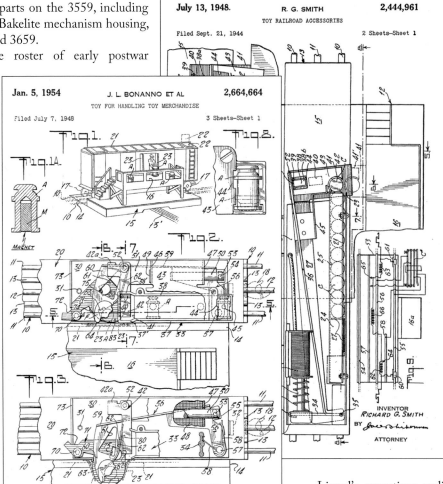

Two patents for the operating milk car. The original from Richard G. Smith, dated July 13, 1948, and the "improvement on the type of accessories described….in the Smith patent…" by Joseph Bonnano and Abram D. Gash Jr. dated January 5, 1954.

In lamenting the drab, heavy look of the updated operating cars a landmark in toy train lore is overlooked. For in 1947, Lionel introduced a car whose appearance and action caught everyone's attention. It featured an attractive white exterior and worked with a green-painted platform. The car, platform, and miniature load dazzled with their chrome details. The model spotlighted the most celebrated animated figure since the automatic gateman arrived in 1935. Please give a hearty round of applause to Lionel's no. 3462 automatic refrigerated milk car.

At a moment when the in-house crew of designers was swamped by the demands of putting out a newly revised line, the milk car "came over the transom" from an outsider. Richard G. Smith, a tinkerer who contributed neat cars to both the Lionel and Flyer lines, shared his ideas for a refrigerator car that came with a figure that appeared to push out tiny milk cans at the press of a button. (The animation was actually caused when an operator energized the electromagnet on a remote-controlled track, which in turn activated a solenoid on the milk car.)

Lionel's executives realized that such a unique car had commercial potential, though they probably underestimated how popular it would be. Members of the engineering staff, including Dale Gash and Vito Bertucci, were instructed to take Smith's ideas and produce an item ready to be mass-produced. The milk car took the public by storm. With few notable changes, it remained a set component and separate-sale item every year from 1947 through 1955 (being renumbered from 3462 to 3472 and then to 3482 before being superseded by a longer version). Lionel is credited with manufacturing hundreds of thousands of these short milk cars.

The financial impact of the milk car was felt immediately at Lionel; the creative impact took longer to surface. No new operating cars hit the market in 1948. Then, a year later, an explosion shattered the quiet. Creative juices that had been diverted into a host of other areas were concentrated on operating cars, and the results were remarkable.

Influenced by the milk car and its clever blending of remote-controlled action with an animated figure and an auxiliary item, Pettit devised an operating car for junior ranchers. He fashioned a special stock car that depended on vibration generated by the remote-controlled electromagnet and solenoid assembly. The animation of the no. 3656 consisted of miniature cows that would creep up a ramp, shimmy along a runway inside the car, and mosey down another ramp into a corral. Lionel had another winner, Pettit recalled in the January 1993 issue of *Classic Toy Trains* magazine, even if the black rubberized cattle occasionally tipped over.

The no. 3464 operating box car, which also debuted in 1949, proved to be another crowd-pleaser. It relied on a remote-controlled plunger mechanism attached to springs in the car to slide open one of the doors and cause a miniature railroad laborer to bound forward. The appeal of this reasonably priced model derived in part from its decoration. Lionel painted the 3464 in solid yet vivid colors and lettered it for two nationally known railroads (New York Central and Santa Fe, the names used on the F3 diesel models introduced in 1948). Most of all, it was the blue rubberized man that captivated observers. He sprang into action only when an operator wanted.

Lastly in 1949, after waiting much too long, Lionel brought out a thoroughly updated version of its prewar floodlight car. The searchlight and housing of the no. 6520 were set atop the die-cast metal frame developed for the no. 2461 transformer car that had entered the line in 1947. A generator, injection-molded out of any of four colors of plastic, was included on the depressed center of the model, adding authenticity and visual appeal to the car. Concealed by the generator was a mechanism that, when activated by a remote-control device, turned on or off the stationary light. Once more, operators would be dousing the overhead lights in attics and basements and letting the bright beam of a searchlight car illuminate their O gauge empires.

Lionel brought out only one truly new operating car over the next three years. For 1950, Pettit developed a version of the hopper car with an electromagnetic plunger. When that device was activated at the touch of a button on the remote controller, it pulled open the bottom doors to release chunks of coal. Neat as this solenoid-activated animation was, Pettit stated that he intended the no. 3456 to be used with the new no. 456 coal ramp and not separately.

By the time the effects of the Korean War were felt most strongly at Lionel, with prices regulated and shortages of materials limiting production, the roster of operating cars seemed unbeatable. Never before had the firm been able to offer so many remote-controlled models. Cars dumped coal and logs, delivered milk, and transported cows. Figures rode inside boxcars and refrigerator cars. Searchlights illuminated work scenes and cities. Only the merchandise cars, which sent tiny packing crates flying without the aid of a hardy laborer, had been dropped. Otherwise, the specially modified flat cars, hoppers, box car, stock car, and more remained prominent members of the O and O27 lines, as components of outfits and items sold separately.

The assorted operating cars shared certain characteristics. All were touted as realistic. For Lionel, realism meant rudimentary decoration, often with solid, dark colors. It also meant replicating the action people associated with railroads: carrying cattle and milk cans, unloading coal and logs, shining bright lights where needed. Realism did not mean manufacturing near-scale models decorated in an assortment of road names. Unfortunately for

Lionel, the last two traits mattered to hobbyists for whom realism was paramount. They cared about authenticity and not animation. So Lionel's campaign to win over the mushrooming contingent of scale modelers by developing what it called "realistic" operating cars was doomed to fail.

Acknowledging that the company should follow a different path made sense. But what would that path look like? A hint of where Lionel would soon travel appeared in 1952 with a new operating box car. The no. 3474 did not differ mechanically from its predecessors. Neither did its general appearance diverge from the pair of 3464s that Lionel continued to catalog. But its decoration represented something fresh and beautiful. More than just being painted shiny silver, the Western Pacific operating box car featured an immense yellow feather decaled across each side to emulate what the actual railroad painted on its latest, highly publicized box cars.

This step forward in decoration revealed that Lionel's leaders were on the verge of retreating from the notion that realism was synonymous with dullness. Rather, they saw that realism could involve greater use of color. Bright hues and elaborate logos and markings would bring Lionel's models back into the realm of toys. Yet not in a silly or childish manner. Designers and salesmen would discover how to blend realism, beauty, and imagination to create products that stand out as among the finest in Lionel's history. Balancing those three elements would take skill and ingenuity. Yet the 3474 Western Pacific car served as a grand starting point.

IV. REALISM MIXES WITH ENTERTAINMENT: 1953-59

The trend quietly launched by the 3474 gathered speed in 1953. Pressed by the up-and-coming American Model Toys, Lionel had introduced near-scale models of extruded aluminum streamlined passenger cars. In 1953, that rival's roster of large, contemporary box cars motivated Lionel to launch its own fleet of big boys in the no. 6464 series. In addition to the four models that inaugurated that well-known class, it offered an identical box car with the operating mechanism and blue rubberized figure that had made the 3464s such moneymakers.

The no. 3484 Pennsylvania operating box car did not represent a step forward from a technological perspective. The mechanical "guts" scarcely differed from those on its short cousins. But from an aesthetic angle, it was a brand-new venture. The near-scale body, painted Tuscan red, made this model seem more realistic than the 3464s or even the 3474. At last, Lionel had an operating box car that met the market's standards for authenticity and play value.

Pleased by the success of the 3484, Lionel proceeded over the next three years to bring out more near-scale and colorful operating box cars. Like General Motors and Ford, Lionel insisted on having a new and more dazzling model out every year. The Pennsylvania car gave way to a similarly decorated one showcasing the Santa Fe. Then, in 1955 and 1956, designers let their artistic skills loose and finished models painted in New York Central, Missouri Pacific, and Bangor & Aroostook "State of Maine" schemes. All of these operating box cars were available as separate-sale items, and most were used to fill out impressive O gauge freight outfits.

The 3484 catapulted Lionel ahead in enlarging its early postwar operating cars. The automatic refrigerated milk car, for

Stock being loaded into a "cattle car" on the Denver and Rio Grande Western Railroad August 26, 1949.

loading and unloading livestock by remote control. To their delight, engineers improved the vibrating mechanism and the animation.

Two other stalwarts, the log car and the dump car, soldiered on. Other than getting magnetic couplers and having tweaks made to their frame, neither had changed much since being introduced in 1946. Lionel did offer a green-painted log car in 1954 (no. 3461-25) in an effort to inject more color into the line. Otherwise, anyone desiring to ship and unload lumber and coal had to be content with basic black models and a mechanism that dumped fast and furiously.

Therefore, updating those two operating cars was long overdue when Lionel announced the nos. 3361 log dump car and 3359 twin-bin dump car in 1955. Both plastic models were longer than their predecessors and came in gray rather than black (too bad the log dump car wasn't produced with the red frame shown in the consumer catalog for 1955). Their animation was slower and more deliberate, due to new mechanisms (using rotating cams) that still worked by remote control. The log car remained plain and functional; the twin-bin dump car at least had two separately controlled troughs and a red motor housing. Neither car would win a beauty contest, but their operation was more reliable and the animation more realistic than before.

example, which continued to sell briskly, was redesigned for 1955. The new no. 3662 near-scale refrigerator car featured a brown roof, ends, and doors. The internal mechanism was improved, and the milk man returned. Ironically, by looking less like a plaything and more like a realistic replica, the milk car sacrificed a good deal of its charm.

Another updating altered the operating cattle car for the 1956 line. Besides modifying the corral so the rubberized animals marched along without tipping over or getting stuck, designers used the near-scale stock car (no. 6356) they had developed two years earlier as the basis for the no. 3356 operating horse car. Stallions and mares replaced the cows that had populated the 3656, although the animation was the same. Youngsters were still

In the midst of updating its stable of operating cars – enlarging some and gussying up others – Lionel developed a new one that skyrocketed up the hit parade like a new record by the McGuire Sisters or Perry Como. This classic encapsulated every element of the quintessential operating car. It combined color with realism. An eye-catching model as it rode around the rails, it produced clever animation. It included a figure, which moved as though he were handling the labor. That work, accomplished by an operator through remote control, could be done anywhere on a layout or in conjunction with an operating accessory. The best aspects of an operating car – activity, entertainment, interaction,

Lionel's 3656 Operating Cattle Car was modeled after the real railroads of the day.

The 3562 was a colorful and animated addition to a collection or layout.

and beauty – characterized the no. 3562 barrel car. No wonder Lionel announced its delivery in 1954 with the pride of a new dad handing out cigars.

To be sure, the first incarnation of the barrel car wasn't likely to stop traffic on the streets of Manhattan. It was painted black and had only a creamy yellow trough (a hue that matched the shade on the no. 362 barrel loader introduced in 1952) to grab attention. Soon, Lionel remembered that cans of other colors were sitting next to the paint spray booths at its factory. Subsequent variations of the 3562 were painted gray or yellow or left as bare yellow or orange plastic. These distinctive models were included in freight sets cataloged between 1954 and 1958.

Technically, the barrel car stood out for its use of a vibrating mechanism to move kegs up its metal ramp. The animation continued as the figure seemed to push the small wooden casks off the car and into a tray at the side of the rails or a waiting gondola parked on a parallel line. Or the barrels might end up on a 362, where they would ride up a ramp and be pushed off. The action of a 3562, designed by Pettit, depended on the wishes of its operator, who had to be sure he or she planned everything correctly and then aimed right. The degree of interdependence was outstanding for an operating car. That factor, along with the car's appearance and animation, exemplified the blend of realism and imagination that Lionel desired and its customers loved.

Another landmark was achieved two years after the 3562 made its debut. In 1956, Lionel first cataloged the 3424 brakeman car. This model stands out for its beauty (the blue scheme with white Wabash Railway markings) and its entertaining action. A brakeman stood upright on the roof until, like a railroader of old, he brushed through the tell-tales erected over the track to warn that a bridge, tunnel, or other low-lying obstacle was near. The figure dipped forward, lying flat atop the car until it passed the danger zone. Reaching a second set of tell-tales, he bolted upright and kept riding. (In reality, the car's wheels brushing against clips inserted into the track at the base of the pole holding the tell-tales activated the internal mechanism that moved the figure.)

For the first time on an operating car, the action was vertical. The brakeman moved up and down and not forward and back, as

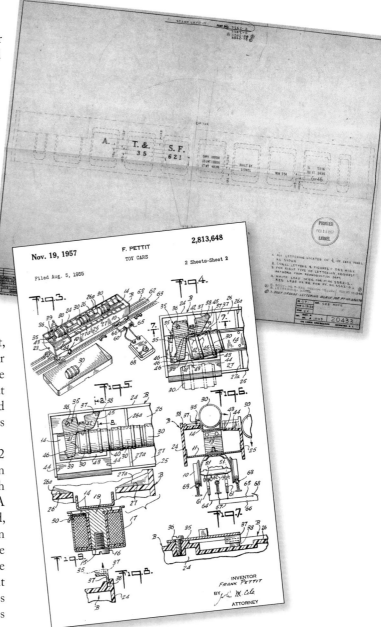

Frank Pettit's patent for the 3562 as well as the 3562 stamping layout dated 3-19-54.

Refrigerator cars being "iced" on the Seaboard Air Line Railroad.

of a tramp and a cop. The officer, his nightstick held high, chased the hobo, ready to beat the guy if the two caught up.

They did not, of course, but the animation was entertaining. The 3444 showed up in freight outfits and as a separate-sale item through 1959. Again, there was nothing for an operator to do except couple the gondola to a train and move the lever. Then he or she sat back and watched the slapstick action, much as kids giggled over the antics of the Three Stooges. The animation on this car was clever, but it had nothing to do with the world of work that had been the focus of Lionel's operating cars right through the development of the barrel car.

If anything, the more Lionel turned to entertaining children, the less appeal its work-oriented operating cars had. The operating box car, which had seemed innovative in 1949 and then been given new life as a realistic model four years later, seemed boring and out of date by 1957. Lionel did catalog two more variations in that year and the next. But the Monon and the Soo Line cars (nos. 3494-550 and 3494-625, respectively) had little to recommend them, except that their Midwestern road names might boost sales in that region. Neither model was included in an outfit, not when it seemed as old-fashioned as a silent movie or a hand-cranked Oldsmobile.

So also did the dump and log cars seem out of place by the late 1950s. Lionel kept the two models it had updated in 1955, but sales suffered as kids spurned models that called on them to supervise the action. Better to be entertained by a brakeman car that could be set off on an adventure and watched than to have to position a log car in just the right spot and then get only gradual movement from it as long as a button was pressed. Who wanted to work when you could catch the action of the cop on the animated gondola sprinting after the hapless tramp?

Little wonder that Lionel recognized a need to update its operating box car to provide more interesting action. On the no.

with the operating box cars and the barrel car. The action related entirely to what happened on railroads, although like the no. 6352 ice car that worked with the no. 352 icing depot (new in 1955), it was a throwback. Few railroads still needed men to ride atop freight cars, presumably to throw the brake wheel at a moment's notice.

But the 3424 was terrific fun to watch. That says much about where Lionel was taking its operating cars by 1956. Unlike the barrel car brought out only two years before, the brakeman car was automatic in its animation. Once an operator put the car on the tracks and positioned the tell-tales, he or she had nothing to do except gaze at it and laugh. A barrel car demanded forethought, constant use of a remote-control device, and coordination. It required interaction of a degree beyond what a child could muster, which enhanced its appeal as a sophisticated model.

The brakeman car was far simpler in its operation and demanded little of whoever was handling the transformer. As such, it had much in common with the television cartoon programs then captivating boys and girls across America. The 3424 shows that Lionel wittingly or otherwise sought to change perceptions of its products. Rather than creating trains that demanded patience and planning, it was selling playthings that promised thrills and laughs, especially if a child cast a tell-tale aside so he could laugh as his brakeman rode head-on into a tunnel portal.

The same wish to appeal to a child's love of physical comedy explains the no. 3444 animated gondola. Almost two decades earlier, Lionel had cataloged a car with a similar name – a remote-controlled model that dumped barrels to imitate honest labor. The car introduced in 1957 had little in common with it. Instead, as with the brakeman car, the animation was automatic, continuous, and silly. By flipping a lever on the car, an operator set in motion spools with sprockets that turned a loop of film on which were attached figures

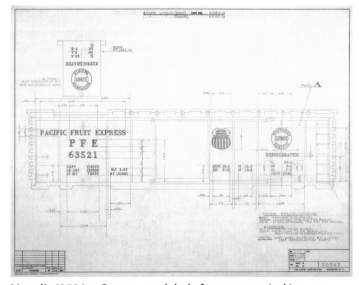

Lionel's 6352 Ice Car was modeled after prototypical ice cars. The stamping layout for the 6352 body and door.

3434 (introduced in 1959), it changed the animation so the little figure moved forward with a broom in hand as though he were sweeping out a stock car packed with chickens. On the no. 3428 (also new in 1959), it tried a mail car in which a magnet held a tiny bag to the figure's midsection. When the man sprang forward, the sudden stop of its momentum caused the bag to be hurled off the car as though a sack of letters had been delivered.

The only concession Lionel made to the view that kids wanted to use their imagination and hands to interact with an operating car came with its searchlight. First in 1956 came the no. 3530 General Motors generator car, followed by the no. 3650 extension searchlight car. Both featured searchlights that could be lifted off the model and placed by the track to illuminate a work scene. Incidentally, 1956 was the last year that Lionel cataloged a version of the basic searchlight car. That model had been improved in 1952 so its light rotated (the no. 3520). Two years later, Lionel updated the searchlight car by installing a vibrating mechanism. Now, as the no. 3620, the model could automatically rotate its beam while coasting behind a locomotive.

Still, as the 1950s closed, the individuals planning Lionel's line realized that their market was changing. Model railroaders had all but abandoned them years before in favor of scale and accurately detailed trains. Operating cars of any nature didn't attract interest from this growing segment of the hobby. About the only hope Lionel had of reaching serious enthusiasts was through the line of HO scale trains it introduced in 1957 and built up over the next few years.

At the same time, Lionel's bread-and-butter market – children and families – kept shifting interests. The operating cars that had once captured the attention of youngsters seemed too simple. The fast-paced world in which they lived, dominated by jet airplanes, intercontinental missiles, and rockets streaming into outer space, made railroads appear dated and boring. As a result, Lionel's O gauge models also looked out of date and unappealing to older boys, the very audience that had the motor skills and coordination to use more demanding, interactive operating cars. Lionel appeared to be left with only younger kids, and for them it had to devise operating cars that could provide ample entertainment merely by being placed on a track and switched on.

The most revealing example of what had happened to Lionel's operating cars was the no. 3435 traveling aquarium, which entered the line in 1959. This model featured images of sea creatures on a roll of celluloid that revolved automatically, thanks to a vibrating motor that an operator switched on. The animation created the illusion that the fish were swimming in the two tanks of a modified box car. The model's fanciful nature likely caused scale modelers to throw up their hands. Youngsters hoping for an accurate replica that performed work and encouraged their interaction would have found this car wanting. Only kids or their parents, waiting to be entertained, appreciated the 3435. It was the television series *Sea Hunt* on wheels, although it probably didn't hold anyone's attention as long as that half-hour adventure show.

The brakeman car, animated gondola, and traveling aquarium indicated a disappointing trend among children and Lionel enthusiasts. Too many of Lionel's models, operating and non-

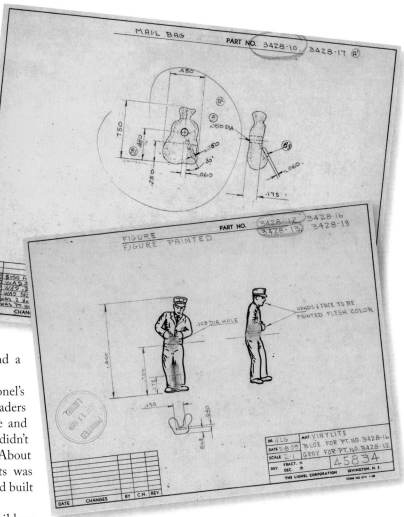

The blueprints for the 3428's mail bag and figure. Note that the mailbag underwent numerous changes.

operating, did seem old-fashioned in a rapidly changing America. They had depended on a child spending time using his or her imagination to dream up a railroading scenario and acting it out by performing tasks, such as unloading freight or shipping livestock. By the end of the 1950s, kids seemed less interested in putting forth much effort with their toys. They demanded color, action, and stimulation, usually from playthings that asked for relatively little from them.

But the "entertainment-oriented" operating models introduced in the late 1950s should remind us of something more positive. They reveal the extraordinarily creative minds employed at Lionel. Individuals there managed to come up with novel concepts long after they had exhausted what could be done with dumping coal and transporting barrels. Good as those familiar operating cars were, one needed only a rudimentary knowledge of railroading to suggest them. Frankly, the most difficult parts of bringing out operating cars in the 1940s and early 1950s related to the design of parts and utilization of mechanisms. To assert this is not to underestimate the achievements of research engineers and their colleagues. Pettit and others working with Bonanno earned every accolade that came their way. Nevertheless, their work on Lionel's early postwar operating cars necessarily emphasized the technological aspects.

Once the obvious operating models had been developed, the

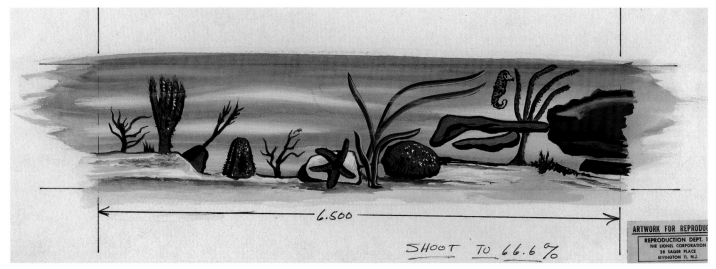

Lionel artist Louis Melchionne's original artwork for the 3435 Aquarium Car.

challenge confronting Lionel's engineers was where to go next and how to build what they envisioned. They explored peripheral areas of railroading and found ways to model activities like a brakeman riding on the roof of a car or a laborer cleaning out a stock car. Designers discovered odd, esoteric rolling stock through research – the generator car or the car modified to carry fish to aquariums – and fashioned models that boasted some level of animation. They also paid attention to outside ideas, as with the no. 6805 atomic energy disposal car (new in 1958). This model, whose animation consisted of blinking lights, was inspired by full-sized cars transporting radioactive materials.

Lionel's crew did not think of everything. Engineers never added an operating passenger car. They studied the American Flyer heavyweight passenger car that delivered and retrieved miniature mailbags, yet did not create something on a par with that model in O gauge. Lionel's counterparts at Gilbert also beat them to the punch with an operating caboose. Only a preliminary O gauge model exists of a caboose with a figure waving his lantern. In contrast, an S gauge "action caboose" was a staple of the American Flyer line from 1955 through 1958. In the latter year, Lionel did catalog a basic model equipped with a smoking mechanism (no. 6557).

Faulting Lionel's designers for not surpassing their rivals at Gilbert is short-sighted. So, too, is the tendency of hobbyists to dismiss the later operating cars. They need to spotlight the wonderfully creative responses that came forth from Lionel as its engineers and model makers recognized that their market was changing. Judging by the engineering samples and mock-ups in the Lionel corporate archives and private collections, even more incredible cars were planned. These different models prove that Lionel remained an inventive toy maker as the 1950s closed.

V. GOING OUT WITH A BANG: 1959-69

The operating cars first released by Lionel in 1959 shed light on that year as being one of transition. The powers-that-be had let go of the notion that children played with an electric train because they wanted to simulate work and learn about the greater world of transportation and commerce. The educational aims that had, for so much of Lionel's history, motivated parents

to purchase outfits for their offspring carried far less weight. Kids considered a train set a source of entertainment, and designers and sales executives at Lionel tried to satisfy them with ingenious, sometimes silly operating cars. Those models, the grandchildren of the Mickey Mouse handcar, played prominent roles in the product line throughout the second half of the 1950s.

But what it takes to entertain children never stays constant. The automatic operation and physical antics of the brakeman car and animated gondola gave way to the visual magic of the traveling aquarium and the surprises of the operating United States mail car.

Then what? Maybe putting more bounce in a couple of traditional models whose appeal was waning might ratchet up the annual sales figures for 1959. Therefore, while still cataloging the nos. 3356 horse car and 3662 automatic refrigerated milk car, Lionel announced the arrival of new versions of those models that it hoped would drive kids to scream, "Gotta have it!"

Lionel molded the horse car and yard out of white plastic and proclaimed them to be the no. 3366 operating circus car and corral. A similar external makeover awaited the milk car and its platform. They emerged as the no. 3672, whose yellow-and-brown

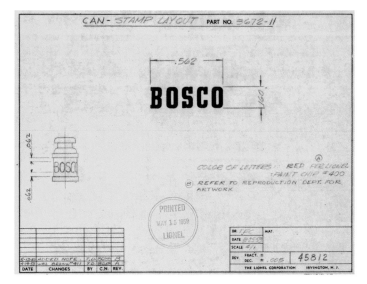

Stamping and color instructions for the 3672-11 Bosco Syrup cans.

color scheme celebrated Bosco, a popular syrup that kids spooned into glasses of milk to give it a chocolate flavor.

Both models were noble efforts, but neither they nor their two staid cousins (the 3356 and 3662) sold well. All but the circus car were gone after 1960. The 3366 survived for another year; later, the basic horse and milk cars returned for a final run that lasted from 1964 through 1966.

If circus steeds and Bosco cans, chicken sweepers and tropical fish weren't the answers that Lionel was searching for in 1959, what might be the key to bolstering sales? Executives once more seized on the need for interaction. Common kinds of labor, notably unloading freight, hardly cut it any more. For insights into what activities left kids genuinely excited, Lionel turned to television, comic books, and, in particular, a new and aggressive player in the toy industry.

Kusan Incorporated, a toy maker based in Nashville, Tennessee, had at the end of 1954 acquired the tooling and inventory of AMT. Three years later, it had developed an O gauge Atomic Train that included a diesel equipped with a movable machine gun and cars that featured flashing lights, artillery, and a rocket. The Satellite Train followed in 1958. It boasted a radar scanner, nuclear containers, a searchlight, and a "Compressortron" (a motor inside this car blew a stream of air upward to suspend a Styrofoam "satellite" above the moving train).

Lionel responded with an array of great trains. Three types of operating cars, each sporting military hardware, strutted forward in 1959. The action they promised varied, although it was, by and large, interactive and not automatic. How that action was generated also varied. For one model, an operator needed a remote controller. For another, he waited to depress a spring-loaded lever. Ironic that springs, which toy trains depended on for their locomotion before electricity was harnessed in the late nineteenth century, constituted the source of animation for many of the operating models of armament on rails that Lionel offered between 1959 and 1964.

To compete with Kusan, Lionel in 1959 trotted out the no.

3540 operating radar scanning scope car. This inauspicious model featured a figure that alertly checked the radar unit automatically revolving while the car traveled. There was nothing terribly exciting about this model, which benefited from the drive-belt and pulley system that Lionel's engineers had recently devised and would later use on the no. 3545 operating TV monitor car, brought out in 1961.

Next in 1959 came the no. 3419 helicopter launching car. This remote-controlled car would, at the touch of a button, release a whirlybird, its main double-propeller rotor spinning over a layout. The 3419 received excellent publicity in the weekly magazines *Life* and *Look* and stayed in the line through 1965. By that time, more versions of this car (linked with the U.S. Navy or Marine Corps) appeared in the cataloged line and a variety of promotional outfits.

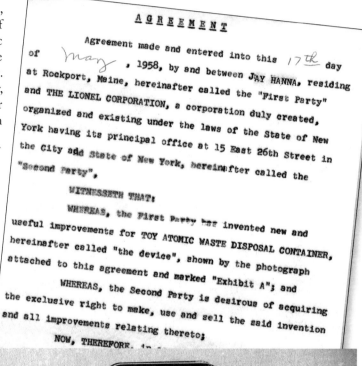

The original Atomic Waste Disposal Container (6805) contract between Jay Hanna and Lionel and a photo of Jay Hanna's original mock-up.

These manual- and remote-controlled models, numbered 3409, 3410, and 3429, along with their 'copters, fall into the Space and Military category, which will be covered in depth in a future volume as part of Project Roar Publishing's Lionel Postwar Encyclopedia Series. For that reason, they, as well as other space and military items, are not covered in this volume.

The third type of operating car Lionel released in 1959 didn't mess around when it came to confronting imaginary foes. The no. 6650 missile launching car did what its name said: At the flick of a spring-loaded lever on the side of the base assembly, it delivered a warhead at whatever target its operator selected. Boys might aim at a younger brother or a bowl of goldfish; Lionel, however, recommended they choose a new item designed to shatter on contact – either a no. 943 exploding ammo dump or a no. 6470 exploding target car. The latter loosely qualifies as an operating car. The main pieces of that red plastic box car were rigged together with a spring-loaded assembly so that, once hit by a missile, they flew high into the air.

The wide range of operating cars available in 1959 suggested that Lionel's leaders were walking a tightrope, as they tried to develop and sell models that might appeal to different segments of the market. They tended to accept that different kinds of operating cars were essential to pleasing those diverse audiences. Cars that operated automatically and entertained visually would win over young kids. Military items requiring interaction might entice older boys.

Occasionally, as with the no. 3512 operating fireman and ladder car (new in 1959), Lionel promoted a model its leaders thought could reach all customers. Unfortunately, this model's intricate operation and fragile parts proved to be frustrating and hurt sales. Still, Lionel persevered, struggling to create both kinds of operating cars and finding models that combined visual effects with the interaction (launching rockets and combating national foes) kids desired.

The overarching philosophy of satisfying all consumers survived well into the 1960s. The tremendous creativity and productivity seen in the operating cars first released in 1959 did not dissipate. Unlike, say, the late prewar period or the early 1950s, a year or two of innovation in the area of operating cars did not give way to quiet and inactivity. Just the opposite occurred. The models introduced between 1960 and 1963 attest to the ingenuity and determination of engineers to stretch the boundaries of what a toy train could do to engage a youngster.

However, a shift in thinking was going on, one that can be traced to the pivotal year of 1959. The inventive minds at Lionel still thought they could entertain kids, though models with automatic operation and outlandish visual effects were losing their effectiveness. Youngsters, the company's leaders realized, increasingly wanted military- and space-oriented operating cars with interactive features that enabled them to send objects into the air and destroy enemy installations.

Evidence of how rapidly Lionel adapted to that changing market can be found by perusing the consumer catalog released in 1960. The coal dumping cars and related accessories were gone, as outdated as steam locomotives. Log cars were gone, too, though, like a fading nightclub crooner, they would make periodic comebacks in the 1960s. The gray car showed up in green in 1961 as the no. 3362, with an inferior dumping mechanism. It carried silver-painted dowels that were supposed to be tanks filled with

helium. A successor (no. 3364) made its debut in 1964, swapping the tanks for three brown-stained logs.

Revised versions of such "old reliables" as the operating box car and the milk car bowed out after 1960. The operating United States mail and poultry dispatch cars, the last descendants of the venerable 3464, would be banished, although the latter returned for a three-year run in 1964. Barrels were nowhere to be seen, as forgotten as the crates ejected by merchandise cars.

No coal, no logs, no barrels – but lots of giraffes! The Lionel operating car that captured the most attention in 1960 was a model on which a plastic giraffe raised and lowered its head through a hole in the roof of a stock car. The nos. 3376 and 3386 cars relied on the track clips and tell-tales that had controlled the 3424 brakeman car between 1956 and 1958. Designers now utilized those parts to put on a show that ran automatically once the Bronx Zoo car was placed on the tracks. Kids who had squealed with joy at seeing the operating poultry dispatch and traveling aquarium must have begged for one of the giraffe cars offered through most of the 1960s.

These models, funny as they were, represented an aberration in a train line that seemed to be administered by the Department of Defense. The changing character of that line coincided with the acquisition by Lionel of businesses that made military and aerospace hardware. To understand how things were changing, consider the sole searchlight car illuminating the skies over Lionelville in 1960. The older models had vanished. In their place stood the no. 3535 security car with rotating searchlight. But this model was unlikely to garner praise from Joshua Cowen, who had turned over control of the firm to his grandnephew Roy Cohn the previous year. For alongside the searchlight and atop the red cab was mounted a revolving antiaircraft gun.

Compared with other artillery strapped to cars in 1960, that antiaircraft gun was firing darts. Packing a more powerful punch was the 6650, which stayed in the line through 1963. Lionel also cataloged a special version of the missile launching flat car (no. 6640). That model, painted olive drab and lettered for the Marine Corps, served as part of an O27 set. New, though it carried lighter ammunition, was the no. 6544 missile firing trail car. Its spring-loaded mechanism could nail a target with four plastic projectiles and reload with the extra four missiles on the car.

Springs were put to greater use over the next few years. In 1961, they helped Lionel send satellites into orbit and fire missiles from a special box car. The remote-controlled no. 3519 automatic satellite launching car joined a manually operated version designated as no. 3509. These models capitalized on the spring-loaded launching device installed on the helicopter launching cars. Meanwhile, the no. 3665 Minuteman missile launching car was putting on quite a show as its firing device rose through the roof halves of the box car in which it was concealed. Additional versions of the missile launching car (no. 6630) and exploding target car (no. 6480) entered the line. Other than their colors, these operating cars were identical to earlier models.

In 1962, a slightly different spring-loaded device was designed for the first versions of the turbo missile launching car (nos. 3309 and 3349). Pressing a tab on the mechanism sent a "missile" spinning upward. Between 1962 and 1965, Lionel had four cataloged and promotional models, differentiated by the number of operating couplers and the color of the unpainted car.

More elaborate was the no. 3413 Mercury capsule launching

The 3512 with a silver lader is a collectors favorite.

car, also new in 1962. A launcher on the car used a tightly wound spring to propel the onboard rocket to a certain height, at which point a string tethered to the car halted its ascent. The rocket's momentum caused the capsule on the nose to lift off and keep rising. On the capsule's way down, a parachute opened to allow it to drift to earth, as occurred on the Mercury spacecraft launched from Cape Canaveral.

Designers intrigued by the possibilities of springs ended up with a special box car from which a helicopter could be launched. The no. 3619 helicopter reconnaissance car also belonged to the Class of '62. A remote-controlled plunger on the near-scale yellow plastic box car caused the two vertical sections of the unpainted black roof to separate. A platform inside the model was automatically elevated, and the HO scale chopper attached to it was sprung into the sky, with its main rotor spinning. The array of special effects was worthy of the latest film from Hollywood.

Finally in 1962, the engineering staff at Lionel developed their own version of Kusan's Compressortron. Known as the aerial target launching car, the no. 3470 featured a motor that, drawing power from the three-rail tracks, generated a stream of air over the car. An inflated balloon rather than a Styrofoam sphere hovered above as the operating car moved on its journey. At any moment, though, a missile might streak over the horizon and knock out the balloon.

Quite an array of space- and military-oriented operating models! Add in the locomotives, motorized units, rolling stock, and accessories, and you can see why Lionel felt confident that it had met the demands of youngsters who wanted the most exciting and up-to-date trains. And just to make sure that other concerns weren't ignored, three humorous, original cars entered the line.

The no. 3370 Wells Fargo operating stock car benefited from the westerns inundating television watchers between 1961 and 1964, when it was cataloged. Plastic figures of a sheriff and an outlaw rose and fell automatically, as though they were aiming six-shooters at each other. What looked like a scene from *Gunsmoke* or *Have Gun Will Travel* was made possible by a special assembly that consisted of a cam on one axle, an actuator lever and pawl, and a ratchet wheel. Fans of the Old West also favored an even simpler

model, featuring the bobbing heads of horses, made available a year later. The no. 6473 horse transport car remained in the catalog from 1962 through 1966 and was eventually brought back in 1969, the end of the postwar period.

The third of these entertaining models was the no. 3357 hydraulic platform maintenance car, which enjoyed a three-year run, beginning in 1962. The wild animation consisted of a police officer and a hobo, who appeared to leap from a box car to an overhead platform in a madcap chase. As the cop rode on top of the car, he bore down on the tramp, standing on the two-piece trestle. The second he jumped onto the platform to catch the hobo, the latter figure moved onto the box car and sped away – until the car passed under the trestle again. The animation was consistent and fun, making the 3357 one of the overlooked jewels of Lionel's operating cars.

Of course, purists may decry the direction that operating cars took in the early 1960s. But a thoughtful assessment lauds the ability of both Lionel's leaders to recognize that the market for their trains was changing and its engineers to repeatedly come up with new models to attempt to satisfy consumers. Once older work-oriented cars no longer sufficed and newfangled models offering automatic entertainment fell short, designers plunged ahead with interactive cars that exploited the interest in space travel and military readiness (both related to underlying anxiety about global tensions). Keeping Lionel afloat meant, or so they believed, creating playthings that provided opportunities to launch satellites, detonate box cars, and protect facilities from enemies.

The real shame is that corporate leaders elected to pull the plug on the engineers' efforts at the end of 1963. To save money, the department was shut down and contracts terminated. Even Bonanno, the chief engineer, was let go. Operating cars introduced between 1964 and 1969 can be categorized in one of two ways. They were either developments that predated that closing (the no. 6651 shell launching car) or reissues of earlier entries (the 3434 poultry dispatch and 3662 automatic refrigerated milk car).

Don't conclude that the imaginative designers working under Bonanno's watchful eye had run out of ideas for operating cars. The quantity and diversity of models brought out between 1959 and 1963 belies that view. So does the extraordinary range of mock-ups reported over the years. Never-cataloged engineering samples of operating cars that launched spacecraft, dispensed candy, handled baggage, transported gorillas and other wild beasts, directed rockets, and lobbed missiles testify to the unstoppable enthusiasm and wide-ranging plans of Lionel's designers.

VI. A SALUTE TO THE CARS AND THEIR DESIGNERS

The little-remembered members of the firm's engineering department are, in some many respects, the heroes of the Lionel saga. Their fresh ideas and innovative models blazed new trails, especially during the post-World War II period, when an electric train was the most exciting and magical gift a child could receive. Designers, model makers, electrical engineers, and draftsmen devised ways to simulate in miniature an amazing variety of tasks and activities, most though not all based on real acts. Their ingenious use of magnets, pulleys, springs, solenoids, and other parts broke new ground in what kids could do with their toy trains.

As you read this comprehensive look at Lionel's postwar operating cars, pause to appreciate the efforts of Frank Pettit and other members of Joseph Bonanno's staff, along with such outsiders as Richard Smith and Kenneth Van Dyck. Thanks to them, Lionel enthusiasts were able to dump timber, eject packing crates, fire missiles, toss barrels, sweep stock cars, unload milk cans, launch satellites, and chase tramps on their O or O27 gauge railroads.

Now read on about the dozens of operating cars that have been delighting toy train fans for generations. You'll learn about how they operate and when they were added to the Lionel line. There is information about the changes that Lionel made in individual cars over the years and how those variations make collecting operating cars enjoyable. We also share insights into what makes each type of operating car significant and worth acquiring to help you decide which models to hunt for so that your roster of postwar operating cars grows and brings more pleasure. Best yet, the information comes straight from thousands of authentic Lionel documents, combined with many years of expert observations, to make this the "Authoritative Guide to Lionel's Postwar Operating Cars."

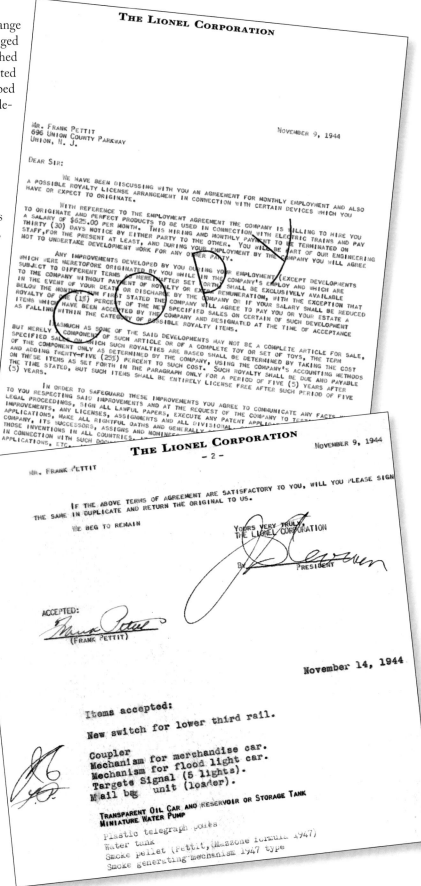

Frank Pettit's 1944 employment agreement detailing his salary, royalty payments and items in which he was to receive royalties.

CHAPTER ONE

Box Cars

3357-1 COP AND HOBO CAR (BOXED VERSION): 1962 - 1965
3357-25 COP AND HOBO CAR (UNBOXED VERSION): 1962 - 1965

Often referred to as a "Hydraulic Platform Maintenance Car", the 3357-1 represented the component *boxed* version of the Cop and Hobo Car, although the "-1" was not printed on the box or the car.

The 3357 Cop and Hobo Car used a modified Scout-type box car, but the action was brand new and exciting. A platform was added to the roof upon which the cop or hobo could be positioned. A two-piece metal trestle was also included, upon which the other figure could be placed. The never-ending action began as the box car, holding let's say the cop, passed under the trestle holding the hobo. As the box car passed under the trestle, the cop would hop onto the trestle, but to his amazement, the hobo would in turn jump off onto the top of the passing box car. Naturally, the action could be repeated.

The 3357 was almost perfectly depicted in the full-color 1962 and two-color 1963 consumer catalogs, except that part of the vertical row of rivets to the left of the double doors was incorrectly missing. In 1964, it didn't fare any better as it was incorrectly depicted as a stock car.

The 3357 used the same shell as the Scout-type box cars (mold no. 1004-3), except its roof was modified to accommodate the gray plastic platform and the other parts necessary for the action of the cop and hobo.

Lionel's operating box cars came in a variety of designs and road names.

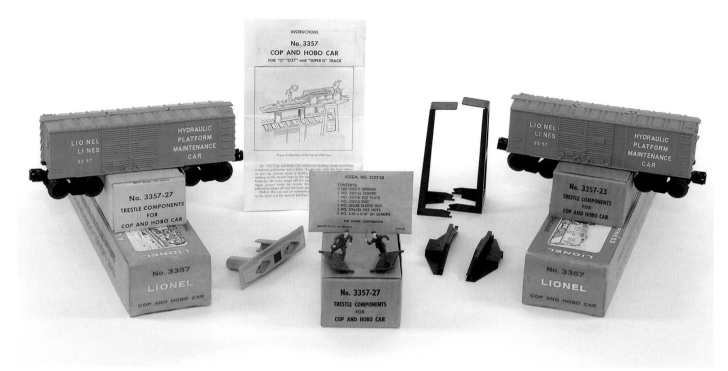

Left: Type IIb regular-production box car. Right: Type IIb teal blue. Left: Type I accessory box in white. Middle: Type II in brown. Right: Type III, which was actually numbered "3357-23" on the brown box. Left: Light Orange Picture box. Right: Dark Orange Picture box.

> Per Lionel Blueprints, two bosses to support platform screws were added to the inside of the frame on 4-10-62 and were quickly followed by two ribs to support them on 5-8-62. Also, the "U" shaped openings on the 3357 body top were originally to be machined (body after machining was 3357-11) but changed to pierced (body after piercing 3357-10).

For 1962, the 3357-1 was offered for separate sale at $7.95 and included in promotional set 19206. The 3357-1 incorporated two AAR trucks with operating couplers following the normal AAR progression. Two complete rows of rivets were to the left of the door, and two complete and two "broken" rows (each with one rivet on the top and two on the bottom) were to the right. With the addition of the 3357's holes on the roof, it is commonly referred to as a Type IIb body (see Appendix A).

> Per Lionel Blueprints, the rivets were removed on 8-22-61. This was the date that they transitioned from Type I to Type IIa.

The 3357-25 was the *unboxed* version of the 3357, although the "-25" was not printed on the car. It was included in 1962 set 11222 and promotional sets through 1965. In this instance, the 3357 was placed *unboxed* within the appropriate set box. The smaller 3357-27 box, which included the peripherals to operate the cop and hobo, was also placed inside.

The 3357's shell was molded in several shades of blue polystyrene (dark blue was predominant), and the lettering was heat-stamped in white.

For 1963, light and medium blue plastic dominated production,

When placed in a set, the 3357-25 also included a 3357-27 accessory box packed loose, as shown in 1962, set 11222.

with "Teal Blue" being the shade collectors covet. A variation of the "Teal" even had a greenish tint to the plastic. The 3357-1 wasn't part of any cataloged sets, but was still offered for separate sale at $7.95. Also, by the end of production, the two vertical rows of rivets to the left of the double doors had been removed, leaving only one rivet on top and two (left) and one (left nearest door) at the bottom (also known as a Type III body).

> Per Lionel Blueprints, the rivets were removed on 8-8-63. This was the date that they transitioned from Type IIb to Type III.

For 1964, the 3357-1 was shown in the consumer catalog for separate sale only and at the same $7.95 price. Therefore, as Lionel cleaned house of leftover 3357-1s, boxed examples could include any of the previously mentioned variations.

For 1965, the 3357 was no longer illustrated in the consumer catalog. However, Lionel wasn't done selling off remaining Cop And Hobo Cars, as boxed 3357-1s were also included in three 1965 promotional sets. This was Lionel's last effort to sell off remaining 3357-1s, although some were probably sold through Madison Hardware Co. of New York City and other key retail outlets.

The 3357-1 was component boxed with a car and a 3357-27 accessory box.

- For Each Box:
  - Tuck Flap Number: 3357-24
  - Box Dimensions: 3¼" x 13½" x 2"
- Box Style Orange Picture (1962 - 1965)
  - Box Date: 6-62 or 11-62 (with logo on opposite end)
- Box Style Dark Orange Picture (1963 - 1965)
  - Box Date: 4-63 (logo on same end)

Each component box included a 3357-27 accessory box (tuck flap 3357-23) containing the 3357-21 Tenite (cellulosic plastic) cop and 3357-16 hobo, two 3357-2 bridge platforms, two 3357-3 bridge sides, a 3357-22 car platform assembly, a 3357-8 instruction sheet and a 3357-28 packed envelope (envelope no. 3357-29) with the remainder of the peripherals. Three variations of the 3357-27 accessory box exist.

- For Each Box:
  - Box Dimensions: 3" x 5½" x 2"
- Box Type I - 3357-27 White (1962 - 1965)
  - Tuck Flap Number: 3357-23B (one end) (1962 - 1965)
- Box Type II - 3357-27 Brown (1962 - 1965)
  - Tuck Flap Number: 3357-23-B (both ends) (1962 - 1965)
- Box Type III - 3357-27 Brown (3357-23 on the box) (1963 - 1965)
  - Tuck Flap Number: 3357-23-B (both ends)

Two versions of the 3357-8 instruction sheet exist: a 1962 version with a one-year warranty dated 6/62 and another version from 1963 - 1964 with a 90-day warranty but also dated 6/62. Lionel likely reverted back to the one-year warranty version in 1965.

Author's Comments: For the Cop and Hobo Car (as well as many others), Lionel made the distinction between boxed and unboxed items in their internal documentation: "-1" for boxed items and "-25" for unboxed.

With this new information herein, collectors can now check to ensure that they have the correct peripherals (3357-27 or 3357-23), instruction sheet (90-day versus one-year) and boxes (Orange or Dark Orange Picture).

Interestingly, the holes added to the mold were plugged for production of other Scout-type box cars. This led to a rare version of the 6050 Swift Premium box car with plugged holes open on top of the roof.

The two most desirable variations are the teal blue car and the white boxed version of the 3357-27, although the Type III variation is a sleeper.

3357		C7	C8	C9	Rarity
Regular Production	-25	10	15	30	R5
Type IIb	-1	40	90	180	R7
Teal Blue	-25	35	75	100	
Type IIb	-1	65	150	275	
Regular Production	-25	25	40	60	R8
Type III	-1	55	115	225	
Teal Blue	-25	50	75	100	
Type III	-1	80	150	250	

3424 OPERATING BRAKEMAN CAR: 1956 - 1958

Introduced in 1956, the 3424 was the first action box car to place a figure outside the car instead of inside. The action began as a low-bridge warning signal pole caused the trainman on top of the car's roof to fall prone before reaching a bridge, tunnel, or other obstruction. After safely passing through, a second signal pole brought him upright again, as all the action was done automatically.

The real work, however, was handled by a coil assembly hidden inside the car, allowing a plunger to activate the bracket and cam

Besides having a white or blue figure, the 3424s shell could be a light blue (left) or a dark blue (right).

assembly, which in turn enabled the figure to move up and down. Naturally, the power was picked up from the track by the use of a special sliding shoe.

Illustrated in the earlier dealer catalogs as an operating "Tell-Tale" car with Baltimore & Ohio Sentinel markings, the 3424's true Wabash identity was revealed when the full-color consumer catalog was issued in 1956.

In 1956, the 3424 was offered for separate sale at $8.95 and included in two O27 and three O gauge sets. It used two bar-end trucks with or without coupler tabs and silver knuckle pins.

The polystyrene plastic shell for the 3424 was identical to the one used for 6464 box cars, except that an .800" x .464" opening was pierced 3.275" (from the bottom inside) in the roof to allow for the swinging action of the brakeman. The top of the shell also revealed a thin line to the left of the brake wheel from the modification caused by the production of the 6352 Refrigerator Car, originally issued in 1955. This line was caused by an insert placed in the box car mold that allowed for the 6352's swinging top hatch and side door. This shell is commonly referred to as a Type IIb.

Although Lionel called for all the shell colors to be "blue 35", the shell for the 3424 was actually molded in light, medium, or dark blue plastic, and the lettering was heat-stamped in white. The vinyl figure came in blue or white and had painted face and hands. Examples of cataloged set 1561WS from 1956 usually have a car with a white figure, whereas cataloged set 2255W from the same year tends to have a blue figure.

> Per Lionel Blueprints, the 3424-33 figure was originally "VNG 9970 Blue 485" and was subsequently changed on 10-22-56 to "VG 9980 White."

With the white figure being in the line longer, this likely explains why they are more common.

For 1957, the separate-sale price was $9.95 and the 3424 was featured in two O gauge sets. The 3424 used the same shell and figures as it had in 1956, yet key features distinguished new production. A support hole was added to the top of the knuckle coupler's drawbar, and in some cases, the connecting wire to the power truck was pale-yellow instead of black. Don't forget about transition, as this leads to some cars having 1956 features in 1957.

In 1958, the 3424 was featured in set 2511W and the separate-sale price remained the same. The car was mechanically the same as in 1957.

Each 3424 came in a Late Classic component box with a 3424-90 corrugated insert that both protected the vinyl figure and stabilized the car inside the box. Included inside the component box was accessory box 3424-100 (see 3424-100 listing), which included an instruction sheet 3424-95 dated 8/56 (1956) or 5/57 (1957). In 1956, a 927-56 service station leaflet was also included.

- Box Style Late Classic (1956 - 1958)
  - Tuck Flap Number: 3424-89
  - Box Dimensions: 4½" x 11¾" x 3⅜"

The 3424-100 included signal poles that were molded in orange polystyrene plastic (see 3376 and 3386 Giraffe Car for darker orange listings).

> Per Lionel Blueprints, the metal support bases change from black oxidized to zinc plated on 5-15-56.

Author's Comments: A common misconception is that a 3424 with a white figure used a white pick-up shoe (collector shoe 474-5), whereas one with a blue figure used a blue shoe. If so, this was totally coincidental. Although the new sliding shoe was special, it is doubtful that Lionel would spend the time or energy on such an arrangement.

The pale-yellow connection wire used during the 1957 production year is an important feature to remember, especially when assembling certain sets, such as 2279WS.

Left: This 3424 box has a rubber-stamped "X" to the right of "Lionel." Right: The other box has a rubber-stamped "O" to the left of "Lionel."

Also, some 3424s had an "O" or "X" rubber-stamped on the outside of the component box. The meaning of these marks is not clear, although the "X" box is known to be part of 1956 set 1561WS, whereas the "O" box was included in 1956 set 2265WS.

Of further interest is that the Lionel mock-up for the Operating Brakeman Car was actually modified from the 1955 mock-up for the 6464-275 State of Maine Box Car. This unique preproduction model is shown in Chapter 8, Prototypes.

> Per Lionel Blueprints, the 3424 was originally scheduled to be heat-stamped in black with a black or yellow door. These were both changed to white on 4-20-56.

3424	C7	C8	C9	Rarity
White Figure	30	45	60	R5
	45	85	150	
Blue Figure	50	70	90	R7
	65	110	180	

3424-75 LOW BRIDGE SIGNAL (SEPARATE SALE ONLY): 1956 - 1957

The 3424-75 was another example of Lionel's ingenuity or thoughtfulness, as customers could replace a *single* pole and base that was lost or broken. Also, the 3424 could be accidentally

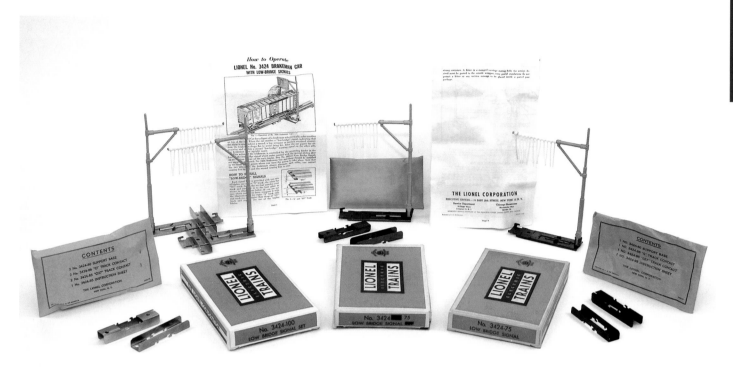

Offered as separate-sale items, the 3424-100 included two poles, while the 3424-75 had only one pole. Also shown are the 3424-75 Late Classic ("-100" over-stamp) and letter-press boxes.

triggered by the grounding clips on a 497 Coaling Station or a 3656 Operating Cattle Car thus leaving the figure in an inopportune position. The "-75" allowed an operator to reset the figure to avoid an accident.

The Lionel 3424-95 instruction sheet explained that 3424-75 Single Low-Bridge Signals could be obtained from the Lionel Service Department for $1.35 each. However, the instruction sheets were dated 8-56, which suggests that the 3424-75 wasn't readily available until the last quarter of 1956.

Therefore, it's logical that very few, if any orders, were ever placed during the 1956 production year, especially since the Christmas holidays were approaching. Lionel dealers and other customers had more important things to consider than a replacement item.

However, whether in late 1956 or early 1957, Lionel used existing 3424-100 Low Bridge Signal Set boxes for those first orders. In this case, Lionel blackened out the "-100", and rubber-stamped "-75" in its place.

> **Per Lionel Changes Affecting Future Production dated 11-10-56, for 1956 use folding box 3424-88 (3424-100 box) in place of 3424-98 (3424-75 box).**

Included in the rubber-stamped box was one 3424-76 signal pole with a 3" x 5½" blank packed envelope (no envelope number), containing one 3424-80 support base, one 3424-86 "O" track contact, one 3424-85 O27 track contact and a 3424-95 instruction sheet dated 8/56.

For 1957, the 3424-75 letter-pressed box was introduced and included either a blank packed envelope or a new 3424-96 3½" x 6½" printed packed envelope (envelope no. 3424-97) that contained the same hardware, but the instruction sheet was now dated 5/57.

> **Per Lionel Blueprints, the metal support bases change from black oxidized to zinc plated on 5-15-56.**

Each 3424-75 came in a Late Classic component box.

- For Each Box:
  - Box Dimensions: 4½" x 7" x 1"
- Box Style Late Classic Over-stamped 3424-100 (1956)
  - Tuck Flap Number: 3424-88
- Box Style Late Classic (1957)
  - Tuck Flap Number: 3424-98

Author's Comments: The 3424-75 wasn't listed as a "Replacement Accessory" in the 1956 consumer catalog or as "Extra Accessories" in the 1957 consumer catalog. Therefore, one way to obtain a "-75" was through the Lionel Service Department.

Also, the *box* is what makes the 3424-75 so special and is rarer than a red-lettered 3562-25 Operating Barrel Car, thus accounting for the assigned rarity

3424-75	C7	C8	C9	Rarity
Over-stamped 3424-100 or 3424-75 Late Classic Box	150	300	500	R10

3424-100 LOW BRIDGE SIGNAL SET: 1956 - 1958

Unlike the 3424-75, the 3424-100 was included in the consumer catalog as a replacement accessory for $2.50 in 1956 and 1957, and $2.95 in 1958, when it was leftover inventory from the previous year's production.

The 3424-100 came component boxed and included two 3424-76 signal poles, and a 3494-93 packed envelope (envelope no. 3424-94) containing two 3494-80 metal support bases, two metal track contacts (both 3424-86 "O" and 3424-85 O27) and a 3424-95 instruction sheet dated 8/56 (1956) or 5/57 (1957). The signal poles were molded in orange polystyrene plastic (see 3376 and 3386 Giraffe Car for darker orange listing). This was perfect for operators wanting to add the "tell-tale" action of the Brakeman Car to another area on their layout.

> Per Lionel Blueprints, the metal support bases change from black oxidized to zinc plated on 5-15-56.

Each 3424-100 came in a Late Classic component box.

- Box Style Late Classic
  - Tuck Flap Number: 3424-88
  - Box Dimensions: 4½" x 7" x 1"

Author's Comments: It's curious that the 3424-75 had a lower suffix number than the 3424-100. This suggests that it was made first. However, the 3424-100 had a lower tuck flap number "-88" than its counterpart "-98", and that suggests the complete opposite.

There is technically no difference between the 3424-100 originally offered for separate sale or included with each 3424. Although the ones designated for separate sale were offered in much lower quantities (April 1957 records revealed that 400 units were contemplated and the following year 200 remained as leftover inventory) it is nearly impossible to tell the difference.

3424-100	C7	C8	C9	Rarity
Late Classic Box	25	35	60	R6

3428 OPERATING MAIL CAR: 1959 - 1960

The 3428 Operating Mail Car replaced the 3494 operating box car series. The colorful 3428 was painted with three horizontal stripes of red-white-blue, although the roof and ends were painted *only* red. The white-painted middle section had black heat-stamped lettering, whereas the other two (top and bottom) had white heat-stamped lettering.

The 3428 provided simple, yet enjoyable animation. A plunger located beneath the car was all that was necessary to generate the action. When the car was placed on an activated remote-control track, the door opened and the postal clerk tossed out a mailbag.

The 3428 was offered in one cataloged set each year (1626W in 1959 and 1640W in 1960), as well as for separate sale at $7.95, which was the same price as the discontinued 3494 box car series. It incorporated two AAR trucks with operating couplers and followed the normal AAR progression.

Most shells were molded in the same blue polystyrene plastic as the 6464-275 State of Maine box car, thus indicating that the two cars probably paralleled each other in production. The inside roof line for these shells introduced during 1958 was ribbed, which collectors call a Type III box car.

Gray shells with a smooth inside roof line were also used and had the 6352's visible line on the roof (see 6352). These shells were phased out during 1958 but continued to be used in 1959 until depleted. These are commonly known by collectors as a Type IIb box car.

The 1.400" tall vinylite figure for the 3428 was gray (3428-15) or blue (3428-18) with painted face and hands. The .750" vinylite mail bags were molded in the same colors as the figure, gray (3428-22) or blue (3428-11), and are often observed paired with a figure of the opposite color.

The blue figure, less common to find than the gray, was most often included with the Type IIb box car. The gray figure was the norm for the Type III. This suggests that the Type IIb box car with blue figure was produced first. In fact, the blue figure was pictured with the 3428 in the full-color consumer catalog for 1959.

> Per Production Control Files dated 4-24-59, "Note: Use mail bag assembly in color opposite of color of figure." Also, per Lionel Blueprints, each 3428 originally was to have three mail bags, but this was changed to one on 5-21-59.

Each 3428 was component boxed, with a 3428-11 or 3428-22 mail bag loose in the car (per the instruction sheet) and a 3428-23 instruction sheet dated 8/59.

The 3428 included either a gray or blue figure with mail bags of the opposite color, as was Lionel's intended production.

- Box Style Orange Perforated (1959 - 1960)
  - Tuck Flap Number: 3428-20
  - Box Manufacturer: CCA
  - Box Dimensions: 3⅜" x 10" x 2⅜"

Author's Comments: Thanks to Lionel's Production Control Files, it was discovered that Lionel intended to have gray mail bags with blue figures and blue mail bags with gray figures. How these were actually produced may never be determined, although blue bags and figures are less common than gray.

The *Lionel Service Manual* incorrectly transposes numbers of the gray and blue mail bags. This has likely led to the confusion over which color combination was intended.

> Also of note, the Lionel Component Parts Index indicated that the shell color was originally supposed to be black, but changed to gray on 5-28-59.

3428	C7	C8	C9	Rarity
Type IIb	85	125	150	R7
Blue Figure & Gray Bag	115	175	225	R8
Type IIb	75	100	125	R7
Gray Figure & Blue Bag	100	150	200	R8
Type III	85	125	150	R7
Blue Figure & Gray Bag	115	175	225	R8
Type III	75	100	125	R7
Gray Figure & Blue Bag	100	150	200	R8

3434 OPERATING CHICKEN CAR WITH SWEEPER: 1959 -1960 & 1964 - 1966

Introduced in 1959, the 3434 was another new action car designed to replace the previous 3484/3494 operating box car series. The 3434 had a magnetically activated plunger beneath the car that opened the box car door and caused an attendant to appear to sweep the car floor with a broom. This clever mechanism had the attendant attached to a frame pivoting on a thin wire assembly. Even though the car's attendant made for a newer, almost adorable, sweeping action, the operating mechanism's fragile interior design often broke, leaving the attendant dangling.

In 1959 and 1960, the car was painted Lionel's color chip #812 tan (really brown), with white heat-stamped lettering. As with the 3428, a gray (3434-10) or blue (3434-19) vinylite figure with painted face and hands was used. However, the earliest gray figures weren't painted at all.

> Per Lionel Blueprints, the early painted figures used Lionel's #502 yellow, but this was changed to #434 "flesh" on 7-22-59.

In 1959 and 1960, the trucks were bar-end with operating couplers and a roller pickup on one truck. Each 3434 was equipped with two light bulbs to backlight the printed celluloid figure plates illustrated with chickens. These chicken plates came in various shades of light colored plastic, and the poultry shades varied as well. The doors were molded in gray plastic, and the first doors were much lighter than the ones that followed in 1964 through 1966. Observations of changes in these features indicate that more than one production run was made in 1959.

In 1959, the 3434 was included with set 2535W and offered for separate sale at $7.95. In 1960 it was offered for separate sale only at $8.95.

Lionel reissued the 3434 in 1964 with plastic AAR trucks, which followed the normal AAR progression. It also featured the AAR version of the roller pickup on one truck. The tan paint and doors were darker than the earliest versions. The 3434 was included in set 13150 from 1964 through 1966 and for separate sale at $7.95 in 1964 and $8.00 thereafter.

The 3434 was component boxed with a car and 3434-21 instruction sheet.

- For Each Box (1959 - 1960 & 1964 - 1965):
  - Tuck Flap Number: 3434-14
  - Box Dimensions: 3⅜" x 12½" x 2½"
- Box Style Orange Perforated (1959 - 1960)
- Box Style Orange Picture (1964 - 1965)
- Box Style Cellophane Window (1966)
  - Tuck Flap Number: 12-228 (3434-24 not on box)
  - Box Dimensions: 3½" x 13¼" x 2½"

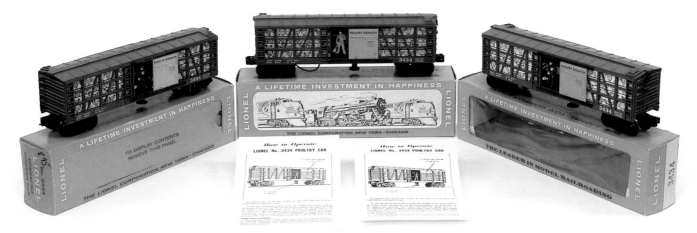

The 3434 came with either a blue figure (left and right) or a gray figure (middle). Also shown (left to right): Orange Perforated, Orange Picture and Cellophane Window boxes, as well as blue- and black-printed instruction sheets.

Three versions of the 3434-21 instruction sheet exist, dated: 8-59 (1959 - 1960); 8-59 with 90-day warranty and Lionel Toy Corporation (1964 - 1965); and 5/66 (1966). The front page of the instruction sheet was the same all five years. In 1959 and 1960 it was printed in blue ink; later, it was black.

The instruction sheets for the 3434 prove that some instruction sheet dates weren't always correct, as the date on the back page of the 1964 sheet was still 8-59. When Lionel reshot these newer versions, they updated the information about warranty, but not the date.

Author's Comments: These cars were likely poor sellers especially since Madison Hardware Co. had hundreds of the 1964 and 1966 versions in stock well into the 1970s. Ironically, finding a boxed 3434 is difficult because the boxes themselves, especially Orange Perforated and Cellophane Window, are hard to find in collector condition.

> Per Lionel Production Planning Records dated 6/20/66, only 800 units of the 1966 Cellophane Window boxes were produced.

In 1964, Lionel brought back the 3434 after a three-year hiatus, along with the 3356 and 3662. It was unusual to reissue cars after this length of time. However, top management had closed Lionel's engineering department after 1963, and it is unlikely that they focused many resources towards newly engineered items.

3434	C7	C8	C9	Rarity
1959 - 1960	75	100	125	R7
With Orange Perforated Box	125	175	250	R8
1964 - 1965	75	100	125	R8
With Orange Picture Box	100	125	200	
1966	75	100	125	R9
With Cellophane Window Box	150	225	300	

3434-50 OPERATING POULTRY CAR: 1960

The Lionel Factory Order for set 2555W (The well-known Father and Son Set) listed a "3434-50 Operating Poultry Car - Red." Why red? Further research indicates that Lionel was going to make a red 3434 to match the red 0834 Illuminated Poultry Car in HO set 5555W (the HO set included with 2555W).

> Per Lionel Engineering Specifications dated 2/15/60, the 3434-50 is identical to operating car (3434-1) with the following exceptions. Metal trucks replaced with plastic trucks (566 and 581); also, the body color has been changed.

Author's Comments: The Factory Order further stated that all 3434-50s were substituted out for 3434-1s. To make this even more intriguing, the consumer catalog shows a 6434 Poultry Car but lists a 3434 instead for 1960. This supports the idea that Lionel may have been thinking about making a 3434 in red, hence the 3434-50.

This item is included for reference only, and price and rarity levels are not applicable. More information on this car and the 2555W is included in the *Authoritative Guide to Lionel Cataloged*

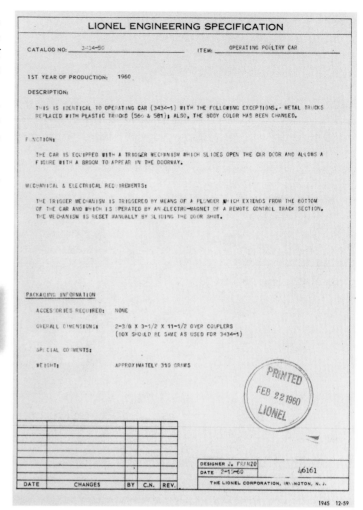

Lionel Engineering Specifications outline Lionel's plans for a 3434-50.

Outfits 1960 - 1969, by Project Roar Publishing.

3435 AQUARIUM CAR: 1959 - 1962

One of the most collectible of all the postwar operating cars, or any car for that matter, is Lionel's exclusive "Fish Bowl" on wheels, the 3435 Aquarium Car.

By the flick of a switch, located at the bottom of the car, rare tropical fish could be viewed swimming inside the illuminated interior of the car. In fact, the fish were actually printed on a celluloid film (moving belt) that attached to rotating pulleys located inside the car at each end and driven by Lionel's "Vibrotor" motor. The background included an underwater scene printed on a celluloid screen panel fitted over the two light bulbs and motor. This panel was held in place by two molded nubs on the inside roof of the shell.

The shell also had two guidance posts molded inside the end with the screw hole. These posts provided stabilization guidance for the plain pulley. The shell was molded in clear polystyrene, but the windows were not painted. These "wavy" windows provided the appearance of fish swimming underwater.

In 1959, the 3435 was included in four cataloged sets and for separate sale at $12.95. The 3435 was shown in the consumer catalog with white or black lettering, but wasn't made that way.

3435 versions (clockwise from left): Type I with gold lettering and Circle "L" and Tank designations, Type II the same but no Circle "L", Type III without Tank designations, and Type IV with yellow lettering.

Based on the different decorations of the 3435, more than one production run was needed. In fact four versions have been observed. All 3435s used a clear polystyrene shell. The first two versions were first painted with a coat of black primer to eliminate any "glowing" effect. This black primer was then covered with a final coat of green.

Both cars used gold-leaf heat-stamped lettering. The earliest example included a gold circle heat-stamped around the Lionel "L." Lionel must have had a difficult time centering the circle, because it soon was omitted. Both versions had the words, "Tank 1 and Tank 2", below the clear window of each car.

> Per Lionel Production Control Files, the 3435-5 "car body painted" was originally to be painted green (color chip #619) only, but was changed to be painted black (#21-313) first and then green.

The next version eliminated the black primer and "Tank 1 and Tank 2." The shell was now just painted green, and silver paint was added to the inside roof of the car. This reflective paint aided in the illumination of the car. At the same time, the drive pulley changed from clear polystyrene to opaque white (natural Zytel® #101) nylon, although the plain (idler) pulley remained clear.

By the end of 1959, Lionel stopped experimenting and found the optimal manufacturing solution, an Aquarium Car with yellow rubber-stamped lettering, which is the most common variation.

Type	Circle Around "L"	"Tank 1 and Tank 2"	Letters	Body Paint	Decorating Process
I	Yes	Yes	Gold Leaf	Black Primer and Green	Heat Stamping
II	No	Yes	Gold Leaf	Black Primer and Green	Heat Stamping
III	No	No	Gold Leaf	Green With Silver on Inside of Roof	Heat Stamping
IV	No	No	Yellow	Green With Silver on Inside of Roof	Rubber Stamping

Guidance Posts

Drive Pully Change

3435 Type I on left and Type IV on right. Notice the differences in the bodies.

In 1960, the 3435 was included with cataloged set 2553WS and for separate sale at $12.95. In 1961 and 1962, the 3435 was offered for separate sale only, and those were leftover inventory from prior years. The price remained at the same $12.95.

All 3435s came with AAR-style trucks and couplers with a roller pickup on one truck. They followed the normal AAR progression.

The 3435 was component boxed with a 3435-33 instruction sheet dated 8-59.

- Box Style Orange Perforated (1959 - 1962)
  - Box Manufacturer: CCA
  - Tuck Flap Number: 3435-34
  - Box Dimensions: 3½" x 11½" x 2⅜"

Author's Comments: The 3435 was yet another example of leveraging concepts already in production, as it was an extension of the 3444. The 3435 used the same frame with modifications, as well as the same operating concept; i.e. celluloid film around two pulleys powered by a "vibrator" motor.

The underwater scene and colorful fish were just some of the creative artwork of long-time employee Louis Melchionne. They added visual excitement to the operation of the car.

Of all the Aquarium Cars, the Circle "L" variation is the rarest, with the same rarity level as a black lettered 3484-25 Operating Santa Fe Box Car.

An early preproduction shell molded in bluish-green plastic was observed without the inside roof nubs and end guidance posts (see Chapter 8). Therefore, it is possible that an early production version with these features exists.

3435	C7	C8	C9	Rarity
Type I - Circle "L"	1,200	1,800	2,700	R10
and "Tank 1 and Tank 2"	1,300	2,000	3,000	
Type II	400	600	800	R9
"Tank 1 and Tank 2"	500	800	1,100	
Type III	250	350	450	R8
Gold Lettering	350	500	650	
Type IV	125	175	225	R6
Yellow Lettering	175	250	325	R7

3454 OPERATING MERCHANDISE CAR: 1946 - 1947

The 3454 was the first new 9¼-inch operating box car made during the postwar era. Before the fun began, each car needed to be manually loaded with six miniature packing cases through the hatch door on the roof. The car's action began at the touch of the unload button. This operation opened the sliding door, and each subsequent activation ejected a plastic packing case onto the 160-1 3" x 7" Bakelite bin included with the car. After several cases were unloaded, the door closed automatically.

Each 3454 was component boxed, with a corrugated liner and early non logo-striped paper that protected the car and nested the bin. Also included was a packed envelope with the instruction sheet and six miniature packing cases (all of the same color), each with "Baby Ruth" molded on the case. The cases came in three colors: burgundy, black, and red. Original cases without "Baby Ruth" were probably from the prewar era.

The 3454 was incorrectly depicted in the 1946 catalog as brown with white lettering, whereas the 3454 was actually painted silver with blue heat-stamped lettering. A limited run of 3454s was heat-stamped with red lettering and are very rare. In fact, less than a dozen are known to exist. Other one-of-a-kind versions were also manufactured and are pictured in Chapter 8.

In 1946, staple-end trucks with the coupler head and coil assembly (TC10) were secured to the bottom frame assembly (TC102) by a swedging and crimping process. In addition, the connecting wires were blue. Also, the roof door (hatch) pin was brass and did not extend through the end of the car. In 1946, the 3454 was included in four cataloged sets and offered for separate sale at $5.95.

In 1947, the 3454 was included in only one cataloged set and available for separate sale at $5.95. The coupler was the same, except it was now secured by a swedging and staking process. The connecting wires were black, and an aluminum pin now extended through the end of the car to facilitate assembly. The heat-stamped lettering was a brighter blue than before.

The 3454 came with six burgundy, six black or six red cases (two of each are shown here).

Left: The 3454 from 1946 lacks an extended hatch pin. Right: The 3454 from 1947 has this pin.

The **3454 was component boxed with a car, a corrugated liner, a 160-1 bin, non logo-striped paper, a packed envelope (envelope no. 3454-51) with six 3814-53 packing cases and a 3454-57 instruction sheet.**

- Box Style Art Deco (1946)
  - Tuck Flap Number: None
  - Box Dimensions: 4"x 11" x 3¼"
- Box Style Art Deco Toy Logo (1947)
  - Tuck Flap Number: None
  - Box Dimensions: 3⅝" x 11" x 3¼"

Author's Comments: Being on the early end of the postwar era, these cars are becoming more difficult to find in collector condition.

Age alone has caused the silver to fade in many of these, and time is also taking its toll on the boxes. Because the 1947 car was included in one set only, it is more difficult to find than the 1946 version.

Also, a brown-painted 3454 is known to exist, but whether this one-of-a-kind car was used for the 1946 catalog illustration is not known.

3454	C7	C8	C9	Rarity
1946 Version	50	100	150	R6
Pin Not Through Car End	100	200	350	R7
1947 Version	75	125	175	R8
Pin Through Car End	125	225	375	R9
Red-Lettered	1,500	2,200	3,500	R10
	1,600	2,400	3,800	

3464-1 N.Y.C. BOX CAR (NEW YORK CENTRAL): 1949 - 1952
3464-50 S.F. BOX CAR (SANTA FE): 1949 - 1952

Lionel's 3464 series included two 9¼-inch operating box cars decorated as New York Central and Santa Fe, each road name having national appeal. These road names also matched the popular F3 diesels that Lionel first cataloged in 1948. What could be better than to add these box cars to a matching F3?

The 3464 took advantage of the track electromagnet, as the model's metal plunger located beneath the car was drawn down, thus allowing the sliding door to open, and a figure to appear. The action was manually reset by closing the door. This was an inexpensive way for Lionel to add action to a basic box car.

Although the NYC did not appear in the 1949 advance and consumer catalogs, it was still made. In fact, it was a primary component of two sets: 2139W that featured a GG1 and 2151W led by a NYC F3.

Analysis of suffixes suggests that the NYC was *considered*, if not made, before the Santa Fe. For instance, although 1949 boxes

3464-1 from left to right: 1949 with Early Classic box, 1949 with Middle Classic box, 1950 with Middle Classic box and 1950 shorter Middle Classic box.

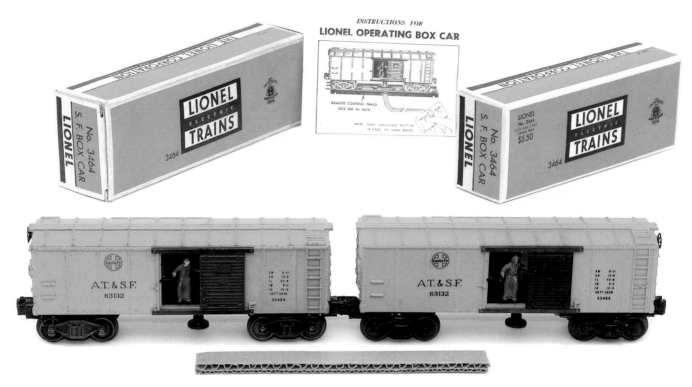

Left: Early 1949 ATSF. Right: 1952 car with OPS Classic box.

lacked a tuck flap number, when it appeared in 1950 it was 3464-25 for the NYC, whereas the Santa Fe was 3464-26. The NYC always had a lower suffix number than a Santa Fe. Also, the part number for a finished NYC shell was 3464-30, whereas the Santa Fe's was 3464-31. These lower suffixes support the view that the NYC was first. But more important, the 1953 advance catalog identified the Santa Fe as a 3464-50, although it was not produced that year.

> **Per Production Control Files, the 3464-30 box car body assembled NYC was dated 5-10-49, which was 17 days before the 3464-31 box car body assembled SF dated 5-27-49.**

The NYC was painted tan, with white heat-stamped lettering; the Santa Fe was painted orange, with black heat-stamped lettering. Because of the number of box cars needed to fill sets,

A 1949 example of the 3464 tan ATSF is extremely rare.

more than one production run was made. This fact would account for differences in the shades of paint on the two box cars (flat and glossy are recognized by collectors).

About the same time, Lionel stamped Santa Fe graphics on a short run in the NYC's color. These tan 3464 Santa Fe cars, reported to be service station replacement shells, were actually preproduction test shots of the Santa Fe stamping.

> The New York Central Car Production Control Files dated 4-29-49 show the body began as a 2454-3 molded in polystyrene and then painted "Brown L 813" to become a 2454-11 box car body painted, then white heat-stamped to become a 3464-18 box car body stamped NYC.
>
> The Santa Fe Lionel Production Control Files dated 5-27-49 show the 3464-33 Santa Fe car body was molded in orange opaque Styron™ and then painted "Orange L 525" to become a 3464-34 box car body painted, then black heat-stamped to become a 3464-32 box car body stamped SF.

Each box car (mold 2454-4) included a pair of chemically blackened die-cast metal doors (3464-20 for a plain door and 3464-22 for a door with a latch and large block), although some of the Santa Fe models used brown-painted doors.

Multiple variations of a 3464 were manufactured in 1949 with the first relating to the body. It appears that Lionel was working to add reinforcement to the catwalk overhang and quickly modified the catwalk which also led to some lost rivet detail.

Both the NYC and the SF shared the same 1949 features. Included were frames with steps, staple-end magnetic trucks and couplers, a "flared" activator flap rivet, and a 3464-17 vinylite figure

with painted face and hands. Some cars have the outdated coil couplers, which could have been due to transition. Also, the 3464-13 figure lever originally used a metal washer underneath on the bottom of the frame. This feature was subsequently eliminated.

Because of the quantities of cars required to fill the six cataloged sets and separate-sale orders (at $5.00), it appears that Lionel ran out of boxes or just ordered more boxes in accordance with company policy. In either case, they changed to Middle Classic boxes.

In 1950, the NYC was illustrated with several sets in the advance catalog but was again omitted from the consumer catalog. Both 3464s experienced changes, as the steps were removed from the frame and the figure was no longer painted. As for the trucks and couplers, the flared rivet was turned around with the round end showing and a hole was punched in the activator flap. Also, by August 1950, Lionel was using flathead door and brake-wheel rivets on some cars.

In 1950, the 3464s were included in eight cataloged sets and for separate sale at $5.00. Consequently, Lionel again needed more boxes during the year. These new boxes, only 8½" long, had no coupler protection flaps because the couplers could now be turned inward.

In 1951, the 3464 was part of four cataloged sets and the separate-sale price increased to $5.95. The car's features repeated, except the frame changed, as three holes and the slot where a 3472's base assembly would be attached were removed. Also during 1951, 3464-42 black polystyrene doors were introduced, and the trigger housing changed from metal to plastic, requiring a frame change from four to eight serrated edges. During the last run, the trucks changed to bar-end magnetic couplers.

In 1952 the 3464 was cataloged in two sets and offered for separate sale at $5.50 (a decrease from the year before).

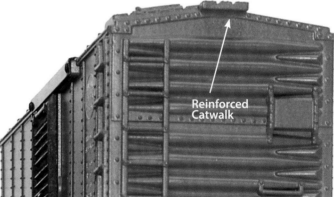

Left: The earliest examples of the 3464 included two extra rivets directly beneath the catwalk. **Right:** These were removed when reinforcement was added.

Top: Early 1949 frame. **Bottom:** Late 1951 frame.

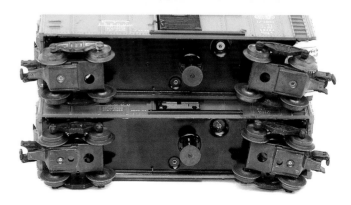

The **3464** was component boxed with a car, a 3464-29 corrugated truck alignment insert and a 3464-28 instruction sheet dated, 3/49 (1949); 1/50, 5/50 or 9/50 (1950); 4/51 or 10/51 (1951 and 1952); or a 3474-14 5/52 (1952).

- For Each Box:
  - Box Dimensions: 3¼" x 10" x 2¼"
- Box Style Early Classic (1949)
  - Tuck Flap Number NYC: None (3464-25 not on box)
  - Tuck Flap Number ATSF: None (3464-26 not on box)
- Box Style Middle Classic (1949 - 1950)
  - Tuck Flap Number NYC: None (1949) (3464-25 not on box)
  - Tuck Flap Number ATSF: None (1949) (3464-26 not on box)
  - Tuck Flap Number NYC: 3464-25 (1950)
  - Tuck Flap Number ATSF: 3464-26 (1950)
- For Each Box:
  - Box Dimensions: 3¼" x 8⅝" x 2¼"
- Box Style Middle Classic (1950 - 1952)
  - Tuck Flap Number NYC: 3464-38 (1950 - 1952)
  - Tuck Flap Number ATSF: 3464-39 (1950 - 1952)
- Box Style OPS Classic (1952)
  - Tuck Flap Number NYC: (Existence unknown)
  - Tuck Flap Number ATSF: 3464-39
- Note the NYC also used over-stamped 3464 Santa Fe boxes

Per Lionel Production Control Files dated 3-4-49, the 3464-29 corrugated insert is to be cut to 8" x 1" using obsolete cardboard.

Author's Comments: Much has been written about which 3464 was made first. The Production Control Files provide definitive documentation that the NYC was made first. In either case it should not matter to most collectors and operators, as both road names were 1949 production line items.

With respect to set contents, it appears that Lionel used the Santa Fe or New York Central box cars interchangeably. Catalogs do not shed much light on this subject. Therefore, we have used our years of observations and research to determine which sets contained which car.

Early 3464s included a 1³⁄₁₆" x 1⅛" piece of cardstock (form no. 927) stating: "Important, To Open Door, Position Car Over Magnet In Remote Control Track, Press 'Uncouple' Button - Not 'Unload.'"

3464	C7	C8	C9	Rarity
3464-1 N.Y.C.	15	25	35	R4
	25	35	50	R6
3464-50 S. F.	15	25	35	R3
	25	35	50	R5
3464-50 S. F. With N.Y.C. Color (Tan)	750	2,000	3,000	R10
	760	2,010	3,025	

3474 W.P. BOX CAR (WESTERN PACIFIC): 1952 - 1953

Introduced in 1952, the attractively decorated 3474 Western Pacific Box Car was a new road name for the 9¼-inch operating box car series. It operated in the same manner as previous cars, specifically, when activated, a figure would appear out the door (see 3464).

Left: The 3474 included a Type I large, unpainted figure in 1952. Right: In 1953 it included a Type II small, unpainted figure.

The 3474 had a promising beginning, as the advance catalog for 1952 depicted it as part of three sets and for separate sale at $5.50. However, when the full-color consumer catalog was released, the 3474 was part of *only* set 1483WS. Although no longer offered for separate sale, the car's component box was letter-pressed $5.50 OPS, and included a corrugated truck alignment insert and a 3474-14 instruction sheet.

In the consumer catalog, the 3474 was incorrectly illustrated as being white. The car was actually painted silver and had black heat-stamped lettering. It also included a 3474-7 yellow-orange feather decal with the slogan "Rides Like A Feather." The 3474 used the same 1952 features as the 3464, except the black plastic doors were painted to match the car.

Per Lionel Production Control Files dated 5-14-52, the heat-stamped lettering was originally to be white.

In 1953, the 3474 was not offered for separate sale but was included in one cataloged set 1511S. The 3464-17 figure was reduced in size. Bar-end trucks were used for both years, but the silver truck pivot studs were phased out in favor of blackened ones. The Middle Classic box no longer had OPS information.

The 3474 was component boxed with a car, a 3464-29 corrugated truck alignment insert and a 3474-14 instruction sheet, dated 5/52 (1952) or 6/53 (1953).

- For Each Box:
  - Box Dimensions: 3¼" x 8⅝" x 2¼"
- Box Style OPS Classic (1952)
  - Tuck Flap Number: 3474-10X
- Box Style Middle Classic (1953)
  - Tuck Flap Number: 3474-10

FIGURES USED WITH LIONEL OPERATING CARS

Operating car figures (left to right): Type IP, Type I, Type II, Type IIP, Type IIP Altered and Type IIPT.

Lionel used both large and small, painted and unpainted figures, during the postwar era. Two part numbers were used for these figures. The first number, 3464-17, was used interchangeably for large or small, painted or unpainted, versions. The second and later number, 3562-62, could also be large or small, but all versions were painted.

The table below provides a summary of each figure used and the operating car with which they came. The types are defined as follows:

- Type I - Large unpainted figure (1⁵⁄₁₆" tall) with raised left arm.
- Type IP - Large painted figure.
- Type II - Small unpainted figure (1³⁄₁₆" tall) with left arm at side.
- Type IIP - Small painted figure.
- Type IIP Altered - Small painted figure with melted slot on bottom.
- Type IIPT - Small painted figure with "T" style slot on bottom.
- Note: All figures were various shades of blue vinylite.

Year	Figure Type	Figure Number	Car(s)
1949	IP	3464-17	3464-1 and 3464-50
1950	IP or I		
1951	I		
1952	I		3464-1, 3464-50, and 3474
1953	II		3474 and 3484-1
1954	II	3562-62	3562-1
1954	IIP		3562-1, 3562-25, and 3484-25
1955	IP		3562-25, 3562-50, 3484-25, and 3494-1
1956	IP		3562-50, 3484-25, 3494-150, and 3494-275
1957	IIP		3562-50 and 3562-75
1957	IIP		3494-275, 3494-550, and 3494-625
1958	IP		3562-75
1959	IIP Altered		6812
1960	IIPT		
1961	IIPT		6812 and 6822
'62 - '66 '68 - '69	IIPT		6822

47

Author's Comments: Collectors and operators are often confused over which 3474 came in 1952 and 1953. The information above should eliminate this confusion and has been validated by the production sample observed in the Lionel Archives. This will help collectors because boxed 1953 cars are much harder to find and are more collectible.

3474	C7	C8	C9	Rarity
1952 Version	50	100	150	R7
With OPS Classic Box	75	150	225	R8
1953 Version	50	100	150	R8
With Middle Classic Box	90	175	275	R9

3484-1 OPERATING BOX CAR (PENNSYLVANIA): 1953

The 3484-1 replaced the 3464/3474 9¼-inch series in the product line and launched the 10½-inch series of operating box cars. This change was Lionel's attempt to provide more scale-like features to their products and respond to the long, realistic O gauge cars already developed by American Model Toys. The 3484-1 mechanically operated in the same manner as the previous series; specifically when the car was activated, a figure would appear out the door.

The 3484-1 (the "-1" was *not* on the car or box) was included in three cataloged sets and for separate sale at $6.50. It is the most common of the 10½-inch series of cars likely due to its road name as the famous Pennsy name provided the perfect add-on to all the customers who purchased Pennsy Turbines (2020s, 671s, or 671RRs) or GG1s.

Like the other 10½-inch operating box cars, the shell for the 3484 was that of a 6464 box car and in this case was a Type I shell. The 3484's shell and doors were painted Tuscan red with the shell having white heat-stamped lettering. The doors used an early design that had only one large block. All 3484s came with bar-end trucks and couplers.

> Per Lionel Production Control Files, the 3484 originally used a 6464-4 box car body in clear polystyrene and changed to a 6464-58 box car body in utility black #39 (Type 666).

The 3464-17 vinylite figure was the same small figure without painted face and hands as Lionel used with the 3474.

Each 3484-1 was component boxed with a car and a 3474-14 instruction sheet, dated 6/53.

- Box Style Middle Classic (1953)
  - Tuck Flap Number: 3484-15
  - Box Dimensions: 3⅜" x 11¾" x 2½"

Author's Comments: The several shades of Tuscan, of which dull and glossy are recognized by collectors, were due to the multiple production runs required because the 3484-1 was a mainstay in many outfits.

Originally, Lionel called both the 3484s and 6464s 11-inch box cars in their 1953 consumer catalog, but then changed to the correct 10½-inches in the 1954 consumer catalog. Did Lionel get a new ruler?

Small Nick In Mold In Fifth Panel

The 3484-1 Pennsylvania used a Type II small, unpainted figure.

A nick appeared in the fifth panel from the right of the roof on the 3484-1 in late 1953.

Also important was the fact that at some point during the final production run, a nick developed on the mold, causing a minor flaw to the car's roof. This imperfection continued until a new mold was introduced in 1958. Although most 3484-1s were made without the imperfection, the nick helps identify early and later production.

3484-1	C7	C8	C9	Rarity
Without Nick	50	70	100	R5
	70	90	125	R7
With Nick	90	120	150	R9
	110	140	175	

3484-25 OPERATING S.F. BOX CAR (SANTA FE): 1954 - 1956

The 3484-25 was the second and last road name introduced in the 3484 series and is mechanically and operationally identical to the 3484-1. More misconceptions exist about the Santa Fe than any other 10½-inch operating box car because it was shown in only the 1954 advance and consumer catalogs and offered for separate sale only at $5.95. After that, it came in only two well-known Sears promotional sets; 505X in 1955 and 9606 in 1956.

The 3484-25 continued where the 3484-1 Pennsylvania left off and also took advantage of a famous road name. Like the 3484-1, the Santa Fe was a popular car and is not as rare as many collectors believe.

Multiple production runs led to numerous variations, including several shades of orange, with dull and glossy being the two most often recognized. The larger single block door also came in dull or glossy orange.

> Per Lionel Production Control Files, the 3484-25 used a 6464-35 Orange Styron™ box car body painted "Orange L-528" to make a 6464-27 box car body painted and then white heat-stamped to make the 3484-26 box car body stamped.

The first Santa Fe cars were as illustrated in the full-color 1954 consumer catalog and had a rare black heat-stamped lettering variation that came on a Type I body. This short-lived variation was replaced by cars with white heat-stamped lettering. Lionel continued to make changes; as the lettering was now *rubber-stamped* white and then a Type IIa body was introduced. The reduction of rivets on this body type made the application of graphics easier.

The small figure used with the 3484-1 in 1953 was included, but now had a painted face and hands. However, Lionel wasn't done making changes, as the last Santa Fe cars manufactured included the new large 3562-62 figure introduced at the end of the 1954 production year.

The 3484-25 used bar-end trucks and couplers throughout its run, and these also went through multiple changes in early 1954. First, the metal knuckle top was engraved instead of smooth. Second, a washer, placed where the truck pivot stud fastened to the frame, was replaced by a raised embossing on the frame.

In 1955, the 3484-25 came in promotional set 505X, which by observation of many cars' features, was packaged late in the year. Although the use of leftover inventory was still a possibility, the cars included the new in 1955 coupler tabs and a mounting (push) clip replaced the horseshoe washer (clip) to attach the trucks. It also included a silver coupler pin (introduced in late 1955), and the new multiple-block door (made for the new 6464-275 State of Maine box car). Also, some Santa Fe cars were painted over red polystyrene shells from the new 3494-1 New York Central Operating Box Car. The most important 1955 identification is that the box car's roof had the visible line to the left of the brake wheel that was caused by the production of the new 6352 Ice Car, hence making it a Type IIb body.

In 1956, the 3484-25 was painted over orange polystyrene shells. Heat-stamped cars were the norm, as was true in 1955 and it was now component boxed in a Late Classic box that no longer had "S.F." printed on the box end.

Left: 3484-25 with black lettering and Type IIP small, painted figure. Middle: White lettering and Type IIP small, painted figure. Right: White lettering and Type IP large, painted figure.

Left: 1954 Type I 3484-25 with Middle Classic box. Right: 1956 Type IIb car with Late Classic box.

The 3484-25 was component boxed with a car and a 3474-14 instruction sheet, dated 11/54 (1954); 12/55 (1955) or 2/56 (1956).

- For Each Box:
  - Tuck Flap Number: 3484-29
  - Box Dimensions: 3⅜" x 11¾" x 2½"
- Box Style Middle Classic (1954 - 1955)
- Box Style Late Classic (1956)

Author's Comments: The 3484-25 was also part of the Sears promotional set 9693 from 1956, but this set is not as well known as the 505X and 9606. In regard to rarity, the black-lettered version and the 1956 box are the rarest (these boxes were often discarded).

This was the last of the 3484 series box cars. Lionel replaced them with the 3494 series as they began experimenting with multi-colored cars.

3484-25	C7	C8	C9	Rarity
1954	1,000	1,500	2,500	R10
Black Heat-Stamped	1,025	1,550	2,600	R10
1954 Version	60	80	120	R7
	80	100	150	R7
1955 Version	60	80	120	R8
	80	110	175	R8
1956 Version	75	100	150	R8
With Late Classic Box	100	175	300	R9

3494-1 OPERATING BOX CAR (NEW YORK CENTRAL): 1955

Introduced in 1955, the two-tone New York Central Pacemaker, like its 6464-125 counterpart, has remained a collector favorite. The 3494 series was the operating car counterpart to the 6464 series, as some of the same cars were issued with and without operation. Except for the 3494-1, each car retained the identical suffix as its 6464 counterpart. The 3494-series cars were primarily decorated using two or more colors. The operation of these cars was identical to the other 10½-inch cars in the 3484/3494 series.

> Per Lionel Production Control Files, the 3494-1 used a 6464-128 red polystyrene box car body painted "Gray L-206" to make a 6464-127 box car body painted and then lettered in white to make the 3494-2 box car body.

The 3494-1 ("-1" is *not* on the box) was included in cataloged set 1541WS and offered for separate sale at $6.95. It had white rubber-stamped lettering with the number "34941" stamped on a Type IIa body. It included the large 3562-62 blue vinylite figure with painted face and hands introduced in late 1954. A tiny mark caused by a defect in the rubber stamping dangles from the third letter in the word "System" in the oval New York Central logo. Collectors refer to this identifying mark as a *cedilla*.

> Per the Lionel Blueprints dated 4-9-54, the New York Central medallion artwork shows no *cedilla*.

The 3494-1 was made earlier in the year than was the 3484-25 Santa Fe; therefore, the NYC retained the earlier 1955 features, notably bar-end trucks and couplers with a black knuckle pin (with or without the new coupler tabs), and the single, large-block door. The trucks were also mounted using a horseshoe washer (clip).

The 3494-1 was component boxed with a car and a 3474-14 instruction sheet date 12/55.

- Box Style Middle Classic
  - Tuck Flap Number: 3494-5
  - Box Dimensions: 3⅜" x 11" x 2½"

Author's Comments: The 3494-1, the first of the new 3494 series, was followed next by the 3494-150 Missouri Pacific and 3494-275 State of Maine, which were both two-tone cars and matched their 6464 counterparts (6464-150 and 6464-275, respectively). It is likely that Lionel didn't think of mirroring the 6464 series with 3494 operating cars until after the 3491-1 was issued. Otherwise, they would have numbered the 3494-1 as "3494-125" to match its 6464-125 NYC counterpart.

Some early NYC cars used white polystyrene shells that were painted red and gray with white polystyrene single, large-block doors that were also painted red.

Left: The 3494-1 NYC was introduced in 1955. Right: The 3494-150 Missouri Pacific in 1956.

3494-1	C7	C8	C9	Rarity
Regular Production Version	75	100	150	R7
	100	130	200	
White Shell and Door	100	150	200	R9
	125	180	250	

3494-150	C7	C8	C9	Rarity
Regular Production Version	75	125	175	R7
	105	155	300	R8

3494-150   OPERATING BOX CAR (MISSOURI PACIFIC): 1956

One of the more colorful and collectible of the 10½-inch operating box cars was the "MoPac", introduced in 1956. It was cataloged for separate sale only at $7.95 and operated in the same manner as the other box cars in this series.

Lionel used a gray plastic Type IIb body shell, with the top and bottom third of the sides painted in blue. The gray area was rubber-stamped with black lettering, whereas the blue area was rubber-stamped with white. The car was actually numbered "3494150." It used bar-end trucks and couplers with tabs and a silver knuckle pin. The 3494-150 still used the multi-block door, and the large 3562-62 blue vinylite figure with painted face and hands.

> Per Lionel Production Control Files, the 3494-150 used a 6464-326 gray polystyrene box car body painted "Blue Z-710" to make a 6464-152 box car body painted and then lettered in white and black to make the 3494-151 box car body.

The 3494-150 was component boxed with a car and a 3474-14 instruction sheet date 2/56.

- Box Style Late Classic
  - Tuck Flap Number: 3494-155
  - Box Dimensions: 3⅜" x 11¾" x 2½"

Author's Comments: This car stands out as one of the most colorful of the 3494 series. For some reason, it is more difficult to find in collectible condition than one would imagine. In fact, it is almost as difficult to find as a 3494-550 Monon or 3494-625 Soo.

A color sample of a 3494-150 is shown in Chapter 8.

3494-275   OPERATING BOX CAR (STATE OF MAINE): 1956 - 1958

Lionel knew a winner and so took advantage of the State of Maine's famous red-white-blue color scheme by making an operating box car to go along with their 6464-275 State of Maine non-operating box car introduced the previous year. Like the other box cars in the 10½-inch series, the operation of the plunger located beneath the car's frame allowed for the front sliding door to open and the figure to appear.

The 3494-275 was the only 10½-inch operating box car in the series to be included in a cataloged set for more than one year. In 1956 it was included in set 1559W and offered for separate sale at $7.95. As with other cars in 1956, a mounting (push) clip replaced the horseshoe washer (clip) that fastened the truck pivot stud to the sheet-metal frame. Bar-end trucks, with or without coupler tabs, continued; silver knuckle pins were the norm.

Early shells were molded in navy (rare) or royal (common) blue polystyrene, and royal blue became the primary color. All cars used a Type IIb body. The bottom third of the side was painted red, and the middle third was white. The top of the side and the roof were left as unpainted blue. Black rubber-stamped lettering was used on the white stripe, whereas white heat-stamped lettering was used on the red and blue. The figure was the large 3562-62 blue vinylite version with painted face and hands.

> Per Lionel Production Control Files, the 3494-275 used a 6464-401 blue polystyrene box car body painted "White Z-107 and Red Z-400" to make a 6464-277 box car body painted and then white heat-stamped and black rubber-stamped to make the 3494-276 box car body stamped.
>
> Per Lionel Blueprints, the 6464-401 changed from "Blue 45" to "Blue 35" on 3-29-56.

Left: The 3494-275 was produced with only "B.A.R." Right: It also came with "3494275" and "B.A.R." designation.

The first box cars were made without the "3494275" stamping below the B.A.R. Lionel soon corrected this oversight and began stamping each car with its correct identifying number, "3494275", just below the B.A.R. This variation is much easier to find than those made without the identifying number. However, a real oddball has State of Maine with only B.A.R on one side and "3494275" and B.A.R. on the other side of the car.

In 1957, the 3494-275 was part of set 2289WS, which was proclaimed to be the "First To Make The Run On Super 'O' Track." It was also offered for separate sale at $7.95, but those cars were leftover inventory from the year before. In fact, internal Lionel sales forecasts from April of 1957 stated that 1,600 operating State of Maine Box Cars remained in inventory.

Also in 1957, a support hole was added to the coupler drawbar toward the end of May. Soon after, two holes were added (punched out) of the frame (different from the frame of a 3424 Operating Brakeman Car). However, the most perceptible change was Lionel's return to the use of the small blue vinylite figure with painted face and hands.

In 1958, the 3494-275 was offered for separate sale only with the price remaining at $7.95. According to internal Lionel sales forecasts, 900 box cars remained in inventory. Since leftover inventory accounted for 3494-275s offered for separate sale in 1957 and 1958, this information helps explain why only a Late Classic box was used and no Bold Classic boxes exist.

The 3494-275 was component boxed with a car and a 3474-14 instruction sheet, dated 2/56 (1956) or 5/57 (1957 - 1958).

- Box Style Late Classic
  - Tuck Flap Number: 3494-280
  - Box Dimensions: 3⅜" x 11¾" x 2½"

Author's Comments: An interesting observation is that the 3562-62 figure originally issued in 1955 for the 3562-50 Operating Barrel Car (yellow) varied from small to large over the years.

For the 3494-275 and other operating cars manufactured only in 1957 (with carryover inventory in 1958), only small figures were used. At the same time in 1957, the 3562-75 Operating Barrel Car (orange) used a large figure. This suggests that the 3562-62

Top: During 1957 production, two extra holes were added to the frame. Bottom: These replaced the earlier version.

was transitioned from small to large in 1957 and stayed large into 1958.

3494-275	C7	C8	C9	Rarity
Regular Production Stamped "3494275"	65	80	100	R6
	90	120	150	
Number "3494275" Missing	125	150	200	R8
	150	200	250	

3494-550   OPERATING BOX CAR (MONON): 1957 - 1958

The pride of the Hoosier Line, the 3494-550 is a favorite with collectors and operators. The Monon and the 3494-625 Soo Line are the rarest of the regular production operating box cars. The 3494-550 operated in the same manner as the 3494-275, but was the first car in the 3494 series that didn't have a 6464 box car counterpart.

Both the Type IIb body shell and the doors for the Monon were molded in maroon polystyrene, with a white stripe painted across the top. The white stripe was heat-stamped with red letters, the graphics for the unpainted section were heat-stamped in white and the car was actually numbered "3494550." The small 3562-62 blue vinylite figure with painted face and hands was used.

The Monon (left) and the Soo Line (right) are two of the most collectible of all the operating cars in the 3494 series.

> Per Lionel Production Control Files, the 3494-550 used a 6464-378 red Styron™ (#375-H-1496) box car body painted "White 31-107" to make a 3494-557 box car body painted and then white and maroon heat-stamped to make the 3494-556 box car body stamped.

For both 1957 and 1958, the Monon was offered for separate sale only at $7.95. As indicated on 1958 internal Lionel sales forecasts, those cars offered in 1958 were actually leftover 1957 inventory.

The Monon used the same frame and bar-end trucks and couplers as the 3494-275. Some of 3494-550s had only a few visible specks of the "Blt-By-Lionel" data stamped to the left of the sliding door on the side where the figure appears. Although this was just a heat-stamping *error*, enough of these cars are known to exist (unlike most factory errors where only a few are known) to justify it being a collectible variation.

The 3494-550 was component boxed with a car and a 3474-14 instruction sheet dated 5/57.

- Box Style Late Classic
  - Tuck Flap Number: 3494-558
  - Box Dimensions: 3⅜" x 11¾" x 2½"

Author's Comments: Lionel realized separate sales of the 3494-1 and 3494-150 weren't taking the country by storm, so the production quantities for the Monon and Soo were cut almost in half when they were introduced.

This car represents the only instance of the Monon road name being used by Lionel during the postwar era. This reduction of quantity and use of a regional road name has led to these cars being in great collector demand.

As mentioned, the Monon didn't have a 6464 counterpart like the 3494-1, 3494-150 and 3494-275. But thanks to internal Lionel documentation, it was discovered that Lionel intended to have a 6464-550 Monon counterpart.

Only a Few Specks Showing

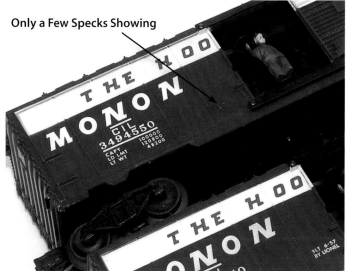

The Monon (bottom) has the built date information to the left of the sliding door, while the top car has only a few specs of white showing.

> Per Lionel documents, the 6464-550 was a reserved number for "Box Car - Monon, Brown with White Lettering, 1957."

3494-550	C7	C8	C9	Rarity
Regular Production Version	250	325	400	R8
	350	500	650	
Stamping Error	250	325	400	R9
	350	500	650	

3494-625 OPERATING BOX CAR (SOO LINE): 1957 - 1958

Offered for separate sale only at $7.95 when introduced in 1957 and carried over as leftover inventory at the same separate-sale price in 1958, the 3494-625 Soo Line is also a coveted piece of postwar Lionel rolling stock. It was the last car in the 3494 series.

Like the other box cars in the 10½-inch series, the operation of the plunger located beneath the car's frame allowed for the front sliding door to open and the figure to appear. Also, this car did not have a 6464 box car counterpart.

Painted brown over a maroon plastic Type IIb body shell, the graphics of this plain car were heat-stamped in white and the car was actually numbered "3494625." The small 3562-62 blue vinylite figure with painted face and hands was used.

Lionel stated in April 1957 internal sales forecasts that 2,600 cars would be produced for separate sale. Naturally, this large quantity would account for noticeable differences in the brown paint used for both the cars and the doors. Cars painted either brown or reddish brown have been recognized by collectors.

> **Per Lionel Production Control Files, the 3494-625 used a 6464-378 red Styron™ (#375-H-1496) box car body painted "Red L-411" to make a 3494-627 box car body painted and then white heat-stamped to make the 3494-626 box car body stamped.**

The 3494-625 Soo used the same frame, bar-end trucks and couplers, and figure as the other two 3494 cars offered in 1957 and again in 1958. There are no major variations of this car other than the different shades of brown or reddish brown paint identified.

The 3494-625 was component boxed with a car and a 3474-14 instruction sheet dated 5/57.

- Box Style Late Classic
  - Tuck Flap Number: 3494-630
  - Box Dimensions: 3⅜" x 11¾" x 2½"

Author's Comments: The Soo Line, just like the Monon, was not prominently featured in the 1957 consumer catalog. They were shown on the same page as the feature illustrated 3444 Animated Gondola Car and 3360 Burro Crane, which Lionel really wanted to push.

The Soo was the last 3494 operating box car produced in the series. It broke tradition by not using a two-tone paint scheme as the cars it followed.

As mentioned, the Soo didn't have a 6464 counterpart like the 3494-1, 3494-150 and 3494-275. But thanks to internal Lionel documentation, it was discovered that Lionel intended to have a 6464-625 Soo counterpart.

> **Per Lionel documents, the 6464-625 was a reserved number for "Box Car - Soo Line, Brown with White Lettering, 1957."**

3494-625	C7	C8	C9	Rarity
Regular Production Version	300	375	450	R8
	500	625	800	

3530   OPERATING GENERATOR CAR: 1956 - 1958

Modeled after a 1,000-kilowatt mobile power station made by the Electro-Motive Division of the General Motors Corporation, the 3530 Operating Generator Car was another exciting new operating car introduced during the stalwart year of 1956.

The 3530 included a searchlight, transformer and pole. Once these items were connected to the generator car, the action was ready to begin. The 3530 received its power from the rails through the use of a track contact roller that is part of the power truck. By connecting the two green wires (called "cables" by Lionel) to the two terminals on the top of the car, power was transferred "through" the pole to the awaiting searchlight.

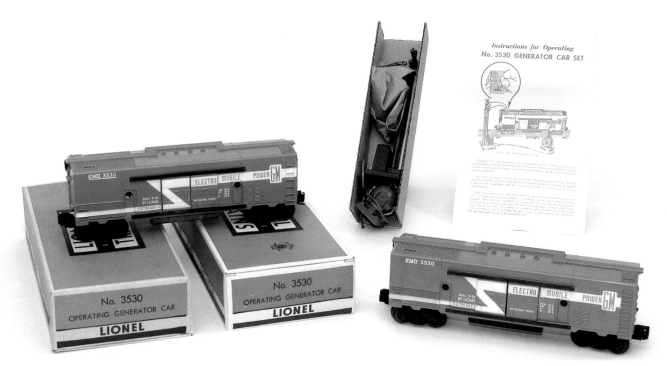

Left: The 3530 has number underlined, a blue fuel tank, a full-length stripe, and no centering rivet. Right: The 3530 was not underlined, the fuel tank is black, the stripe does not extend the full length of the car, and the centering rivet is in place.

A switch is attached to the left door (when the car is viewed with the brake wheel on the left) that, when opened, makes contact inside the car. A light inside the car is activated, highlighting the huge diesel-electric generator. In turn, the generator begins to hum, the ventilating fan begins to turn, and the searchlight positioned outside the car shines brightly. In fact, if the room lights are turned off during evening hours, the searchlight actually works like a spotlight and is fun to watch.

In 1956, Lionel offered the 3530 as only a separate-sale item at a cost of $12.95. The illustrations of this car in the black-and-white advance and accessory catalogs did not accurately depict it. However, by the time the full-color consumer catalog was released in the fall of 1956, the illustration was almost perfect. Considering all the changes that Lionel put this car through, this confusion is understandable.

The 3530's shell was molded in blue polystyrene, with a white-painted lightning bolt (stripe) on each side. The blue polystyrene doors were painted in such a way as to complete the design. The unpainted blue area had white heat-stamped lettering, whereas the white area was heat-stamped with blue. The 3530 used bar-end die-cast trucks, with or without coupler tabs, and the knuckle pins were silver.

The first 3530s were very rare (see author's comments), as the "EMD 3530" was underlined in white and there was no rivet in the center of the top door guide, (on the same side as the door that activates the switch). This variation had a stripe that ran the full-length of the car and might have been used as a salesman's sample. Also, the belly (fuel) tank was blue polystyrene, but the pole's transformer base was black.

> **Per Lionel Blueprints dated 6-5-56, the car was shown with the "EMD 3530" underlined.**

However, Lionel suddenly stopped underlining the "EMD 3530", and the white stripe no longer ran the full length of the car. A rivet was added to the center of the upper door guide (on the same side as the door that activates the switch), and the fuel tank was finally color-coded to match the black transformer base.

> **Per Lionel Production Control Files, the 3530-27 fuel tank was originally TMD-5151 blue polystyrene #35 but changed to TMD 6000 black polystyrene #75.**

But Lionel still wasn't satisfied, and a full-length stripe returned during the final run, when the tank and base probably were still color-coded. At this time, Lionel brought out the separate-sale 3530-50 Transformer Pole set.

In 1957, the 3530 was included in two O gauge sets (2291W and 2295WS) and offered for separate sale at $12.95. The white stripe ran the full length of the car, as it had during the last run of 1956. Other features included a modified inside roof line, coupler drawbars with a support hole, and two new holes punched out of the frame.

The fuel tank and transformer base were now color-coded in blue, and some of the poles were molded in maroon instead of brown plastic. Some 3530s were even molded in a lighter shade of blue polystyrene.

In 1958, the 3530 was cataloged as part of set 2519W and the separate-sale price remained the same. However, with fewer than 2,000 sets anticipated to be produced, the 3530s used to fill this set, possibly came from leftover inventory.

Each 3530 was component boxed with a car, a 3530-40 corrugated insert, a 3530-42 transformer pole and searchlight assembly, TP-6 9" x 9" tissue paper and a 3530-45 instruction sheet dated 11/56.

- Box Style Late Classic
  - Tuck Flap Number: 3530-39
  - Box Dimensions: 5⅜" x 11¾" x 2⅜"

Author's Comments: Other than the rare underlined version, the 3530s are fairly common. But, the underlined version is so rare that less than a dozen are known to exist. One example belonged to former Lionel salesman Ken Negri and might have been used by him as a sample when he visited distributors and other retail outlets.

It is understandable that Ken had this version because Lionel, like any other manufacturer, wouldn't hesitate in providing their sales force with the most decorative items imaginable, thus allowing them to show off their products to prospective customers.

Although Ken owned the rarest variation, his Late Classic box was the same as used from 1956 through 1958. Inside his boxed version, the car was held in place by a 3530-40 corrugated insert that housed the transformer and pole. A small, crumpled-up piece of Lionel striped-logo wrapping paper was placed next to the transformer and pole to help hold them in place. An instruction sheet was also placed inside the car, and it described the operations of the car.

The instruction sheets are rather interesting, as they were printed on white paper in 1956, but changed to yellow in 1957, as did many other instruction sheets.

Finally, the underlined version of the 3530 is so rare, that the price for the car in any condition would probably be the same whether its original box was included or not. This statement holds true when offered for sale in C9 condition, as it's the rarity of the car that demands the highest value - and not the box. In fact, for the underlined version, the box is nothing more than icing on the cake.

3530	C7	C8	C9	Rarity
Underlined Version	1,500	2,500	3,500	R10
	1,600	2,700	3,800	
Long-Striped Version	120	150	200	R6
	150	200	325	
Short-Striped Version	90	125	175	R8
	120	175	300	

Separate-sale Transformer Pole sets came with either a black (left) or a blue (right) transformer base.

3530-50   TRANSFORMER POLE: 1956 - 1957

Along with the 3530 Operating Generator Car, Lionel issued a separate-sale accessory to enable operators to repeat the action of a 3530 on any section of their layout (though a 3530 was required to provide power to this accessory). The 3530-50 was offered as a Replacement Accessory in the 1956 consumer catalog for $1.25. However, the following year the price rose to $3.50, with the 3530-50 referred to as an Extra Accessory. Since only 200 examples remained in inventory for 1957, Lionel thought the increase in price was justified. Transformer bases were molded in either blue or black polystyrene.

> Per Lionel Production Control Files, the 3530-30 service transformer was molded in both TMD 5151 blue polystyrene #35 and TMD 6000 black polystyrene #75.

Each 3530-50 was component boxed with a 3530-42 transformer pole and searchlight assembly that included a 150-3 telegraph pole, a 3530-30 service transformer and all the necessary peripherals.

- Box Style Late Classic
  - Tuck Flap Number: 3530-38
  - Box Dimensions: 2⅛" x 9" x 1⅞"

Author's Comments: The 3530-50 wasn't a great seller, as it continued to sit on dealers' shelves well into the early 1970s. This was indicative of the larger issue that Lionel dealers began experiencing during the late 1950s. Dealers had been buying at record numbers; however, the items weren't selling and Lionel was overproducing based on prior expectations. With items still filling their shelves, dealers were reluctant to reorder. Smaller dealer sales meant lower profits, and Lionel's yearly growth began to decline.

3530-50	C7	C8	C9	Rarity
Black Transformer Base	75	100	150	R8
Blue Transformer Base	100	125	175	R8

The 3854 complete with box, liner, packed envelope and Kimpak wadded paper.

3854 OPERATING MERCHANDISE CAR: 1946 - 1947

The 3854 was a postwar car derived from a prewar model. It was incorrectly shown in the 1946 advance and consumer catalogs with Pennsylvania lettering to the left of the sliding doors, when in reality it was heat-stamped "Automatic Merchandise Car." The operation for the 3854 was the same as the 3454, as the car's door opened and closed by the touch of a remote-control button. Six miniature packing cases were then unloaded to a waiting 160 bin or other device provided by the operator.

Included with each car was a packed envelope with an instruction sheet and six miniature packing cases (all of the same color), each with "Baby Ruth" molded on the case. The cases came in three colors: burgundy, black, and red. Original cases without "Baby Ruth" were probably from the prewar era.

A Remote Control Track was required to operate the 3854. With the car being so long, the trucks were equipped with two pickup shoes. Some earlier examples may have only one shoe, before Lionel realized the potential problem.

The 3854 was painted brown with white heat-stamped lettering. It was made out of Bakelite (a compression-molded plastic), as were the prewar scale box car and the heavyweight passenger cars. As with these cars, the paint can flake off a 3484 and cause it to look worn. In 1946, Lionel experimented with both brown-painted (less common), and chemically blackened doors, before deciding that black was the better choice.

In 1946, the 3854 was part of set 2113WS and offered for separate sale at $10.75. The car had staple-end trucks with coupler heads secured to the bracket by a swedging process. By 1947, however, the heads included four stake marks (see Appendix C). In 1947, the 3854 was included in set 2129WS and offered for separate sale at $10.75.

The 3854 was component boxed with a car, a corrugated liner, prewar-style Kimpak wadded paper, a packed envelope (envelope no. 3454-51) with six 3814-53 packing cases, and a 3454-57 instruction sheet dated 5/46 (1946) or 5/47 (1947).

- For Each Box:
  - Box Dimensions: 4" x 13" x 3⅝"
- Box Style Art Deco (1946)
  - Tuck Flap Number: None
- Box Style Art Deco Toy Logo (1947)
  - Tuck Flap Number: None

Author's Comments: Because it was made in 1946, the rarer brown-painted door version was actually different from its prewar predecessor. This prewar connection was probably responsible for the illustrations in both the advance and consumer catalogs, which showed the 3854 incorrectly with Pennsylvania markings instead of the correct "Automatic Merchandise Car" markings.

The 1947 version of the Art Deco Toy Logo box is more difficult to find than the 1946 Art Deco version without the American Toys Logo.

3854	C7	C8	C9	Rarity
Brown Door Version (1946)	800	1,200	1,800	R10
	1,000	1,600	2,500	
Black Door Version (1946)	400	700	1,000	R8
	650	1,100	1,700	
Black Door Version (1947)	400	700	1,000	
	650	1,100	1,700	

Left: 6434 with Bold Classic box. Right: 6434 with Late Classic box.

6434   POULTRY CAR: 1958 - 1959

Lionel must have had great plans for the 6434, because that car was included in five cataloged sets and offered for separate sale at $6.95. However, by 1959, it was part of only one cataloged set and shown for separate sale again at $6.95. The cars issued in 1959 probably represented unsold 1958 inventory. With Lionel bringing out so many brand-new items at this time, the 6434, after such a great introduction, just seemed to get lost in the shuffle.

Although the 6434 was illuminated, it technically was not an operating car. Its production led to changes that also appeared on other operating cars. Therefore, it is included in order to complete the chronology of these changes.

The polystyrene body was painted various shades of red and heat-stamped with white lettering. The gray plastic doors were heat-stamped in black.

> Per Lionel Production Control Files dated 4-7-58, the 3493-3 body was originally to be molded in red Styron™ #475-H-1496 #71 and not painted; however, this changed to utility black #59 and was subsequently painted red 21-420 to become a 6434-9 car body painted.

The 6434 used the same body as the 3356 Operating Horse Car and the 6556 Missouri-Kansas-Texas stock car. Each 6434 came equipped with four 6434-7 translucent polystyrene panels that depicted four rows of chickens. To hold the panels in place, the inside body was modified by adding eight small gussets, or stiffeners, to the design. Naturally, the gussets became part of the design for the 3356 and 6556. The 6434 used bar-end trucks, with or without coupler tabs, and silver knuckle pins.

Each 6434 was component boxed with just a car. An instruction sheet does not exist.

- Box Style Late Classic (1958 - 1959)
  - Tuck Flap Number: 6434-10
  - Box Dimensions: 3⅜" x 12½" x 2½"
- Box Style Bold Classic (1958 - 1959)
  - Box Manufacturer: Berles Carton Co.
  - Box Date: BC588
  - Tuck Flap Number: 6434-10
  - Box Dimensions: 3⅜" x 12¼" x 2½"

Author's Comments: The color of the panels and chickens for the 6434 varied, just as they did for the 3434.

This car can be an eyesore when the red paint starts to chip. In 1960, Lionel may have considered bringing back the 6434 as a 3434-50 Operating Poultry Car. However, the idea was short-lived (see 3434-50 entry).

6434	C7	C8	C9	Rarity
Regular Production	50	75	90	R6
With Late Classic Box	75	100	125	
With Bold Classic Box	100	150	200	R9

CHAPTER TWO

Gondolas

3444 ANIMATED GONDOLA CAR: 1957 - 1960

In the April 1957 issue of *All Aboard at Lionel* (an internal newsletter provided to employees and later major customers), the 3444 was heralded as one of the "Stars of 1957." It lived up to that early billing and was an immediate hit, as the never-ending action of the cop and hobo delighted audiences of all ages. The car's action was a direct result of a vibrating motor, concealed beneath the packing crates, that ran a 16-millimeter Cronar® (DuPont's Polyester Film Base) belt on which a hobo and a policeman were attached. An on-off switch, which protruded through the crates, triggered the action. Two pulley drums, located at each end of the car beneath the crates, allowed for the movement of the belt, which was also referred to as a "Conveyor Assembly" by Lionel.

In 1957, the 3444 was included in two cataloged sets and the separate-sale price was $9.95. The car had a red polystyrene body, with white heat-stamped lettering in the Hastings font. The tan plastic packing crates had black heat-stamped lettering. The gray hobo and blue policeman had "flesh" painted face and hands.

> Per Lionel Blueprints dated 11-5-56, the 3444-31 hobo is made of vinylite VND 9970 gray #335 measuring 1.187" tall and the 3444-32 cop is made of vinylite VND 9950 blue #1125 measuring 1.75" tall.

Bar-end trucks and couplers, with or without coupler tabs and silver knuckle pins, were used each year. However, early on, the 3444 came with only one pickup truck, but a second was subsequently added.

> Per Lionel Production Control Files, the number of 481-1 "light coupler truck complete" changed from one to two on 10-29-57.

Because of the number of cars needed to fill orders, more than one production run was made. This accounted for subtle differences in the red polystyrene and the painting of the cop and hobo. The first 3444s had a smooth frame, with the appropriate number of punch-outs for the placement of the pulley drums, motor assembly, on/off switch, and so forth.

Operating gondola cars offered loads of entertainment value as well as exciting colors.

Left: 3444 regular production. Right: Two versions of truck combinations.

To improve the rotation of the belt, the frame was modified by embossing the area (visible from below) where the two screws held the crates in place. The *Lionel Service Manual* showed this change.

In 1958, the 3444 was included in two cataloged sets and the separate-sale price remained the same. A metal washer was added

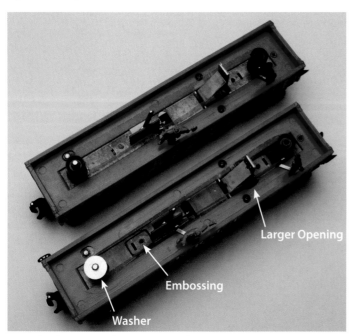

Top: The first 3444s had a smooth frame. Bottom: They eventually were modified to include a raised frame, a metal washer, and a cutout above the motor.

to the pulley closest to the on/off switch. Soon after, the walkway, where the cop chased the hobo, was slightly cut on both sides directly above the motor.

In 1959, the 3444 continued to be offered for separate sale at $9.95, but those numbers probably represented leftover inventory. It was, however, included in one cataloged set (2533W), and what a set it was. The 2533W is desirable and difficult to obtain in collector condition.

In 1960, the 3444 was offered for separate sale *only* in the advance catalog. The price was $10.95, which was a dollar more than before. However, by the time the consumer catalog was released, the 3444 had been dropped from the product line. This probably happened because advance orders, taken before the consumer catalog was produced, reduced the total inventory to a point where it was no longer feasible to illustrate any 3444s. Or distributors and retail outlets, such as Madison Hardware Co. of New York City, purchased Lionel's remaining inventory after noticing 3444s were still offered for sale in the advance catalog.

The 3444 was component boxed with a 3444-33 instruction sheet (on 9½" x 6¼" yellow or smaller white paper) dated 5/57 (1957 - 1958) or 5/59 (1959 - 1960).

- Box Style Late Classic
  - Tuck Flap Number: 3444-36
  - Box Dimensions: 3½" x 11¾" x 2⅛"

Author's Comments: Publishers and collectors have incorrectly referred to the 3444 as "the cop and hobo car." Of course, the 3357 was *the* "Cop and Hobo Car." Even so, the Animated Gondola

Car was a groundbreaking achievement for Lionel, as the use of belts and pulleys paved the way for other operating cars. Cars like the 3435 Aquarium Car, introduced in 1959, used the same principles as established by the Animated Gondola, as the 3435 took advantage of two pulleys and a belt-type apparatus.

The intended production (per Lionel Production Control Files) included two brake wheels; however, many are found with only one.

Cars like the 3444, and those that followed, have provided countless hours of entertainment for both young and old. Maybe we should end this section by offering a hardy thank-you to the developer of the "Vibrotor" motor - Mr. Frank Pettit!

3444	C7	C8	C9	Rarity
Early 1957 Version	50	90	125	
(No Embossing on Frame)	65	110	150	R4
1957 - 1960 Version	50	75	100	
	65	95	125	

3562-1   OPERATING BARREL CAR (BLACK): 1954

Introduced in 1954, the operating barrel cars were the perfect companion for the 362 Barrel Loader, which had made its debut two years before. Lionel also designed these cars, which all had AT&SF markings, for stand alone use, because not every operator owned a 362 Barrel Loader. Each barrel car came with a small box: a 362-100 barrel set with six stained 362-78 wooden barrels (marked "362-78" on the box). These needed to be manually placed on the car by the operator.

The car's action was attributed to the vibration of a spring-loaded conveyor (called a "trough" by collectors), which was activated by an electromagnetic coil hidden inside the car. This vibration allowed for miniature barrels to travel along the conveyor until released by the figure positioned at the end of the conveyor. One by one they dropped into the 160-2 3½" x 8⅜" polystyrene bin that was included with the car.

The first barrel car (3562-1) introduced by Lionel was painted black with white heat-stamped lettering. The suffix "-1" was stamped on the car as "35621", but not on the box.

The 3562-1 was part of set 1521WS and, except for the figure, was perfectly illustrated in the full-color consumer catalog. The problem was the figure in the catalog had painted face and hands. However, the black barrel car was issued with the same small unpainted vinylite figure as Lionel used on the 3474 Western Pacific Operating Box Car from 1953. Even so, the last black barrel cars made in 1954 probably paralleled the assembly of the gray barrel car (see 3562-25) also manufactured that year. Gray barrel cars included figures with painted face and hands, so some black cars may have come this way too. This is called a "transition" of parts (see Definitions section). However, Lionel was also using the large 3562-62 figure in 1954 on the 3484-25 Operating Box Car (per Lionel Archives sample dated October 27, 1954); thus it is possible they were used on the 3562-1 and 3562-25 as well.

Lionel also experimented with the trough (conveyor), as both yellow-painted and black examples were made. The 3562-1 came equipped with bar-end trucks and couplers with black knuckle pins.

> Per Lionel Production Control Files dated 4-13-54, the 3562-21 conveyor assembly was originally painted ivory S-305 and was changed to black S-306.

The 3562-1 was not illustrated in the 1954 consumer catalog for separate sale; instead, the 3562-25 was featured for $8.95. However, 3562-1s were probably available for separate sale just the same, if those orders were placed according to Lionel's sales and delivery policy at that time.

Each 3562-1 component box included a car, a 3562-52 packed envelope (envelope no. 3562-53), a 362-100 barrel set (with six stained wooden barrels marked "362-78" on the box), a 160-2 bin and a 3562-61 corrugated insert.

> Per Lionel Production Control Files, a 362-100 barrel set is comprised of six 362-78 barrels in a 362-79 folding box.

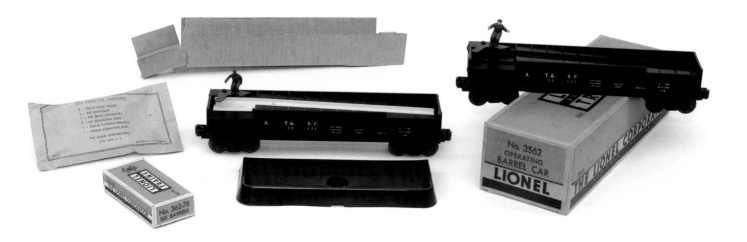

The 3562-1 came with either a yellow trough (left) or black (right), as well as the associated peripherals.

The 3562-52 packed envelope included a 96C controller, two 3562-51 track spacers, a 3562-48 platform extension, an OTC-1 lockon, two 24-4 auxiliary rail clips, two 81-32 24" RC wires and a 3562-54 instruction sheet dated 6/54.

For the 3562-1:
• Box Style Middle Classic
  – Tuck Flap Number: 3562-60
  – Box Dimensions: 4" x 12½" x 3"
For the 362-100 (362-78 on box):
• Box Style Middle Classic
  – Tuck Flap Number: 362-79
  – Box Dimensions: 1⅞" x 4" x 1"

Author's Comments: Previous observations note that the yellow (ivory) trough version matched the paint used on the 3656 Operating Stock Yard. While true, this overlooks the more important fact that it matched the conveyor ramp of the companion 362 Barrel Loader.

3562-1	C7	C8	C9	Rarity
Black Trough Version	125	150	200	
	175	250	350	R8
Yellow Trough Version	150	175	225	
	200	275	400	

3562-25 OPERATING BARREL CAR (GRAY): 1954 - 1955

The 3562-25 also debuted in 1954, and both the car and the box had the "-25" suffix stamped; the car was stamped "356225." The 3562-25 was painted gray with blue heat-stamped lettering, and it operated in the same manner as the other operating barrel cars in this series. Bar-end trucks and couplers with black knuckle pins were the norm for 1954.

In 1954, the 3562-25 was included in four cataloged sets and offered for separate sale at $8.95. Therefore, more than one production run was needed to fill those orders. Multiple runs resulted in cars with various shades of gray paint and blue lettering. Dull or glossy gray, and royal or navy blue, are the colors recognized by collectors. The trough now matched the car and was also painted gray.

Lionel also heat-stamped some gray cars with red lettering, known as components of set 2217WS. Rarer than these is a red-lettered example stamped with the black barrel car's "35621" number.

> Per Lionel Blueprints dated 3-19-54, the 3562-25 is to be stamped in red leaf or equivalent. Subsequent Production Control Records show this changing to blue heat-stamping.

When the gray barrel car was introduced, Lionel remembered its promise of more color for 1954, as the small figure with painted face and hands returned to the product line. Of course, don't forget about transition and the possibility that the black barrel car could have the same type of figure at this point in production (see 3562-1).

In 1955, the 3562-25 was included in three cataloged sets (1533WS, 1537WS and 2245WS), but wasn't illustrated for separate sale in the consumer catalog; instead, the yellow operating barrel car (3562-50) was shown. In fact, the 3562-25 wasn't illustrated anywhere in the 1955 consumer catalog, but was manufactured just the same.

For instance, set 1533WS included either gray or yellow barrel cars, although the gray barrel cars may have been leftover inventory from 1954. The gray barrel car was also included in set 1537WS. To be correct, however, this barrel car should have 1955 features (a new molded catch to hold the cam in place, new interior molded posts, and possibly new coupler tabs). Even the large 3562-62 painted figure returned for good.

Left: 1954 red-lettered heat-stamped example. Right: 1955 blue-lettered heat-stamped example with a molded catch. Note that the packed envelope contents changed.

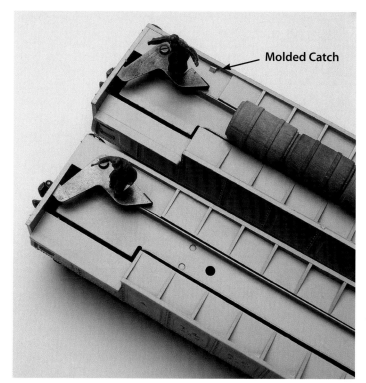

Molded Catch

Top: A molded catch became part of the barrel car's design in 1955.

Each 3562-25 component box included a car, a 3562-52 packed envelope (envelope no. 3562-53), a 362-100 barrel set (with six stained wooden barrels marked "362-78" on the box), a 160-2 3½" x 8⅜" polystyrene bin and a 3562-61 corrugated insert.

> Per Lionel Production Control Files, a 362-100 barrel set is comprised of six 362-78 barrels in a 362-79 folding box.

In 1954 the 3562-52 packed envelope included a 96C controller, two 3562-51 track spacers, a 3562-48 platform extension, an OTC-1 lockon, two 24-4 auxiliary rail clips, two 81-32 24" RC wires and a 3562-54 instruction sheet.

For 1955, the packed envelope number remained the same, but now the envelope number was 3562-73. This change signified the removal of the 96C controller and the addition of a 90-1 controller loosely packed.

For the 3562-25:
• Box Style Middle Classic
  - Tuck Flap Number: 3562-57
  - Box Dimensions: 4" x 12½" x 3"
For the 362-100 (362-78 on box):
• Box Style Middle Classic
  - Tuck Flap Number: 362-79
  - Box Dimensions: 1⅞" x 4" x 1"

The 3562-54 instruction sheet came as three versions, dated: 6/54 or 8/54 (1954); and 8/54 or 8/55 (1955).

Author's Comments: Red-lettered cars are the rarest, but the 1955 cars with the molded catch are more difficult to find than most

collectors realize. Also, some instruction sheets were confusing because they depicted the molded catch, yet were dated 1954. They turned out to be 1955 sheets with an incorrect date.

Although not generally known, Lionel even used silver polystyrene bodies and painted them gray with blue or red lettering. This was done during 1954 production and is validated by observations of 1954 gray-painted 6417-50 Lehigh Valley Cabooses also painted this way.

One final note: Pay particular attention to red-lettered gray barrel cars. Make sure you are not selling a red-lettered "35621" for the price of a "356225"!

In fact, this entire volume gives you plenty of examples of unpublished variations that can be used this way and so makes this new Project Roar Publishing volume even more valuable.

Although the red-lettered gray barrel car came both as "356225" and "35621", the "-1" version is much rarer, with fewer than six examples verified to date (see Chapter 8).

3562-25	C7	C8	C9	Rarity
1954 Version Without Molded Catch	35	50	75	R4
	90	75	200	
1955 Version With Molded Catch	35	75	100	R8
	50	100	175	
"356225" With Red Letters	300	400	600	R9
	325	500	800	
"35621" With Red Letters	1,800	2,400	3,000	R10
	1,850	2,500	3,300	

3562-50 OPERATING BARREL CAR (YELLOW): 1955 - 1957

New for 1955, yellow operating barrel cars, which operated in the same manner as the other cars in this series, were illustrated on the front cover of the consumer catalog as part of three sets. In this instance, Lionel may have been searching for the "right" color, and yellow, which is bright, would look good on any catalog cover. However, set 1537WS, which was featured on the front cover of the 1955 consumer catalog, actually used gray 3562-25 operating barrel cars instead. Both the yellow car and the box had the "-50" suffix stamped, with the car stamped "356250."

Yellow operating barrel cars were included in three cataloged sets (2237WS, 2251W and 2249WS) and offered for separate sale at $8.95. They also have been observed, as were gray 3562-25s, in sets 1533WS and 2245WS.

The 3562-50 was molded in yellow polystyrene with black heat-stamped lettering. However, the first cars made were painted yellow over gray polystyrene and came with or without the molded catch. Various shades of the painted cars exist, with yellow-orange being the most vibrant. However, the rarest example was a yellow-painted car stamped with the gray car's "356225" number. Some yellow cars were even packaged in the gray car's box, with only a "Y" printed on the box for identification. A large 3652-62 figure with painted face and hands and bar-end trucks and couplers with black knuckle pins were the norm.

> Per Production Control Files dated 4-11-55, the 3562-69 car painted yellow S-524 was replaced on 6/6/55 by 3572-70 car body molded in TMD-5151 yellow and not painted.

Left to right: 3562-50 yellow-painted with a "-25" (stamped "Y") or "-50" Middle Classic box (1955), yellow molded with "-50" Late Classic box (1956), 3562-75 orange plastic with Late Classic box (1957 or 1958).

In 1956, the yellow polystyrene car continued, and the specifications were pretty much the same as before. The only difference was that the knuckle pins were silver and not black. This car was included in five cataloged sets and offered for separate sale at $8.95.

In 1957, the 3562-50 was shown in the consumer catalog for separate sale at $9.95, with a short run possibly needed to finalize production. In fact, internal Lionel sales forecasts from April of 1957 stated that 700 yellow operating barrel cars remained in inventory, with an additional 600 to be made available for May delivery. The specifications for these cars were the same as before.

Each 3562-50 component box included a car, a 3562-52 packed envelope (envelope no. 3562-73), a 362-100 barrel set (with six stained wooden barrels marked "362-78" on the box), a 160-2 3½" x 8⅜" polystyrene bin, a 90-1 controller and a 3562-61 corrugated insert.

Per Lionel Production Control Files, a 362-100 barrel set is comprised of six 362-78 barrels in a 362-79 folding box.

The 3562-52 packed envelope included two 3562-51 track spacers, a 3562-48 platform extension, an OTC-1 lockon, two 24-4 auxiliary rail clips, two 81-32 24" RC wires and a 3562-54 instruction sheet.

For the 3562-50:
• For Each Box:
  - Tuck Flap Number: 3562-64
  - Box Dimensions: 4" x 12½" x 3"
• Box Style Middle Classic (1955)
• Box Style Late Classic (1956 - 1957)
• Note: The 3562-50 also used 3562-25 boxes with a "Y" stamped on them.

For the 362-100 (362-78 on box):
• For Each Box:
  - Tuck Flap Number: 362-79
  - Box Dimensions: 1⅞" x 4" x 1"
• Box Style Middle Classic (1955)
• Box Style Late Classic (1956 - 1957)

The yellow-painted 3562-50 stamped as "356225" is very rare.

The instruction sheet (3562-54) came in three versions, dated: 8/54 or 8/55 (1955) and 4/56 (1956 - 1957).

Author's Comments: The yellow-painted cars are not as rare as collectors and operators have been led to believe. What is incredibly rare, however, is a yellow-painted 3562-25, made without the molded catch. This was actually a 3562-50 stamped with the gray barrel car's "356225" number.

3562-50	C7	C8	C9	Rarity
Regular Production Unpainted Yellow	35	50	75	R4
	50	90	125	
Yellow-Painted	80	110	150	R8
	100	150	250	
Yellow-Painted Stamped "356225"	2,000	2,700	3,500	R10
	2,100	2,900	3,800	

3562-75 OPERATING BARREL CAR (ORANGE): 1957 - 1958

The 3562-75 was the last operating barrel car produced, and it operated in the same manner as the other cars in this series. It was molded in orange polystyrene, with black heat-stamped lettering.

In 1957, the orange operating barrel car was included in two cataloged sets, but wasn't illustrated in the consumer catalog for separate sale. It used bar-end trucks and couplers, with or without tabs, and silver knuckle pins. Another feature for 1957 was that the 3562-75 came equipped with a support hole in the coupler drawbar.

Both the car and the box had the "-75" suffix with the car numbered "356275." The intended production included the large figure with painted face and hands. The large figure had the highest probability for production, but a transition was always possible, as was the case with most cars having a figure.

In 1958, the 3562-75 was included in one cataloged set and illustrated in the consumer catalog for separate sale at $9.95. The specifications were the same as before, and unsold inventory was included in promotional set X-225. This was done to help reduce inventory until other sales outlets could be considered.

Each 3562-75 component box included a car, a 3562-52 packed envelope (envelope no. 3562-73), a 362-100 barrel set (with six stained wooden barrels marked "362-78" on the box), a 160-2 3½" x 8⅜" polystyrene bin, a 90-1 controller and a 3562-61 corrugated insert.

Per Lionel Production Control Files, a 362-100 barrel set is comprised of six 362-78 barrels in a 362-79 folding box.

The 3562-52 packed envelope included two 3562-51 track spacers, a 3562-48 platform extension, an OTC-1 lockon, two 24-4 auxiliary rail clips, two 81-32 24" RC wires and a 3562-54 instruction sheet dated 5/57.

For the 3562-75:
- Box Style Late Classic
  - Tuck Flap Number: 3562-79
  - Box Dimensions: 4" x 12½" x 3"

For the 362-100 (362-78 on box):
- Box Style Late Classic
  - Tuck Flap Number: 362-79
  - Box Dimensions: 1⅞" x 4" x 1"

Author's Comments: To be correct, the orange barrel car should have 1957 features, such as couplers with silver knuckle pins and any combination of coupler tabs and drawbars with the support hole.

The 3562-75 wasn't illustrated in the 1957 full-color consumer catalog for separate sale, but was shown in the full-color 1958. Internal Lionel sales forecasts from April of 1957 showed that the 3562-50 would be offered for separate sale and that 700 remained in inventory, with a short run production of 600 additional yellow operating barrel cars to be delivered by May. When the full-color consumer catalog came out in the fall of 1957, only the yellow operating barrel car was illustrated for separate sale. So apparently the 3562-75 was included in only two cataloged sets: 2281W and 2291W.

However, 1958 internal Lionel sales forecasts further explained that 1,000 barrel cars remained in inventory, but no distinction was made as to whether those cars were 3562-50 or 3562-75. Only the 3562 (with no suffix) barrel car was listed, although shown as an orange car in set 2511W. This explanation suggests that yellow cars were available for separate sale in 1958 or orange cars were also available in 1957.

Even so, this volume will follow Lionel's full-color consumer catalog and 1957 internal Lionel sales forecasts and show that 3562-50s were available for separate sale in 1957 and 3562-75s in 1958.

3562-75	C7	C8	C9	Rarity
Regular Production Version	75	100	150	R6
	100	175	300	R7

Lumber Cars

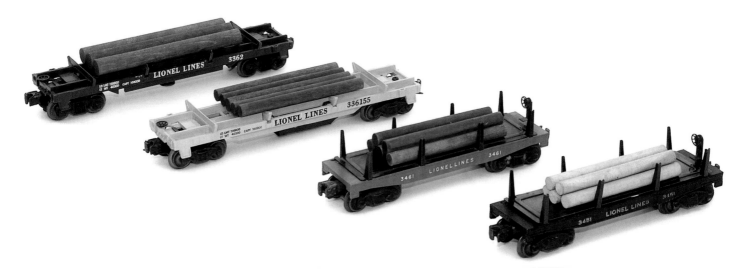

3361 OPERATING LUMBER CAR (PACKAGED WITH BIN): 1955 - 1961
3361X OPERATING LUMBER CAR (PACKAGED WITHOUT BIN): 1955 - 1961

Advertised in the 1955 consumer catalog as a scale-detailed 11-inch logger, the unpainted gray plastic 3361 was incorrectly illustrated in the 1955 consumer catalog as a red flat car in both set form and for separate sale. The following year the oversight was corrected, and it was correctly shown as a gray flat car. Lionel considered the 3361 as something special, because it was included in 14 cataloged sets during its seven-year run. With such a long production span, the gray plastic varied from light to medium to dark, and the lettering varied as well.

> Per Lionel Component Parts Index, the 3361 was originally intended to be painted, but on 7-20-55 part 3361-4 frame painted and stamped was deleted.

The operation of the 3361 was rather simple with a solenoid and plunger mechanism, located beneath the car, doing the work. With a touch of a remote-control button, the mechanism turned a plastic geared cam, which caused the dumping frame (3361-5) to rise one notch. As the frame rose one notch at a time, the logs were released one by one into a waiting bin that was included with each 3361. Once the frame reached its maximum height, it returned (dropped) to its normal starting position.

In 1955, the 3361 was part of two cataloged sets and offered for separate sale at $7.95. It had black rubber-stamped lettering, and the number "336155" appeared to the right of "Lionel Lines." Bar-end trucks were used throughout the production of the 3361.

When offered for separate sale, the 3361 was packaged in its own box that included five stained 5" logs and a 160-2 3½" x 8⅜" polystyrene bin. These items were protected and secured by a corrugated insert. When included with a boxed set, the car and logs were boxed without the bin. This 3361X version of the car came in a smaller box, and the bin was placed loose in the set box.

> Per Lionel Blueprints, the 3361-21 logs were birch and stained dark brown. "Stain used must be non-toxic." They were 5" (+/- ¹⁄₁₆") long by ⁷⁄₁₆" (+/- ¹⁄₃₂") in diameter.

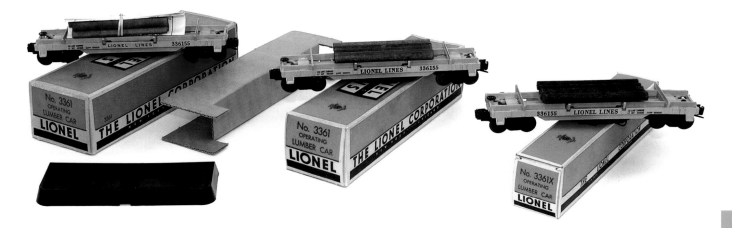

Left to right: 3361 sans-serif lettering with a Middle Classic separate-sale box; serif lettering and "336155" to the right of "Lionel" with a Late Classic separate-sale box; serif lettering and "336155" to the left with a 3361X Late Classic box.

Lionel experimented with two styles of lettering. The more common is rubber-stamped "serif" lettering; other versions have what is termed "sans-serif" lettering. Both styles were shown in the 1955 consumer catalog.

> **Per Lionel Blueprints the serif font was Cheltenham Bold and the sans-serif font was Gothic.**

Lionel used a two-cavity mold in the production of the 3361, as indicated by a "1" or a "2" on the bottom of the plastic body. Although both appeared the same, the "2" had an extra rivet on the top of the body.

In 1955, the bar-end trucks included black knuckle pins with or without tabs. Turning the car upside down reveals two other identifying features: The gear cam (3361-14) was molded in several shades, including orange, white and black Zytel® (Dupont's brand of nylon plastic), and the insulating washer (600-129 or -29) was red, like the one used with the new 155 Ringing Highway Signal. When trying to identify the 1955 version, look for a black knuckle pin and a red insulating washer.

In 1956, the 3361 came in a Late Classic style box. It was part of four cataloged sets and was offered for separate sale at $7.95. Silver knuckle pins became the norm, and serif lettering was used, although transition was a possibility. "336155" was stamped to the right of "Lionel Lines", but by the time set 2267W was released, Lionel had moved the "336155" to the left. Also in 1956, the *Lionel Service Manual* mentioned that in order to help unloading lumber to the lumber loader, the finger underneath the dump frame was increased by about 1/16".

For 1957, "336155" moved back to the right, and the hole in the knuckle drawbar continued until the end of production. The 3361 was once again offered as part of four cataloged sets, and the separate-sale price remained the same. In 1958, the car continued without change, and it was included in three cataloged sets, with the same $7.95 separate-sale price.

In 1959, the 3361 was included in only one cataloged set, and the separate-sale price remained the same. Those cars were probably left over from previous years, or a short production run was made. Either way, they still came in Late Classic style boxes.

In 1960 and 1961, a sufficient supply of 3361s remained in inventory to allow Lionel to feature them in the advance catalog, though not enough to make the consumer catalog. Lionel also decided to bury the remaining 3361s (both boxed 3361s and 3361Xs) in several promotional sets.

The 3361 was component boxed with a car, a corrugated insert, a 160-2 bin, five 3361-21 logs and a 3361-29 instruction sheet rubber-banded (with a #10 rubber band) around the logs.

- Box Style Middle Classic (1955)
  - Tuck Flap Number: 3361-25
  - Corrugated Insert: 3361-26
  - Box Dimensions: 4" x 12½" x 3"
- Box Style Late Classic (1956 - 1961)
  - Tuck Flap Number: 3361-34
  - Corrugated Insert: 3361-35
  - Box Dimensions: 3¼" x 12½" x 3"

The 3361X was also packed with the instruction sheet rubber-banded around the logs, but without the bin. It was held in place with coupler protection flaps instead of an insert.

- For Each Box:
  - Tuck Flap Number: 3361-28
  - Box Dimensions: 2¼" x 11¾" x 2½"
- Box Style Middle Classic (1955)
- Box Style Late Classic (1956 - 1961)

The 3361-29 instruction sheet came in five versions, dated:
- 9/55 (1955); 2/56 or 3/56 (1956); 6/57 (1957) and 6/58 (1958 - 1961)

Author's Comments: This car was the first plastic operating log dump car in the log dump car series. Its design was subsequently used for many other operating and non-operating cars, including the 3362, 3364, 6361 and 6362. It became a mainstay in sets, as it was an interesting and versatile car that could be used alone or with an operating accessory.

For variation collectors, the 1955 version with sans-serif lettering is the most desirable, especially when paired with the correct Middle Classic style box. Overall, collectors value the 3361 box much more than the 3361X version. This fact is reflected in the price table.

3361		C7	C8	C9	Rarity
"336155" To The Right	Serif	25	40	50	R4
	With 3361X Box	40	65	100	R7
	With 3361 Box	50	125	200	R8
	Sans-Serif	50	100	150	
	With 3361X Box	65	125	200	R8
	With 3361 Box	75	185	300	
"336155" To The Left		30	45	75	R7
With 3361X Box		45	70	125	
With 3361 Box		55	130	225	R8

3362-1 HELIUM TANK UNLOADING CAR (BOXED VERSION): 1961 - 1963 & 1965
3362-25 HELIUM TANK UNLOADING CAR (UNBOXED VERSION): 1961 - 1962

New for 1961, the Helium Tank Unloading Car used the same body as the 3361 Operating Lumber Car, except that it was molded in green plastic and had white rubber-stamped lettering. This "new" car was created simply by swapping the five logs of the 3361 for three helium tanks and cheapening the unloading mechanism. This was a quick way for Lionel to add additional play value and variety to their line.

Unlike its 3361 predecessor, the 3362 is activated by a spring-loaded dump frame that was less complex to manufacture. In this instance, when a remote-control operating track was activated to pull down the plunger beneath the car, the dump frame sprang upwards and dumped the tanks in one swift movement.

> Per Lionel Blueprints and Component Parts Index, the 3362-14 tanks were maple or equal and with a silver (aluminum) finish. They were 5.5" (+/- .030") long and .625" (+/- .015") in diameter.

The Helium Tank Unloading Car used AAR trucks with a three-piece metal knuckle coupler. It also had the prestige of being selected as part of the first cataloged set for 1961, and for separate sale at $5.95. When included with set 1641, the car was unboxed (3362-25) within the set box. However, when offered for separate sale, the car came boxed (3362-1).

In 1962, the 3362 used the new one-piece Delrin® (Dupont's brand of acetal plastic) coupler that was introduced at the end of 1961. The boxed version, 3362-1, was included in one cataloged set, and the separate-sale price increased to $6.95. Interestingly, 3362-1s packaged with set 13048, usually retained early 1961 AAR three-piece trucks. Furthermore, the 3362 was illustrated in the 1962 advance catalog for separate sale, but only mentioned (not shown) by the time the consumer catalog was released.

In 1963, the 3362 was no longer offered for separate sale, but appeared in set 13118. The features of the car were often the same as 1962, suggesting that Lionel used unsold stock intended for set 13048 and left over inventory and placed them in 13118.

The 3362 was no longer cataloged after 1963, but after a lapse of a year, Lionel disposed of its last twelve units of Helium Tank Unloading Cars by packaging them in Sears promotional set 19435 as a substitution for the 3413-1 Mercury Capsule Car.

The 3362-1 came component boxed with a car, three 3362-14 tanks, a #10 rubber band and a 3362-15 instruction sheet dated 6/61. When unboxed (3362-25), the instruction sheet was placed loose in the set box.

- Box Style Orange Picture (1961 - 1963 and 1965)
  - Tuck Flap Number: 3362-18
  - Box Manufacturer: Shuttleworth
  - Box Dimensions: 2¼" x 11⅞" x 2½"

Author's Comments: Western Auto set E-5009 (Lionel 19330) is shown with a 3362 in their 1964 Christmas catalog. The Factory Order for 19330 initially lists this as a 3362-25 (4-23-64), but subsequently changed it to a 3364-25 (5-2-64). It appears that Lionel originally thought of using the 3362-25, but did not. Therefore, the 3362 is not listed as appearing in 1964.

The 3362 car may have been modeled after a mock up of a helium tank car shown in the April 1952 issue of *Toy Trains* magazine. In that issue, an article details how to make your own helium tank car and shows pictures of one based on Lionel parts. Were Lionel engineers reading this magazine?

The 3362 Helium Tank Car (left) and 3364 Log Unloading Car on (right) (note 3362 on frame) used a modified 6361 frame (top).

The 3362 Helium Tank Unloading Car was reissued in 1969 (see 3362/3364).

3362	C7	C8	C9	Rarity
Regular Production	-25	35	50	75	R5
Version	-1	50	75	125	R8

3362/3364 OPERATING UNLOADING CAR: 1969

Cataloged in 1969 only, the 3362/3364 was truly an oddball as it could be either a 3362 Helium Tank Unloading Car or a 3364 Log Unloading Car. The box, which generically listed a "3362/3364 Operating Unloading Car", allowed Lionel to deplete their inventory of helium tanks (3362) or logs (3364). Three tanks or logs were the correct load, but some had only *two*, as Lionel's inventory probably ran short. Keep in mind that by 1969, Lionel was actively soliciting offers for their toy train business, and they already contracted with General Mills by April 1969. They were doing whatever they could to show as much profit as possible and keep the train business an ongoing concern. It is likely there were no new 3362s or 3364s manufactured in 1969, just repackaging or assembling of earlier production.

This "new" car was still molded in green plastic, but the majority of the time the rubber-stamped lettering was absent. However, the 1969, as well as the 1966 and 1968 catalog illustrations showed the lettering being present, although they were all missing "3362" to the right of "Lionel Lines" on the car. The 3362/3364 was offered for separate sale only at $7.00.

The car's 1969 trucks and couplers were typical 1966 or later production and included one AAR operating coupler and one dummy, both with open journal boxes. If the leaf spring had a washer attached with the leaf spring rivet, it was likely assembled in 1966.

The 3362/3364 was component boxed with a 3364-10 instruction sheet dated 4/65.

- Box Style Hagerstown or Hillside Checkerboard (1969)
  - Tuck Flap Number: 12-278
  - Box Dimensions: 3⅝" x 10½" x 2½"

Author's Comments: According to Lenny Dean, who supervised the Service Department in the 1960s and served on a team in charge of operations in 1968 and 1969, "There was an abundance of either helium tanks or logs, and Lionel was just cleaning house at that time."

The Checkerboard box is more valuable than the car. In fact it is one of the tougher Checkerboard boxes to find.

3362/3364	C7	C8	C9	Rarity
Regular Production Version	50	75	100	R8
	100	150	225	R9

3364-1 LOG UNLOADING CAR (BOXED VERSION): 1965 - 1966 & 1968
3364-25 LOG UNLOADING CAR (UNBOXED VERSION): 1964 - 1967

As Lionel was dumping their leftover stock of 3362 Helium Tank Unloading Cars, they suddenly had a change of heart. They returned to the load that was a favorite with young and old since the prewar days . . . logs. The 3364 Log Unloading Car, like the 3362, was molded in green plastic with white rubber-stamped lettering. The 3364 was the same as a 3362, except that it came with three logs rather than three helium tanks. In fact, Lionel did not even bother to renumber the car: a "3364" was still stamped "3362."

The car's operation was the same as the 3362, with a plunger being activated by a remote-control operating track. This caused the tray on which the logs were placed to spring upwards and dump.

> Per Lionel Blueprints, the 3364-8 logs were brown stained (non toxic) wooden dowels and measured 6" long (+/- ⅛") by ⅝" in diameter (+/- 1/16") and weighed 19.6 (+/- 3) grams.

The Log Unloading Car was not introduced in time to be mentioned or illustrated in the 1964 consumer catalog or the *Lionel Service Manual*, but it can accurately be linked to 1964 through Lionel Factory Orders. It was included unboxed (3364-25) in seven promotional sets, such as 19335 (J.C. Penney no. X 924-0672 A). In 1964, features included an AAR operating and a

The 3362/3364 Operating Unloading Car came with either helium tanks (left) or logs (right).

dummy coupler, with *only* the latter's having open journal boxes. In 1965 and after, both the operating and dummy couplers had open journal boxes.

In 1965, the 3364-25 came unboxed in set 11520, and the 3364-1 was boxed for separate sale at $6.00. The *Lionel Service Manual* correctly listed the 3364 as a Log Unloading Car, and the consumer catalog illustrations showed the "3362" number on the right side of the car.

In the 1966 full-color consumer catalog, the 3364-25 was correctly illustrated when shown with set 11520. However, when pictured for separate sale at the same price as before, the 3364-1 omitted the "3362" altogether. In 1967, the 3364-25 appeared in one promotional set, 19705 (Sears T49 C9733).

Lionel used the same incorrect 1966 photograph of the 3364-1 when it was cataloged for separate-sale in 1968; however, the price had jumped from $6.00 to $7.00. This same picture showed up again in the 1969 consumer catalog in the listing for the 3362/3364.

The 3364-1 came component boxed with a car, three 3364-8 logs, a #10 rubber band, a 3364-10 instruction sheet dated 4/65 (1965 - 1966 and 1968) and a 1-165 warranty card (1965 - 1966). The 3364-25 also included the logs, a rubber band and a 3364-10

instruction sheet dated 6/64 (1964) or 4/65 (1965 - 1967) loose in the set box.

- Box Style Hillside Orange Picture (1965 - 1966 and 1968)
  - Tuck Flap Number: 3364-12
  - Box Dimensions: 2¼" x 11⅞" x 2½"

Author's Comments: The 3364 was a drab addition to the line in 1964. Instead of modifying the 3362 with the addition of logs, Lionel should have issued new road names or colors, thus giving operators and collectors something to add to their collections. This repackaging of an existing design reflected Lionel's lack of creativity after the departure of Joseph Bonnano, Lionel's chief engineer, in 1963.

The 3364-25 was first issued unboxed in 1964, thus the only source of its true name came from the 1964 no. 3364-10 instruction sheet dated 6/64. This listed the car as an "Unloading Car" instead of a Log Unloading Car. It wasn't until the internal Lionel documents used for this volume were examined that the true name (Log Unloading Car) for the 1964 version was verified.

3364		C7	C8	C9	Rarity
Regular Production	-25	35	50	75	R3
Version	-1	50	75	125	R8

Top left: The 3451 with silver rubber-stamped lettering. Top right: A 3461 with white heat-stamped lettering. Front: A 3461-25 with white heat-stamped lettering. Note that the polystyrene tray shown with the 3461-25 is larger in this case.

3451 AUTOMATIC LUMBER CAR: 1946 - 1948

Introduced in 1946, the die-cast metal 3451 was the postwar answer to the operating sheet-metal log cars from the prewar era. Included in three cataloged sets and offered for separate sale at $5.75, the black-painted 3451 was perfectly illustrated in the consumer catalog.

The 3451 took advantage of a new solenoid and plunger, which were activated by a pair of sliding shoes on the car's trucks. When the coil was energized, the motion of the plunger lifted the car's hinged floor platform, while the lumber-retaining stakes on the hinged side of the car swung down through their own weight to allow the lumber to roll down into a bin or awaiting accessory.

In 1946, the 3451s featured silver rubber-stamped lettering, blue connecting wires, and staple-end trucks with non-staked coil couplers. Also included were five unstained (natural color) wood logs, and a 160-1 3" x 7" Bakelite bin.

> **Per Lionel Blueprints, the 164-64 logs were birch dowels measuring 4⅜" (+/- ¹⁄₁₆") long by ⁷⁄₁₆" (+/- ¹⁄₃₂") in diameter.**

In 1947, the 3451 was offered in two cataloged sets and the separate-sale price remained the same. Also during the year its features changed; now white heat-stamped lettering, black connecting wires, and staple-end trucks with staked couplers were regular production. Starting in late 1947, a molded ridge, or fillet, running the entire length underneath the car on the solid stake side, was added at about a 45-degree angle, possibly to reinforce the center hole. Also, the diameter of this hole changed from about 1⁵⁄₁₆" in 1946 to about 1³⁄₁₆" and then 1¼" in 1947, and finally to about 1⅛" (see 3461) near the end of 1950's production year.

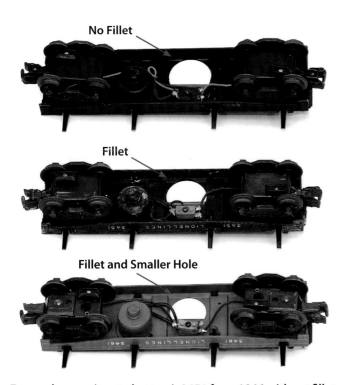

Frame changes (top to bottom): 3451 from 1946 without fillet, 3451 from 1947 with fillet, and 3461-25 from 1954 with a smaller hole and fillet.

In 1948, the 3451 was included in four cataloged sets and the separate-sale price increased to $6.50. The car was the same as in 1947, with the exception of the box decreasing in size.

The 3451 came in a 3451-25 (part number not on box) component box with a 3451-40 liner, five 164-64 logs, a 160-1 bin and a 3451-27 instruction sheet rubber-banded (with a #10 rubber band) around the logs.

- For Each Box (1946 - 1947):
  - Tuck Flap Number: None (3451-25 not on box)
  - Box Dimensions: 4⅜" x 10¼" x 3½" (1946 - 1947)
- Box Style Art Deco (1946)
- Box Style Art Deco or Art Deco Toy Logo (1947)
- Box Style Art Deco Toy Logo (1948)
  - Tuck Flap Number: None
  - Box Dimensions: 3⅜" x 10⅜" x 3¼" (1948)
- Box Style Early Classic (1948)
  - Tuck Flap Number: None
  - Box Dimensions: 2½" x 10⅛" x 2⅛" (1948)

The 3451-27 instruction sheet came in four versions, dated:
- 5/46 (1946); 5/47 (1957) and 2/48 or 4/48 (1948)

Left: 3451 Art Deco (1946). Right: Art Deco Toy Logo smaller box (1948).

Author's Comments: The rubber-stamped 3451 was offered in at least three sets and for separate sale, so it's not as rare as often thought. However, finding one with clean, crisp lettering is another story. "Speckled" Bakelite examples of the 160-1 bin are very collectable.

The 3541 was the first postwar version of an automatic lumber car and has endured time well, as many are still found in operating condition.

3451	C7	C8	C9	Rarity
Rubber-Stamped Version	35	50	75	R7
	45	85	175	
Heat-Stamped Version	25	40	50	R4
	35	75	90	

3461 AUTOMATIC LUMBER CAR (SEPARATE SALE): 1949 - 1953
3461X AUTOMATIC LUMBER CAR (INCLUDED WITH BOXED SET): 1949 - 1953

The 3461 was an update of the 3451 and came equipped with staple-end magnetic couplers instead of the 3451's staple-end, coil-

The rubber-stamped 3461 is very rare.

wound couplers from 1948; hence, the new number. It operated in the same manner as the 3451.

In 1949, the 3461 was perfectly illustrated in the consumer catalog, as part of four sets and for separate sale at $6.50. The black-painted 3461 had a die-cast metal frame with white heat-stamped lettering. Lionel did rubber-stamp some 3461s in silver, just like the 3451, but these 3461s are very rare. The staple-end truck and couplers included a flared activator flap rivet, and some examples had a smaller base plate hole.

When offered for separate sale, the car was packaged in a 3461 box that included five wood logs, an instruction sheet, and a 160-1 3" x 7" Bakelite bin. When included with a boxed set, the same car was packaged in a smaller 3461X box that included the same wood logs and instruction sheet, but the 160-1 bin was placed loose within the set box.

> Per Lionel Blueprints, the 164-64 logs were birch dowels measuring 4⅝" (+/- ¹⁄₁₆") long by ⁷⁄₁₆" (+/- ¹⁄₃₂") in diameter. On 1-17-49, the following note was added: "Stain dark brown and raise grain as much as possible. Stain used must be non-toxic."

In 1950, the 3461 was included in six cataloged sets and the separate-sale price remained the same. The flared rivet was replaced by the round-end version, and a hole was punched out of the activator flap (armature assembly). Of course, don't forget about transition in that earlier trucks and couplers could be present. In 1950, mint examples confirm the existence of the stained logs mentioned in Lionel blueprints; they were probably also included with late 1949 separate-sale examples. By late 1950, the diameter of the opening on the frame had been reduced from 1¼" (see 3451) to about 1⅛".

In 1951, the 3461 was offered in only one cataloged set and the specifications were the same as before. The 3461 was also offered for separate sale, with the price jumping from $6.50 to $7.75. During this year, with the Korean War in progress, dealers were issued a packet of pre-priced gummed OPS labels to be placed on each separate-sale box. But with a possible shortage of raw materials, the 3461s may have been leftover inventory from prior years, with a short production run made to fill in the gaps.

In 1952, the OPS information was letter-pressed directly on the box and bar-end trucks were normal production. The 3461 was once again offered in only one cataloged set, and the price for separate sale dropped to $7.25.

The 3461 made its final catalog appearance in 1953. It was illustrated in two cataloged sets and for separate sale at the 1952 price. The car specifications were the same as 1952.

The 3461 was component boxed with a car, a 3451-40 corrugated liner, a 160-1 bin, five 164-64 logs and a 3461-11 instruction sheet that was rubber-banded (with a #10 rubber band) around the logs.

- For Each Box:
  - Box Dimensions: 3⅜" x 10⅜" x 3¼"
- Box Style Early Classic (1949)
  - Tuck Flap Number: None (3461-10 not on box)
- Box Style Middle Classic (1949)
  - Tuck Flap Number: None (3461-10 not on box)
- Box Style Middle Classic (1950 - 1951 and 1953)
  - Tuck Flap Number: 3461-10
- Box Style OPS Classic (1952)
  - Tuck Flap Number: 3461-10
- Note: The 3461 also used over-stamped 3451 boxes.

The 3461X was also packed with the instruction sheet rubber-banded around the logs, but without the bin. It was held in place with coupler protection flaps instead of a corrugated liner.

- For Each Box:
  - Box Dimensions: 2½" x 10⅛" x 2⅛"
- Box Style Early Classic (1949)
  - Tuck Flap Number: None
- Box Style Middle Classic (1950 - 1953)
  - Tuck Flap Number: 3461X-5
- Note: The 3461X also used over-stamped boxes.

The 3461-11 instruction sheet came in nine versions, dated:
- 2/49 or 11/49 (1949); 2/50, 3/50, 4/50 or 9/50 (1950); 10/51(1951); 2/52 (1952) and 2/53 (1953)

Author's Comments: Although existing reference guides mistakenly state that the five "Stained Logs" debuted in 1954, logic and internal Lionel documentation suggests otherwise. Besides the *facts* provided in the 3461 summary, each of the three illustrations showing a 3461 in the 1952 full-color consumer catalog featured five stained logs. Of course, the artist's rendition probably came from a previous year's example, which in turn goes back to 1951. Finally, mint examples and Lionel blueprints observed provide the final confirmation that these were likely used as early as 1949.

When included in a boxed set, the 3461X was the version always used.

The 1953 *Lionel Service Manual* stated incorrectly that the 3461 was first made in 1948.

3461	C7	C8	C9	Rarity
Regular Production	25	40	50	R4
With 3461X Box	35	55	75	R6
With 3461 Box	40	65	100	R8
Rubber-Stamped Version	500	1,000	2,000	
With 3461X Box	510	1,015	2,025	R10
With 3461 Box	515	1,025	2,050	

3461-25 AUTOMATIC LUMBER CAR (SEPARATE SALE): 1954 - 1955
3461X-25 AUTOMATIC LUMBER CAR (INCLUDED WITH BOXED SET): 1954 - 1955

In the 1954 consumer catalog, Lionel promised vibrant colors, so the green-painted 3461-25 was a colorful alternate to the black-painted 3461. This die-cast metal car came with white heat-stamped lettering and operated in the same manner as the 3451 and 3461.

The packaging of the 3461-25 copied that of the 3461. When offered for separate sale, a 3461-25 used a larger box and a 160-1 3" x 7" Bakelite bin or 160-2 3½" x 8⅜" polystyrene bin was stored inside. When included in a set, a 3461X-25 used a smaller box and the bin was placed loose inside the set box. Both versions included five stained birch logs and an instruction sheet.

The 3461-25 had the same features as the 3461 from the year before, except the top of the bar-end knuckle coupler was engraved (not smooth) and included a 160 bin. The 3461X-25 was included in three cataloged sets, and the 3461-25 was offered for separate sale at $7.25.

In 1955, the 3461X-25 was included in only one cataloged set. Cars offered for separate sale were similarly priced and probably leftover inventory from 1954. Other features were the same as 1954.

The 3461-25 was component boxed with a car, a 3461-20 corrugated liner, a 160-1 or 160-2 bin, five 164-4 logs and a 3461-11 instruction sheet dated 1/54 that was rubber-banded (with a #10 rubber band) around the logs.

- Box Style Middle Classic
  - Tuck Flap Number: 3461-15
  - Box Dimensions: 3¾" x 10½" x 3½"

The 3461X-25 was also packed with the instruction sheet rubber-banded around the logs, but without the bin. It was held in place with coupler protection flaps instead of an insert.

- Box Style Middle Classic
  - Tuck Flap Number: 3461-32
  - Box Dimensions: 2½" x 10⅛" x 2⅛"

Author's Comments: The 3461-25 is the most desirable of the automatic lumber cars with its color making it an attractive offering.

Even though this car was cataloged for two years, it is unlikely that it was made during 1955 because no examples have been observed with 1955 mechanical features.

3461-25	C7	C8	C9	Rarity
Regular Production	35	50	75	R5
With 3461X-25 Box	45	75	100	R7
With 3461-25 Box	60	125	225	R8

Green-painted 3461-25 with a Middle Classic box and 160-1 bin.

CHAPTER FOUR

Dump Cars

Lionel offered dump cars in the prewar era. These early postwar cars carried on the tradition. They also demonstrate Lionel's attempt to introduce different color schemes.

3359 OPERATING DUMP CAR: 1955 - 1958

New for 1955, the 3359 was designed after a twin-body automatic air dump car made by the Magor Car Corp. and used by the City of New York. The O gauge car's operation included the use of two separate dumping trays, which were activated through the use of a 3359-16 geared cam concealed beneath the trays. The gear totaled 16 teeth or steps. Seven steps are required to raise a bin to its maximum height, while the eighth allowed the bin to drop down to its normal position. The next eight steps repeated this sequence for the second bin.

In 1955, the 3359 was included in three cataloged sets and for separate-sale at $8.95. It used a sheet-metal frame, with a red (maroon) polystyrene plastic under frame.

> Per Lionel Blueprints, a .095" hole was added to the 3359-3 sheet-metal frame on 3-9-56. Also, the 3359-26 under frame was originally intended to be black, but was changed to red (maroon) on 10-11-55.

The tray assembly and doors were molded in gray polystyrene, with black heat-stamped lettering in the Gothic style. The car came equipped with a bag of 207-1 artificial coal and a 160-2 3½" x 8⅜"polystyrene bin. When boxed, a corrugated insert held the car and peripherals in place.

During 1955, the car's features also included bar-end trucks, with or without the new uncoupling tabs, and black knuckle pins. It also included gray or black connecting wires.

In 1956, the 3359 was included with three cataloged sets and the separate-sale price remained the same. Silver knuckle pins become the norm.

By 1957, the graphics of the car's 3359-80 packed envelope changed. During the year, bar-end knuckle couplers had a support hole in the drawbar. The 3359 had bragging rights, as it was included in 2289WS, the very first set to make a run on the brand-new Super "O" track. The separate-sale price increased a dollar to $9.95. According to internal Lionel sales forecasts, the 2,500 cars offered for separate sale were leftover inventory from 1956.

The twin dumping action of the 3359 was another fine addition to the Lionel line. The packed envelope is shown in both styles.

In 1958, the specifications were the same as before and the 3359 was cataloged in one set only. The separate-sale price jumped another dollar to $10.95. Internal Lionel sales forecasts indicated that 600 units were leftover inventory, while a balance of 400 would be delivered to the trade by August.

The 3359 was component boxed with a 3359-76 insert to stabilize the car. Also included were a 3359-80 packed envelope (envelope no. 3359-78), a bag of 207-1 artificial coal and a 160-2 bin. Each 3359-80 packed envelope included two OTC-1 lockons, four 24-4 rail clips, a 90-1 controller, three 81-32 24" RC wires and a 3359-79 instruction sheet dated 9/55 or 12/55.

- For Each Box:
  - Tuck Flap Number: 3359-75
  - Box Dimensions: 3⅞" x 14¼" x 3¼"
- Box Style Middle Classic (1955)
- Box Style Late Classic (1956 - 1958)

Author's Comments: Although the 3359 is a common car, its twin dumping action provided more play value than earlier dump cars. The car was also included in 1958 set 2513W, pulled by the brand-new 2329 Virginian Rectifier. This set is extremely popular and collectible because it also included the 6556 MKT Stock Car and 6427-60 Virginian Caboose, both made only in 1958. Because of this set's popularity, the 3359 has become a lot more collectible and valuable, especially when complete with all peripherals and matching box.

3359	C7	C8	C9	Rarity
Regular Production Version	35	50	75	R5
	55	85	150	R7

3459 AUTOMATIC DUMPING ORE CAR: 1946 - 1948

Introduced in 1946, the 3459 included a black frame and silver metal tray with Lionel Lines heat-stamped on both sides in blue. The full-color consumer catalog incorrectly illustrated it with Baltimore & Ohio markings.

Left to right: 3459 from 1946 painted silver, metal bin, and Art Deco box; 3459 from 1946 painted black, Bakelite bin, and Art Deco box; and 3459 from 1948 painted green and Art Deco Toy Logo box.

The 3459 was the first newly designed dump car in the postwar era. Like the 3451 Automatic Lumber Car, it took advantage of a new solenoid and plunger, which were activated by a pair of sliding shoes on the car's trucks. When the coil was energized, the motion of the plunger lifted the tray and dumped the coal.

Included in three cataloged sets and offered for separate sale at $7.00, the rare silver version was replaced by a black-painted, white heat-stamped example later in the year. Also, some silver 3459s were heat-stamped on only the swinging door side and are considered factory errors. Unlike most factory errors, where only a few are known to exist, enough unstamped 3459s exist to consider it a collectible variation.

> Per Lionel Production Control Files dated 12-30-47, the 3459-21 tray assembly was painted "Black S-306" and could be painted at the rate of 405 minimum to 540 maximum units per hour.

In 1946, the 3459 included staple-end trucks with non-staked coil couplers, blue connecting wires, and shiny handrail screws that eventually gave way to blackened ones. This car came with either a bin made of metal or a 160-1 3" x 7" Bakelite bin, although the 3459 is shown in the 1947 full-color consumer catalog with the metal bin. The car also came equipped with a bag of 207-1 artificial coal.

In 1947, the 3459 was offered for separate sale at $7.00 and came with two cataloged sets. The black-painted version dominated and included staked couplers and black connecting wires. Missing was the "knock mark" (heat-stamped depression) on top of the tray, which prevented the tray dumping activation pin from getting stuck and thereby helped the tray return to a closed position.

In 1948, the separate-sale price increased from $7.00 to $7.75 and it was also included in five cataloged sets. A green-painted 3459 now joined the black one. It also had white heat-stamped lettering, and the specifications were the same as before.

The 3459 was component boxed with a 3459-26 corrugated liner to stabilize the car. Also included were a bag of 207-1 artificial coal, a metal bin (1946) or a 160-1 Bakelite bin (1946 – 1948) and an instruction sheet.

- For Each Box:
  - Tuck Flap Number: None (3459-25 not on box)
  - Box Dimensions: 3¼" x 10¼" x 3¼"
- Box Style Art Deco (1946)
- Box Style Art Deco or Art Deco Toy Logo (1947)
- Box Style Art Deco Toy Logo (1948)

The instruction sheet came in five versions:
- 3459-28 dated 5/46 or 7/46 (1946)
- 3451-27 dated 5/47 (1947) and 2/48 or 4/48 (1948)

Author's Comments: Many collectors are not familiar with the metal bin included with the 1946 version of the 3459. Although the bin was perfectly illustrated on page 22 of the 1947 consumer catalog, many were possibly discarded as a non-train related item. Also of note, the 1948 consumer catalog incorrectly lists a 206 bag of coal in set 1449WS.

When it comes to rare items, few surpass the yellow-painted 3459 (see Chapter 8), which was featured on the front cover of the December 1948 issue of *Science Illustrated* magazine.

Also known to exist is a possible one-of-a-kind red-painted example.

Right: The silver 3459 has no heat-stamped lettering on the side opposite the swinging door. Note the original metal bin rather than a Bakelite example.

3459	C7	C8	C9	Rarity
Silver Version	200	300	400	R8
	250	375	500	
Black Version	40	60	90	R6
	60	100	150	
Green Version	60	75	125	R6
	80	115	185	
Silver Factory Error Version	100	200	250	R10
	150	300	400	
Yellow-Painted Version	4,000	6,000	8,000	R10
Red-Painted Version	7,000	8,000	10,000	R10

Dump Cars

3469 AUTOMATIC DUMPING ORE CAR (SEPARATE SALE): 1949 - 1955
3469X AUTOMATIC DUMPING ORE CAR (INCLUDED WITH BOXED SET): 1949 - 1955

Introduced in 1949, the 3469 was an update to the 3459 and came equipped with staple-end magnetic couplers instead of the 3459's staple-end, coil wound couplers from 1948; hence, the new number. It operated in the same manner as the 3459.

The 3469 came with a black die-cast frame and a black-painted tray with a swinging door, both of which had white heat-stamped lettering. The handrails had a screw opening as part of the new design.

In 1949, this new car was included in six cataloged sets and priced for separate sale at $7.75. It featured staple-end trucks with a flared activator flap rivet. Also, a "rainbow" effect was visible on the bottom of the frame where lubricant was used to insert the rubber grommets holding the wires in place.

In 1950, the 3469 was offered for separate sale at $7.75 and included in six cataloged sets. Staple-end trucks continued, but the flared rivet process was now replaced by a round-end type and a hole was punched out of the activator flap (armature assembly). Also in 1950, the rainbow effect vanished. Of course, don't forget about transition as earlier features could also appear.

In the Korean War year of 1951, the 3469 was included in only two cataloged sets and the separate-sale price increased to $8.95. For cars offered for separate sale, dealers were to place a pre-priced gummed OPS label on each box. Lionel would provide a packet of these to each dealer.

An envelope of OPS labels as provided to dealers by Lionel.

With a possible shortage of raw materials, some 3469s may have been leftover 1950 inventory. However, since the 3469 was included in two carryover sets and also available for separate sale, in 1951 it is unlikely that sufficient inventory was available, thus a production run was required. The 3461 was in a similar situation (see 3461). The specifications for the 3469 were the same as before, except some 3459-27 frame covers were orange rather than red. Another change was the way the three rivets were applied to the back of the tray as the round-end rivet was visible on the outside, whereas before it had been on the inside.

In 1952, the 3469 was included in one set and offered for separate sale at a reduced price of $8.50. When offered for separate sale, the box now had OPS letter-press information rather than a label. The car remained as before, except bar-end trucks became the norm.

In 1953, the 3469 was included in two cataloged sets and the separate-sale price remained the same. The 3469's features were the same as before. For some reason, the 3469X box developed a flaw that continued through 1955. Specifically, the "N" in "LIONEL" (to the left of the American Toys logo) bulged out to the right.

In both 1954 and 1955, the 3469 was part of one cataloged set

Boxes for the 3469 (left to right): Middle Classic (1949), Early Classic 3459 over-stamp, Middle Classic 3461 over-stamp, Middle Classic (1950) with OPS Sticker, OPS Classic (1952) and Middle Classic larger size (1954 - 1955).

and the separate-sale price remained at $8.50. The specifications were the same as before, except that the truck and couplers had the tops of the coupler drawbar engraved rather than smooth. In 1955, leftover inventory was probably used to fill orders, especially since the brand-new 3359 Operating Dump Car was the item Lionel really wanted to push.

When offered for separate sale, the car was packaged in a 3469 box that included a bag of 207-1 artificial coal, a 160-1 3" x 7" Bakelite bin (1949 - 1953) or a 160-2 3½" x 8⅜" polystyrene bin (1954 - 1955), and a 3461-11 instruction sheet, all protected by a corrugated liner.

- For Each Box (1949 - 1953):
  - Corrugated Liner: 3459-26
  - Box Dimensions: 3¼" x 10¼" x 3¼"
- Box Style Middle Classic (1949)
  - Tuck Flap Number: None (3469-10 not on box)
- Box Style Middle Classic (1950 - 1951 & 1953)
  - Tuck Flap Number: 3469-10
- Box Style OPS Classic (1952)
  - Tuck Flap Number: 3469-10
- Box Style Middle Classic (1954 - 1955)
  - Tuck Flap Number: 3469-19
  - Corrugated Liner: 3469-20
  - Box Dimensions: 3½" x 10¼" x 3⅛"
- Note: The 3469 also used over-stamped 3461 or 3459 boxes

When included with a boxed set, the same car was packaged in a smaller 3469X box that included a bag of 207-1 artificial coal and a 3461-11 instruction sheet, but the 160 bin was placed loose within the set box.

- For Each Box:
  - Box Dimensions: 2½" x 10⅜" x 2½"
- Box Style Early Classic (1949)
  - Tuck Flap Number: None
- Box Style Middle Classic (1950 - 1952)
  - Tuck Flap Number: 3469X-2
- Box Style Middle Classic with Box Flaw (1953)
  - Tuck Flap Number: 3469X-2
- Box Style Middle Classic with Box Flaw (1954 - 1955)
  - Tuck Flap Number: 3469X-2

> Lionel Production Control Files dated 10-28-54, stated that as an alternate to the 3469 box, use a 12-8 folding box and imprint end panels. Also, on 11-23-54 as an alternate to the 3469X box, use a no. 12-10 folding box and imprint end panels.

The 3461-11 instruction sheet came in ten versions, dated:
- 2/49 or 11/49 (1949); 2/50, 3/50, 4/50 or 9/50 (1950); 10/51 (1951); 2/52 (1952); 2/53 (1953) and 1/54 (1954 - 1955)

Author's Comments: The small box was stamped "Automatic Dump Car", and the large one was stamped "Automatic Dumping Ore Car." Of interest, in 1950 and 1951 the 3469 was listed as a 3469X in the consumer catalog, whereas in other years the catalog listed it as a 3469.

With a seven year run, dull or glossy paint variations exist. Also near the end of 1949 Form 900, informing of a change of address of the Lionel Service Department, was included with some separate-sale items

3469	C7	C8	C9	Rarity
Regular Production Version	30	60	90	R3
With 3469X Box	40	75	125	R5
With 3459 Box	45	85	150	

3559 AUTOMATIC DUMP CAR: 1946 - 1948

The 3559 was a carryover from a similar prewar 3659 model (and a larger 3859 model). In fact, except for the postwar staple-end trucks and couplers, most of the parts on the *new* 3559s were just prewar carryovers, still with prewar numbers. The 3559 was introduced to the postwar era as part of two cataloged sets as well as promotional set 3103W. It was also offered for separate sale at $5.50.

The operation for the 3559 was rather simple. All an operator needed to do was center the car over a section of remote-control track and press the unload button on the controller. The car's tipple action did the rest of the work, as coal was unloaded onto a waiting bin.

In 1946 the 3559 had a black sheet-metal frame with steps and a red-painted hopper. The motor was covered with a black Bakelite motor housing that had a molded Lionel "L" in a circle. There was also silver rubber-stamped lettering on the underside of the frame. The 3559 also included blue connecting wires and staple-end trucks with non-staked coupler heads. Some 3559s even used the earlier style trucks that had a flying shoe and fiberboard insulator.

In 1947, the 3559 was included in two cataloged sets and the separate-sale price remained the same. Staple-end trucks with staked coupler heads and black connecting wires were now the norm. A rare variation with a brown Bakelite motor cover was included in set 2123WS.

In 1948, the 3559 was included in only one cataloged set, with the separate-sale price remaining at $5.50. There were no changes to the car, but a new Early Classic box was used.

Each 3559 was component boxed with a car, a bag of 207-1 artificial coal, a 160-1 3" x 7" Bakelite bin and an instruction sheet, all protected by a corrugated liner.

- For Each Box (1946 - 1947)
  - Tuck Flap Number: None
  - Box Dimensions: 3½" x 9½" x 3¼"
- Box Style Art Deco (1946)
- Box Style Art Deco Toy Logo (1947)
- Box Style Early Classic (1948)
  - Tuck Flap Number: None (3559-20 not on box)
  - Corrugated Liner: 3559-21
  - Box Dimensions: 4" x 8¾" x 3½"
- Note: The 3559 also used over-stamped 3659 prewar dump car boxes

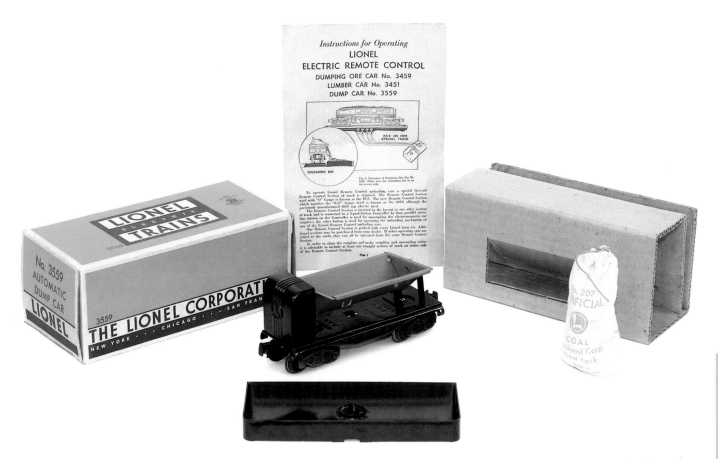

The 3559 was a carryover from a similar prewar design. This version from 1948, with all the peripherals, came in an Early Classic box.

A 3559 (left) with a black motor cover is more common than one with a brown cover (right).

The 3559 included two different instruction sheets in five versions:

- 3559-4 dated: 1/46 or 5/46 (1946)
- 3451-27 dated: 5/47 (1947) and 2/48 or 4/48 (1948)

Author's Comments: The 3559 was a relatively common car, although the brown motor-cover variation is considerably harder to find.

Right after World War II, Lionel was scrambling to get new rolling stock into their line. Simply adding the new postwar trucks and couplers was a quick fix. It also allowed them to use up their inventory of prewar parts. Many prewar manufacturing methods were still used, including the stamping of the part number on the bottom of the frame.

3559	C7	C8	C9	Rarity
Black Motor Cover Version With Flying Shoe Trucks	50	75	100	R9
	70	110	175	
Black Motor Cover Version	40	60	80	R6
	60	90	150	R8
Brown Motor Cover Version	50	75	100	R9
	70	110	175	

5459 AUTOMATIC DUMPING ORE CAR WITH ELECTRONIC CONTROL: 1946 - 1949

In 1946, the 5459 was included in Lionel's new "Electronically Controlled" O gauge freight set 4109WS, which was heralded as "The only train of its kind in the world." The 5459 came with a black die-cast frame and a black-painted tray with a swinging door, both of which had white heat-stamped lettering.

However, the full-color 1946 consumer catalog incorrectly illustrated it as a silver dump car with Baltimore & Ohio markings. That's understandable, because the first 3459 Automatic Dumping Ore Car examples, on which the 5459 was based, were also illustrated in 1946 advance catalog as silver dump cars with Baltimore & Ohio markings. No production models of either a silver 3459 or 5459 dump car with B&O markings have been found.

The 5459 was part of the famous Electronic Control Set (with Art Deco box and peripherals).

The 5459 operated in the same manner as the 3459, except that to activate the car, a button on the ECU-1 Electronic Control Unit, unique to the Electronic Control Set, was pushed and held down. If not held down, it would only uncouple the car.

The die-cast frame for a 5459 was modified to include a small opening in the side of the frame, whereby using a small screwdriver, one could adjust the frequency of the receiver inside the car. Many of the 5459 frames were actually modified 3459 frames and Lionel included the same data as on the 3459 cars, but they had a "5459" number. Authentic 5459 with "3459" numbered frames were also produced by Lionel.

> **Per Lionel Production Control Files, the 5459-4 Zamak #5 frame was molded in a one-cavity mold and used inserts for the 5459-4.**

In late 1946, the 5459 included staple-end couplers with a staked-coupler head. This reinforcing staking process, introduced at this time, may also have been used with the Irvington passenger cars.

In 1947, set 4109WS was cataloged again. The 5459's features were the same as before, although the staked-couplers became the norm.

In 1948, the new 4110WS Electronic Control Set now included accessories, such as a 151 Automatic Semaphore and 97 Remote Control Coal Elevator. Even so, the specifications for the 5459 included examples with either staked or non-staked couplers.

In 1949, the 4110WS was cataloged again, but most likely represented unsold inventory from the year before. In fact, with a suggested retail price of $199.95, it's easy to understand why this set didn't sell well in the first place.

In 1950, Lionel offered the 4333WS Electronic Set in the consumer catalog, but doesn't appear to have ever manufactured those sets, although leftover sets from previous years were probably still available. Therefore, this volume lists the 5459 as being cataloged from only 1946 through 1949.

Each 5459 was component boxed with a car, a bag of 207-1 artificial coal and a 160-1 3" x 7" Bakelite bin. The entire package was protected by a 3459-26 corrugated liner. The instructions for operating the car were included separately with the Electronic Control 12-page operating manual (Form No. ECU-50).

- For Each Box:
  - Tuck Flap Number: None (5459-15 not on box)
  - Box Dimensions: 3¼" x 10¼" x 3¼"
- Box Style Art Deco (1946)
- Box Style Art Deco Toy Logo (1947 - 1949)

Author's Comments: The 5459 was not offered for separate sale, as it was included in only Lionel's series of Electronic Sets. Even so, Madison Hardware Co. of New York City still had a few boxed examples for sale into the early 1980s.

Some leftover 5459 frames may have been used in the making of the 3459 and 3469, as they all used the same mold (mold no. 3459-T-4A).

5459	C7	C8	C9	Rarity
Regular Production Version	100	150	200	R8
	125	300	400	

CHAPTER FIVE

Lights + Cameras = Action

3520 OPERATING SEARCHLIGHT CAR: 1952 - 1953

Introduced in 1952, the 3520 was a follow-up to the 6520 Searchlight Car, last cataloged in 1951. Based on the same gray-painted die-cast body, it included black rubber-stamped lettering. It also included an orange polystyrene plastic diesel motor assembly that modeled a General Motors generator. The 3520-12 searchlight housing was molded in gray Zytel® (Dupont's brand of nylon plastic), left unpainted and fitted with a clear polystyrene searchlight lens.

Whereas the 6520's light was stationary, the 3520 now featured a light mounted on a universal swivel post that rotated 360 degrees when the on-off switch beneath the car was activated. The actual work was done through the use of an electric driving coil and a rubber-driving washer mechanism.

In 1952, the washers were positioned with the rubber fingers pointed upwards. The following year, the fingers were cemented in a downward position.

> **Per Lionel Blueprints, the washer was changed from a 3520-16 driving washer to a 3420-42 adhesive washer on 3-24-53.**

The 3520 was the first searchlight car to use bar-end trucks. It was included in one cataloged set, and the separate-sale price was $7.75. Lionel experimented with both rubber-stamped serif and sans-serif lettering before deciding on sans-serif.

The 3520-7 searchlight housing base assembly was redesigned from the 6520. As the full-color 1952 consumer catalog suggested, the base was blackened with eight small slits on the top that

Many different types of action cars highlighted Lionel's line during the postwar era.

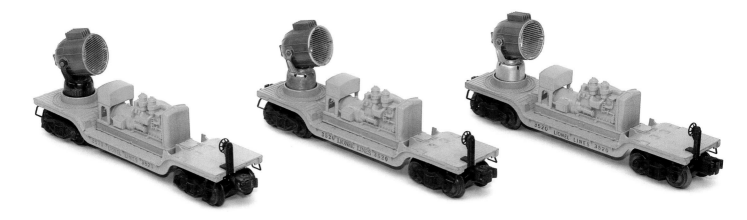

Variations of the 3520 (left to right): sans-serif lettering and blackened base with eight slits; serif lettering and cadmium-plated base with eight slits; and sans-serif lettering and cadmium-plated base with four slits.

probably dispatched the heat off the coil. By the time the separate-sale car was packaged, the base was no longer blackened, and the box was given OPS letter-press information.

> **Per Lionel Blueprints, the 3520-7 searchlight housing base assembly was originally Pentrate (black-oxide) and changed to cadmium-plated on 11-24-52.**

In 1953, the 3520 was included in three cataloged sets and the separate-sale price remained the same. Bar-end trucks continued to be the norm. Because of the quantity required to fill demand, more than one production run was needed, which accounted for different shades of gray paint for the frames (some being glossier than others).

Also, the 3520-7 cadmium-plated base continued, but it now had four slits instead of eight. Of course, don't forget about transition, where earlier bases or features could still appear in 1953.

When component boxed, a car and a 3520-33 instruction sheet (dated 5/52, 2/53 or 6/53) were protected by a 3520-38 corrugated insert.

- For Each Box:
  - Box Dimensions: 3¼" x 11" x 2⅛"
- Box Style OPS Classic (1952)
  - Tuck Flap Number: 3520-30X
- Box Style Middle Classic (1952 - 1953)
  - Tuck Flap Number: 3520-30

Author's Comments: The 3520s are very common, but the "8-slit" 1952 cadmium-plated housing base version or serif lettering variation are harder to find. The 3520 was a step in the right direction for the original Lionel Corporation because the 360-degree sweep added play value for both young and old and was just the beginning of some great new innovations that would be introduced in the coming years. The only downside to this car was that it would have been great to see it issued in additional road names.

3520	C7	C8	C9	Rarity
1952 Serif Lettered Version	100	150	200	
With Middle Classic Box	125	175	250	R8
With OPS Classic Box	145	215	310	
1952 Black Housing Base Version	50	60	70	R7
With Middle Classic Box	60	90	125	
With OPS Classic Box	80	130	185	R8
1952 Cadmium-Plated 8-Slit Housing Version	100	125	175	
With Middle Classic Box	125	150	225	R8
With OPS Classic Box	145	190	285	
1953 Version	30	40	60	R6
With Middle Classic Box	40	60	80	R7

3540 OPERATING RADAR SCANNING SCOPE CAR: 1959 - 1960

In 1959, the 3540 received limited catalog space, but was still part of one cataloged set and offered for separate sale at $7.95. The flat car was molded in red polystyrene and had white heat-stamped lettering in the Cheltenham Bold font. It used a 6511-2 frame which had a light, medium or dark gray polystyrene platform mounted on top. Other features included a vinyl figure with painted face and hands, a constantly lit radar screen that came in several shades of green (most often with six "blips" but also has been observed with seven), and a three-piece yellow polystyrene antenna.

> **Per Lionel Components Parts Index and Blueprints, the 50-84 fixed painted crewman was manufactured using vinyl and was the same as the one used on the 50 Gang Car. The 3540-16 radar screen was originally to be made of vinylite, but was changed to translucent white styrene frosted on one side on 6-5-59.**

The 3540 was also equipped with a 3540-5 radar antenna that rotated while the car was moving along the tracks. The actual work was done by a rubber drive belt wound around one of the wheel axles. The belt turned the pulley and shaft that the radar antenna was attached to. Unfortunately, the belt had a tendency to self destruct or over time melt to the axle. The screen was illuminated through the use of a 581-10 roller assembly that picked up current from the track.

3540 shown with the insert that protects the radar antenna.

The 3540 incorporated two special AAR trucks with three-piece metal knuckle couplers. One included a pick-up, and the other had the wheels mounted "rigidly" to the axles, thus allowing the axle to turn the radar antenna.

In 1960, the 3540 was part of one cataloged set and the separate-sale price remained the same. It was also offered in Sears promotional set 9694, which included a white Allstate box for the 1063 transformer. Some AAR trucks also featured a notch in the top of the side frame.

The 3540 was component boxed with a car, a 3540-36 insert to protect the radar antenna and a 3540-38 instruction sheet dated 9/59.

- Box Style Orange Perforated (1959- 1960)
  - Tuck Flap Number: 3540-35
  - Box Manufacturer: Berles Carton Co.
  - Box Date: BC597
  - Box Dimensions: 4⅜" x 12⅛" x 2⅜"

Author's Comments: The 3540 was not a big seller as indicated by dealers still having stock during the early 1970s. Also, those offered for separate sale in 1960 were probably leftover inventory, with a possible short run to fill orders for 1960 set 2549W.

Finally, the box for a 3540 was longer than the one used for a 3545. It lacked a tuck-in flap, but a corrugated insert was placed inside to protect the fragile radar antenna from breaking.

3545 used the same figures as the 50 Gang Car.

Radar Scanning Scope Car. The key differences were that, instead of the 3540's rotating radar screen, the 3545 had an operator-manned TV camera that rotated full circle and the 3540's antenna was replaced by a reflector stand (bank of lights).

The 3545 used an unpainted black polystyrene 6511-2 frame with white heat-stamped lettering in the Cheltenham Bold font. The platform was molded in blue polystyrene and a non-illuminated screen displayed a moving locomotive. The 3545 included the same vinyl figure (50-84 as the 50 Gang Car) with painted face and hands.

3540	C7	C8	C9	Rarity
Regular Production Version	70	125	175	R7
	110	175	275	R8

Per Lionel Blueprints, the 3545-14 printed screen was 170lb. white index paper.

Per Lionel Blueprints, there must have been fragility issues with the reflector stand as they reinforced it on 5-15-61.

3545 OPERATING TV MONITOR CAR: 1961 - 1963 & 1965

The 3545 was basically the same car as the 3540 Operating

The operation was accomplished in the same manner as the 3540, with a system of a pulley and shaft being run by a drive belt assembly. The only difference being that the 3545 used a 3545-13 counterweight that was attached to the 3545-20 camera complete. The 3545 incorporated AAR operating trucks with three-piece metal knuckle couplers until depleted, and then Delrin knuckle couplers became the norm. One truck had the wheels mounted "rigidly" to the axles, allowing the axle to turn the camera.

Although the 3545 was offered for separate sale in 1961 and 1962 at $7.95, it was included in only one cataloged set (2573 from 1961). It did make an appearance in one promotional set in 1961 and several in 1962 and 1963, until being finally depleted in set 19432 in 1965.

The 3545 was component boxed with just a car, as an instruction sheet does not exist.

- Box Style Orange Picture (1961 - 1963 and 1965)
  - Tuck Flap Number: 3545-17
  - Manufacturer Logo: "Die" in a "C"
  - Box Dimensions: 4¼" x 11¾" x 2⅜"

Author's Comments: The 3545 offered enough additional play value for Lionel's engineers to consider launching it despite the 3540's poor sales. It required minimal additional tooling and added something new to the line.

The 3545's box is very fragile and has a tendency to self-destruct. Be careful when opening and closing this valuable box.

The mock-up for the 3545 used a red plastic 3540 flat car painted black. The number "3545" and the name "Lionel" were decals. The superstructure (platform) was painted blue over gray plastic, which undoubtedly had originally been targeted for a 3540. Both the TV and the antenna were preproduction mock-ups that were painted (rather than molded) yellow (see Chapter 8).

3545	C7	C8	C9	Rarity
Regular Production Version	100	150	200	R7
	175	225	300	R8

3620 ROTATING SEARCHLIGHT CAR: 1954 - 1956

The 3620, introduced in 1954, allowed Lionel to further reduce costs by eliminating the on/off switch and fiberboard from the earlier 6520/3520 design. In this way, the 3620's searchlight (with a four-slit cadmium-plated base) rotated continuously as long as the track power was on.

In 1954, the 3620 was part of three cataloged sets and the separate-sale price was $7.95. The die-cast frame was painted gray, with sans-serif (Gothic) lettering rubber-stamped in black. The car also included an orange polystyrene plastic diesel motor assembly that modeled a General Motors generator. Also, more than one production run was needed, so frames could be dull or glossy gray. Some earlier examples used leftover 3520 frames; these can be identified by the absence of an extra hole on the bottom that was used for wiring. Bar-end trucks were used, and they had black knuckle pins.

Searchlights typically were gray Zytel® nylon as before, although Lionel also molded some in orange nylon and painted them gray. Of interest was page 20 of the 1954 consumer catalog, where the searchlight was depicted as orange in set 2221WS. It's not likely that any 3620s with unpainted orange searchlights were ever manufactured for separate sale or targeted for a boxed set, as Lionel's quality control personnel would easily have noticed the discrepancy.

In both 1955 and 1956, the 3620 was included in three cataloged sets and the separate-sale price remained the same. Features in 1955 included the new coupler tabs with black knuckle pins and a diesel motor housing that was a more vivid orange (before it was more of a pale orange).

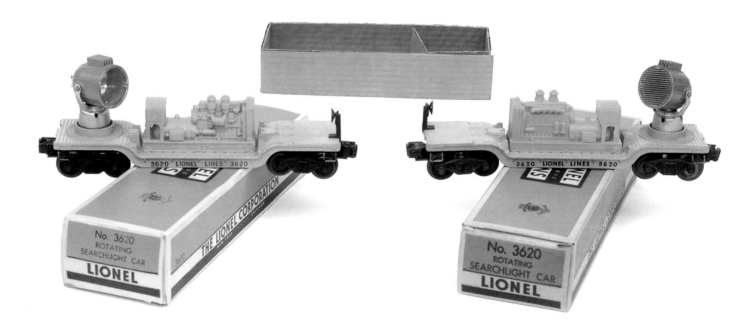

Left: This early 3620 had a painted searchlight with a Middle Classic box. Right: A 1956 version with an unpainted searchlight as well as a darker generator, bolder lettering and a Late Classic box.

In 1956, silver knuckle pins became the norm, the rubber-stamped lettering was noticeably bolder, and the box changed to the Late Classic design.

When component boxed, the 3620 was protected by a 3520-38 corrugated insert included a 3620-14 instruction sheet dated 4/54 (1954) or 4/55 (1955 - 1956).

- For Each Box:
  - Box Dimensions: 3¼" x 11" x 2⅛"
- Box Style Middle Classic (1954 - 1955)
  - Tuck Flap Number: 3620-10
  - Other Box Features: Four Dots or Five Dots on both sides, between New York and Chicago (1954)
- Box Style Late Classic (1956)
  - Tuck Flap Number: 3620-10

> **Lionel Production Control Files dated 11-23-54, stated that as an alternate to the 3620 box, use a 12-7 folding box and imprint end panels.**

Author's Comments: The 3620 was manufactured with only a gray 3520-12 searchlight housing (unpainted gray or gray painted over orange plastic). Any unpainted orange searchlights were originally painted gray and subsequently stripped of their paint. Therefore, this is not a valid 3620 variation because it was not intended production.

The 1956 bold-lettered car paired with the correct Late Classic box is a desirable combination.

3620	C7	C8	C9	Rarity
Gray-Painted Searchlight (1954)	125	150	200	R9
	150	180	250	
Unpainted Gray Searchlight (1954 - 1955)	40	50	65	R5
With Middle Classic Box	50	65	90	R6
Unpainted Gray Searchlight (1956 Bold Version)	45	60	75	R7
With Late Classic Box	80	125	185	R8

3650 SEARCHLIGHT EXTENSION CAR: 1956 - 1959

New for 1956, the 3650 was an almost perfect companion for the 3530 Operating Generator Car because both models featured a detachable searchlight that worked well for evening railroad jobs.

The 3650 was equipped with a searchlight held to a steel plate through the use of a magnetic searchlight base. The searchlight was illuminated through the use of two-wire cables connected to the car's pick-up roller. The cables can actually be unwound by hand with the use of a separate crank-handle. In turn, the handle could be placed for safe keeping in a small opening in the base of the flat car. The information on Form 1629, and later the instruction sheet, reminded owners that the cable ends were held inside the reel by spring tension.

In 1956, the 3650 was part of two cataloged sets and offered for separate sale at $8.95. Its frame looked very similar to the 3620's, but there were enough differences to support a new die-cast mold or a major modification was made.

Left: 3650 with a light gray frame, 1956 instruction sheet and Form 1629 (white and yellow). Right: 3650 with a dark gray frame and a 1957 instruction sheet.

The die-cast frame was painted gray, with black rubber-stamped lettering, and each 3650 came equipped with a dark gray polystyrene generator motor, a nylon searchlight and polystyrene base, a red polystyrene spool, a Cycolac® (GE Plastics' ABS plastic) support structure that included a 5-foot extension cord and a die-cast handle to unwind and wind the cord. Bar-end trucks, with or without coupler tabs, were the norm, and the coupler pins were silver. These features continued through 1959.

> Per Lionel Blueprints, the 3650-9 frame is identical to part 6561-4 Cable Car frame except the 6561 has two keyway (for the elastic band that held the cable reels) slots omitted 3-5-56.

In 1957, the 3650 was included in three cataloged sets and the separate-sale price remained the same. Because so many 3650s were made, the shades of the die-cast frame and the shades and sizes of the rubber-stamped lettering varied. Otherwise the features were the same as before, although a second production run later in the year would introduce two important changes. Less noticeable was the drawbar with the support hole that distinguished earlier trucks from later, but the noticeable change, the one collectors covet, had the frame painted dark gray. In fact, some dark gray examples even had a nylon searchlight painted gray.

In 1958, the 3650 was cataloged in one set only and the separate-sale price increased to $9.95. A price increase sometimes indicated that Lionel was trying to make an extra dollar when ridding itself of unsold inventory. This was one of those times, as April 1958 internal Lionel sales forecasts noted that more than 4,000 units remained in stock. A dark gray frame with an olive tint also made an appearance in 1958.

In 1959, the 3650 was included in cataloged set 2537W, but was not offered for separate sale in either the advance or consumer catalog. The photograph in the consumer catalog, however, pictured the 3650 with a red frame (flat car) with white lettering instead of the regular production colors. 3650s with red frames were not put into production, but at least one example is known to exist (see Chapter 8).

The 3650 was component boxed with a car, a 3520-38 insert, a 3650-22 handle and a 3650-38 instruction sheet dated 7/56 (1956) and 2/57 or 7/57 (1957 - 1959). Earlier boxed cars also included Form 1629 Cable Reel Notice, which had at least two versions with slightly different wording as well as colors of paper used. The information on this form was included on later versions of the 3650-38 instruction sheet, and the form was no longer used.

- Box Style Late Classic (1956 - 1959)
  - Tuck Flap Number: 3650-35
  - Other Box Features: Five Dots on one side and Four Dots on other, between New York and Chicago (1956 - 1957)
  - Other Box Features: Five and Five Dots: (1956 - 1959)
  - Other Box Features: Four and Four Dots: (1957 - 1959)
  - Box Dimensions: 3¼" x 10⅞" x 2⅛"

Author's Comments: The dark gray-framed 3650 with an olive tint is a known component of 1958 set 2509WS and probably

continued into 1959.

However, a key question relating to the 3650 concerns whether a short production run was made in 1959. The 3650 wasn't offered for separate sale in that year, but was cataloged in the very desirable 2537W New Haven F3 set. As noted, there were more than 4,000 cars in inventory at the start of 1958, so it is highly unlikely that any additional production runs were needed. Also, there are no known 3650s from 1959 in Orange Perforated boxes. Therefore, if any were made in 1959, they were packaged with leftover Late Classic boxes.

3650	C7	C8	C9	Rarity
Regular Production Version	40	50	75	R6
	60	80	125	R7
Dark Gray Base	75	100	125	R7
	95	130	175	
Dark Gray Base With Olive Tint	300	375	500	R9
	350	450	600	

6520 SEARCHLIGHT CAR: 1949 - 1951

Lionel introduced the 6520 in 1949 as part of five cataloged sets and a separate-sale item at $6.50. It had a die-cast frame painted gray, with serif lettering that was rubber-stamped in black. The 6520 used a modified frame from the 2461 Transformer Car introduced in 1947. It also included a polystyrene diesel motor assembly that modeled a General Motors generator.

> Per Lionel Components Parts Index and Blueprints, the 6520-17 was known as a Diesel Motor Assembly and was 3½" long by 1⁵⁄₃₆" wide.

The operation for the 6520 was rather simple. For O gauge operation, a UCS remote-control section of track was needed, whereas a 6019 was needed for O27 use. In either situation, the operator had only to position the 6520 directly over the electromagnet of the remote-control track section to actuate the switch that turned on the stationary searchlight. Once on, the searchlight would continue to burn brightly anywhere on the track.

In 1949, a green polystyrene diesel motor housing was probably the first produced, as suggested by the illustrations in the full-color consumer catalog. However, a more common orange polystyrene type soon followed.

Lionel also experimented with either an enameled black or "gray crackle" die-cast searchlight housing before deciding on the latter. The same was true with the fiberboard switch mechanism, as a brownish red version replaced the black. Other 1949 features included staple-end trucks and a flared activator flap rivet.

In 1950, the 6520 was included in four cataloged sets and the separate-sale price dropped to $5.95. The orange generator continued, but since more than one production run was needed (just as in 1949), a maroon example soon followed. The searchlight housing also changed, as an enameled gray version soon replaced the gray crackle one. Other truck and coupler features included a hole in the activator flap and the rivet being applied with the round-end visible.

In 1951, the 6520 was offered for separate sale only and the

Four variations of the 6520 (clockwise from bottom left): gray, maroon, green and orange diesel assemblies.

price increased to $7.25. These examples were probably left over from previous years, but Lionel still issued dealers pre-priced, gummed OPS labels because of the Korean War.

When component boxed, a 6520 was protected by a 6520-21 or 6520-40 (1951) corrugated insert and included a 6520-23 instruction sheet dated 5/49 (1949 - 1950) and 5/50 (1950 - 1951).

- For Each Box:
  - Box Dimensions: 4" x 11" x 2⅛"
- Box Style Early Classic (1949)
  - Tuck Flap Number: None (6520-20 not on box)
- Box Style Middle Classic (1950 - 1951)
  - Tuck Flap Number: 6520-20

Author's Comments: Since the 6520 with the maroon generator was shown for the first time in the full-color 1951 consumer catalog, some observers mistakenly assume that 1951 was the only year of production. However, it actually was introduced the previous year and carried into 1951.

As to rarity, the 6520 with the green generator is the one coveted by collectors, and is about as scarce as a 3494-550 Monon Operating Box Car. However, a gray plastic version, which may have been an early test sample, is almost impossible to find.

6520	C7	C8	C9	Rarity
Green Diesel Assembly	250	300	350	R8
	275	350	450	
Orange Diesel Assembly	30	40	50	R5
	45	60	80	
Maroon Diesel Assembly	40	60	75	R6
	55	85	125	
Gray Diesel Assembly	1,500	2,000	3,000	R10
	1,525	2,100	3,100	

6805 ATOMIC ENERGY DISPOSAL CAR: 1958 - 1959

Introduced in 1958, the 6805 carried two containers that simulated the concrete ones used by atomic research installations. These containers held "hot" waste material, and the railways were the perfect way of transporting them to the proper destination. In fact, young engineers could position their toy soldiers along certain railroad crossings and pretend that the U.S. Army was protecting each crossing from any outside interference. The 6805 was equipped with flashing lamps installed in each container that facilitated the realism of safety lights. In fact, just turn off the lights in the room, and the 6805 puts on a rather good show.

Per Lionel Blueprints, the 6805-6 Containers were molded in utility black polystyrene and painted gray to match paint chip #234.

Lionel's quality control varied, as these containers are observed in light, medium or dark gray, with the glossy gray variation being the one that collectors covet. Furthermore, the containers had the words "Radioactive Waste" heat-stamped in black letters, and the word "Danger" heat-stamped in red. When the 6805 was boxed, the two containers were held in place by two rubber bands that are almost always missing.

In 1958, the 6805 was included in four cataloged sets and offered for separate sale at $6.95. It was almost perfectly illustrated in the 1958 consumer catalog; however, the cars included in three of those sets incorrectly depicted the 6805 with its number to the right, while the other had no number illustrated at all. In reality, the flat car was molded in red translucent polystyrene, with white heat-stamped Cheltenham Bold lettering to the left of Lionel.

The 6424-11 mold was modified by adding an insert, or plug, that formed four plastic stops (two at each end of the car) and held the two rails in place. The 6805 used four rail clips to center the two rails and received current from a pick-up roller. Because of the items needed to operate the 6805, four openings were permanently

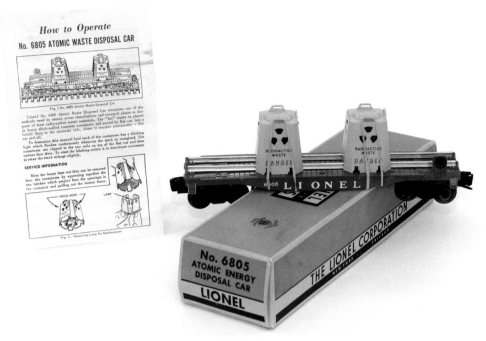

A 6805 with light gray containers.

made in the 6424-11 mold to accept the four rail clips.

In 1959, the 6805 was available for separate sale only at the same price as before. It was finally dropped from the line in 1960. For both years, the 6805 incorporated bar-end trucks with or without coupler tabs and silver knuckle pins.

When component boxed a 6805 included a 6805-22 instruction sheet dated 8/58 (1958 - 1959).

- Box Style Late Classic (1958 - 1959)
  - Tuck Flap Number: 6805-20
  - Box Manufacturer: Berles Carton Co.
  - Box Date: BC585
  - Box Dimensions: 3⅝" x 12⅛" x 2½"

Author's Comments: According to 1958 internal Lionel sales forecasts, 12,750 Atomic Energy Disposal Cars were needed to fill cataloged sets and another 12,500 for separate sale. Lionel probably had an overrun of 6805s to account for breakage or other types of manufacturing deficiencies that can occur during production.

Because of these large quantities, it is likely that Lionel had plenty of 6805s for both 1958 and 1959. Supporting this assumption is the fact that Orange Perforated boxes are not known to exist for a 6805.

The insert, or plug, used to create the rail stops on the 6805 also appeared on some other cars. Specifically, a 6424 Automobile Flat Car with these end stops is well known among collectors, whereas it is extremely unusual (rarity R10) to find a 6830 Flatcar With Submarine or a 6844 Missile Carrying Car with this feature.

6805	C7	C8	C9	Rarity
Light Gray Containers	100	125	150	
	150	225	300	
Medium Gray Containers	100	125	150	R6
	150	225	300	
Dark Gray Containers	125	175	225	
	150	275	400	

6822-1 NIGHT CREW SEARCHLIGHT CAR (BOXED VERSION): 1961 - 1966 & 1968 - 1969
6822-25 NIGHT CREW SEARCHLIGHT CAR (UNBOXED VERSION): 1963
6822-50 NIGHT CREW SEARCHLIGHT CAR (UNBOXED VERSION): 1963 - 1966

The 6822 was the last searchlight car produced by Lionel during the postwar era. Like the earlier 6520 Searchlight Car, its searchlight required manual operation to revolve.

In 1961, the 6822-1 (boxed version) was included in one cataloged and two promotional sets and offered for separate sale at $7.95. It used a red polystyrene flat car (mold 6511-2), that had white heat-stamped Cheltenham Bold lettering. Over its lifetime, the 6822 varied from dark to light red, with dark and medium red plastic being the norm during the first three years. Light red, which was more translucent, dominated production from 1964 through the final year.

The car came with a vinylite figure with painted face and hands. Although the figure retained the earlier 3562-62 part number, its base was altered and was now "T" shaped, instead of having just a horizontal slot. This modification was actually introduced as part of the 6812 Track Maintenance Car.

In 1961 and 1962, the maintenance structure was molded in black polystyrene and paired with a gray nylon searchlight. At this time, the 6822 used AAR trucks with three-piece operating metal knuckle couplers. Delrin one-piece operating couplers became the norm in 1962. Of course, Lionel used the three-piece couplers until they were depleted. In 1962, the 6822-1 (boxed version) was part of one cataloged and one promotional set and offered for separate sale at $7.95.

In 1963, the 6822-1 continued as before and was included in two promotional sets; the separate-sale price remained the same. The Night Crew Searchlight Car was also unboxed as part of cataloged set 11375. As was true with so many O27 sets that year, certain cars were "cheapened" and given new suffix numbers. Specifically, a 6822-1 became a 6822-50, with "-50" indicating

Three variations of 6822-1 (left to right): Black structure and gray searchlight (1961), gray structure and black searchlight (1964), and the rarest, marked "6828" (1966).

one operating and one dummy coupler instead of two operating couplers.

The Lionel Factory Order for promotional set 19227 mentions a 6822-25, which would have been an unboxed 6822-1 with two operating couplers. However, a dual operating coupler 6822 never came unboxed; thus, the Factory Order was updated with a 6822-50. In other words, the 6822-25s existed on paper only, and this information is provided to complete the chronology. The 6822-50 was included in seven promotional sets. Also changing was the maintenance structure, which was molded in gray polystyrene paired with black Cycolac® searchlight.

> Per Lionel Engineering Specifications, on 1-21-63 the material for the searchlight housing was changed from Zytel® Gray #637 to Cycolac® Black #6416. The material for the base was changed from TMD-6000 Black 75 to TMD-6000 Gray 55, Lionel #687.

In 1964, the 6822-1 was included in three promotional sets and offered for separate sale at $7.95. It was also cataloged as part of four O gauge sets. At the end of 1964 production, Lionel began fitting 6822-1 searchlight cars with one operating and one fixed coupler.

Also, Lionel began placing 6822s in over-labeled 6650 Missile Launching Flat Car boxes. In this instance, a white label was placed over the information at each end, and a "NO. 6822" was rubber-stamped. These cars were 6822-1s with one operating and one dummy coupler.

As for the 6822-50, in 1964 it was included in one promotional set. The 6822 continued as before, but the dummy couplers came with open journal boxes. From 1965 through 1969, both the dummy and the operating couplers had open journal boxes.

The 6822-1 was part of one cataloged set in 1965 and 1966 and the separate-sale price increased to $8.00 in 1965. The car was also included in the Sears 1258 operating car assortment in 1965 and 1966. Its companion, the 6822-50, was included in one promotional set in 1965 and three the following year. Starting in 1966, Lionel often attached a washer with the leaf spring rivet, and some frames had an extra hole punched.

In 1968 and 1969, the 6822-1 was offered for separate sale only and, although the price remained the same, those cars offered

were likely leftover inventory. Whether the car had one or two operating couplers was not an issue with Lionel, as they were just selling off the remaining inventory. By the end, 6822s were packaged in plain, white generic boxes with coupler protection flaps at each end.

Each 6822-1 was component boxed with just a car, as an instruction sheet does not exist.

- For Each Box:
  - Box Dimensions: 4" x 11⅛" x 2⅜"
- Box Style Orange Picture (1961)
  - Tuck Flap Number: 6822-21
  - Box Manufacturer: Shuttleworth
- Box Style Dark Orange Picture (1963 - 1964)
  - Tuck Flap Number: 6822-21
  - Other Box Features: Title and Cities Outlined in Blue
- Box Style Orange Picture (1962 - 1966 & 1968 - 1969)
  - Tuck Flap Number: 6822-21
- Box Style Plain White (1968 - 1969)
  - Tuck Flap Number: None
- Note: The 6822 also used over-labeled 6650 boxes.

Author's Comments: Although the 6822 is a common car, it has plenty of variations. In fact, when Lionel brought back the 6828 Harnischfeger Truck Crane Car in 1966, some 6822 Night Crew Searchlight Cars were incorrectly stamped "6828", instead of the correct 6822. These 6828 Night Crew Searchlight Cars are extremely rare, especially when originally packaged by Lionel in a Plain White box.

Also, this volume updates and corrects previously printed 6822 material by placing the cars in the proper years cataloged and the correct sets, both cataloged and promotional.

6822		C7	C8	C9	Rarity
Regular Production Version	-25 or -50	35	50	65	R5
With Orange Pict. Box	-1	50	75	100	R7
With Plain White Box		80	120	175	R9
6828 Production Version		2,000	2,500	3,000	R10
		2,050	2,575	3,100	

CHAPTER SIX

Rolling Stock with Accessories

Lionel's rolling stock with accessories include some of the greatest innovations in Lionel's history, including the milk car, cattle car and horse car.

3356-1   OPERATING HORSE CAR AND CORRAL: 1956 - 1960 & 1964 - 1966
3356-110 OPERATING HORSE CAR AND CORRAL (OUTFITS ONLY): 1966

The 3356 was the perfect follow-up to the 3656 Operating Cattle Car, which was discontinued in 1956. In fact, the new car offered better play value because the vinylite horses moved more freely inside the car and through the corral. They didn't get jammed up as easily, although they still fell over without any warning.

The 3356-1 and "-110" (only in outfit 13150 in 1966) contained a 3356-25 car and all peripherals packaged in one box. When packaged for separate sale, the component boxed car was numbered 3356-2, horses 3356-100 and corral 3356-150.

When the 3356 was activated, the doors dropped down and the vibrator coils in both the car and corral caused the runway within the car and corral to vibrate rapidly. Each horse had angled prongs on the underside of its base that allowed it to move through the car and around the corral, again and again. This movement simulated the loading and unloading of the horses.

> Per Lionel Blueprints dated 2-28-56, the 3356-41 horses were made of black vinylite and measured 1.203" x 1.218". Per Lionel Production Control Files, the horses used the 3356-T-41A six cavity mold and stated that the operator "clean flash on neck."

In 1956, the 3356 was included in one O27 set and one O gauge set and offered for separate sale at $15.95. The car was illustrated correctly in the consumer catalog, with its shell molded in

3356 component boxes (left to right): Bold Classic, Late Classic, Orange Picture (top) and 3356-110 Orange Picture with Horse Corral Graphic (bottom). The packed envelope on the left is a 3366-34 during 1959 - 1960 and a 3356-77 from 1964 - 1966; both used same envelope number. On the right is a 3356-77 from 1956 - 1958.

green polystyrene with yellow heat-stamped lettering; although, when shown for separate sale, the illustration incorrectly included gray doors and interior.

The Operating Horse Car had Santa Fe and Railway Express Agency markings. The choice of Santa Fe was somewhat appropriate because the 3356 debuted in O27 set 1567W, which was headed by a 2243 Santa Fe F3 diesel.

The car used the same shell as the 6376 Circus Car, but after the production of the 6376 was completed, the shell was modified for the 3356 by adding internal molded door stops at each end.

The 6376 inherited the door stops starting in 1957. Bar-end trucks, with or without coupler tabs, and silver knuckle pins were used through 1960.

The corral was molded in brown polystyrene. It was partially painted green to take on the appearance of grass and was surrounded by white polystyrene fences. This was depicted quite well in the full-color consumer catalog, but the actual car came with nine black horses and not the multi-colored ones cataloged.

In 1957, the 3356 was included in one cataloged set and the separate-sale price jumped to $17.95. The specifications for the car

Left: 3356 with the molded door stop and the brake wheel on the right side. Right: 3356 with a boss (large rivet) to the left of "FE" and the brake wheel on the left side.

and corral were the same as before, except the coupler drawbar had a support hole. The catalog *incorrectly* illustrated the car with white lettering; it came with only yellow.

In 1958, the 3356 was part of one cataloged set and the separate-sale price remained the same. Once again, the lettering was incorrectly illustrated as white in the catalog. With the introduction of the 6434 Poultry Car, the 3356's shell also changed, as the tooling was reworked. Eight small gussets, or stiffeners, were added to the inside design, the brake wheel was moved to the left side of the car, and a molded boss (looks like a large rivet) became part of the design between the front sliding door and the "FE" part of "SANTA FE." Also, inside the car the color of the solenoid coil changed from copper to red.

> **Per Lionel Blueprints dated 4-23-58, a small boss was added to the shell.**

In 1959, leftover inventory probably accounted for the 3356s included in set 2541W. The car was offered for separate sale in 1959 and 1960 at $17.95, although a short production run may have occurred just prior to Lionel changing the style of boxes.

When the 3356 was included in Super "O" sets, all the peripherals necessary came in a combination of the packed envelopes with the set and 3356. In 1959, a 39-25 packed envelope (envelope no. 39-26) became the norm in Super "O" sets. This new packed envelope didn't include the necessary 36-7 control blade to operate the horse car. This led to a new 3356 packed envelope being issued, which now included a 36-7 remote-control blade and a 36-8 control blade screw. Although the packed envelope part number changed to 3366-34, the envelope number remained the same (3356-79).

After a three-year absence, the 3356 returned in 1964 as part of set 13150, headed by the reissued 773 Hudson, and as a separate-sale item at $19.95. The car was the same as before, except that the front sliding door had the inside molded stop (see 3366) and "Blt 5-56 By Lionel" was removed during the production run.

> **Per Lionel Blueprints dated 11-20-64, "Blt By Lionel" was removed from the shell stamping.**

In 1964, AAR trucks with operating couplers (one with an armature plate and pickup; the other with ground spring) and closed journal boxes were the norm. The corral was the same as before and would continue the same way through 1966. However, in the 1964 and 1965 consumer catalogs, one white horse was illustrated, although only black horses were included.

In 1965, the 3356 was once again included in set 13150. The specifications were the same as before, except that the AAR trucks and couplers now had open journal boxes. This car was also offered for separate sale at the increased price of $20.00. The solenoid coil used a green or red insulating material. The way the coil was wound lacked the workmanship of prior years, although don't forget about transition.

In 1966, Lionel offered the 3356-1 for separate sale at $20.00 but changed the box style and updated the instruction sheets to create 3356-110, which was included in the 1966 version of set 13150. The AAR bottom frame assembly changed, as it now had a half circle cut-out to provide extra room for the coupler disk and some AAR trucks with washers attached with the leaf spring rivet. Except for some solenoid coils with a yellow tint, all other specifications mirrored that of 1965.

The 3356-1 and 3356-110 were component boxed with a 3356-25 car, a 3356-42 corral complete, a 3356-72 corrugated liner and the following peripherals:

Year	Packed Envelope	Env. No.	Instruction Sheet	Sheet Date	3356-100 Horses	Other
1956	3356-77	3356-79	3356-78	9/56	Late Classic	927-56 Service Station Leaflet
1957 1958				5/57		
1959 1960	3366-34		3366-33	5/59		
1964	3356-77		3356-78	6/64	Plain White	1-165 Warranty Card
1965				6/65		
1966 "-1"			3356-78 3356-112	6/65 10/66		
1966 "-110"			3356-111 3356-112	8/66 10/66		

From 1956 to 1958, the 3356-77 packed envelope contained an OTC-1 operating car lockon, a 364C-1 controller, four 81-32 24" wires, two 24-4 adjusting clips and the appropriate instruction sheet. From 1959 to 1960 for 3366-34 and 1964 to 1966 for 3356-77, each of these packed envelopes added a 36-7 control blade and a 36-8 control blade screw. The envelope number always remained 3356-79.

- For Each Box:
  - Tuck Flap Number: 3356-70
  - Box Dimensions: 6⅛" x 12½" x 4⅞"
- Box Style Late Classic (1956 - 1958)
- Box Style Bold Classic (1958 - 1960)
  - Box Manufacturer: Berles Carton Co.
  - Box Date: BC588
- Box Style Orange Picture (1964 - 1966)
- Box Style Hillside Orange Picture with Horse Corral Graphic (1966 for 3356-110)

Author's Comments: Lionel learned from earlier experiences with the cattle car by improving the interior design of the 3356 to obtain smoother operation.

Because the 3356 was issued over eight years and with at least as many variations, specializing in this car is a major undertaking. Even today, it still provides operating and collecting excitement.

A Lionel Factory Order indicated that 96 of these were packaged for separate sale on 3/30/67. These were leftover inventory as manufacturing had ceased by then.

3356	C7	C8	C9	Rarity
1956 - 1960 Car Only	40	55	70	R5
Car & Corral	80	100	120	
Boxed	125	150	300	R7
1964 - 1966 Car Only	50	75	100	
Car & Corral	90	120	150	R8
Boxed	150	200	350	
1966 With "Half Circle" Frame Assembly	75	95	125	R8
Car & Corral	115	140	175	
Orange Picture "Horse Corral Graphic" 3356-110 Boxed	350	500	1,000	R9

3356-2 OPERATING HORSE CAR: 1956 - 1957

The 3356-2 Operating Horse Car was offered as a replacement accessory in 1956 for $8.95 and an extra accessory a year later for $9.95. By 1957, only 35 remained in inventory. The specifications mirrored that of the 3356-1 mentioned earlier.

The 3356-2 included a 3356-25 horse car complete in a component box.

- Box Style Late Classic (1956 - 1957)
  - Tuck Flap Number: 3356-75
  - Box Dimensions: 3½" x 12⅝" x 2½"

Author's Comments: Naturally, it's the box that makes the 3356-2 so valuable and achieves its R10 rating. Without the box, its value is minimal (see 3356-1).

Although this item has an R10 rating, the ones that exist are usually found in C9 condition with the correct 1956 version of the car. This is likely because Madison Hardware Co. of New York City was still selling these in the 1980s. These cars were likely purchased by collectors and kept in collectable condition.

3356-2	C7	C8	C9	Rarity
Regular Production Version	1,000	1,300	1,700	R10

3356-100 FIGURES FOR HORSE CAR: 1956 - 1959

Each 3356-1 or 3356-110 came packaged with a 3356-100 box of nine black vinylite horses. The 3356-100 was available for separate sale in 1956 and 1957 for $1.25 and in 1958 and 1959 for $1.50. Although the 1964 - 1966 version was not offered for separate sale, examples still show up in the marketplace; therefore, pricing is included.

- For Each Box:
  - Tuck Flap Number: 3356-71
  - Box Dimensions: 1½" x 3" x 1¼"
- Box Style Late Classic (1956 - 1960)
- Box Style Plain White (1964 - 1966)

Author's Comments: Although the Plain White box was not originally intended for separate sale, Madison Hardware Co. had them for separate sale into the 1990s.

When offered for separate sale, the horse car came packaged in its own box.

3356-100 Figures for Horse Car. Left: 1956-1960. Right: 1964-1966.

3356-100	C7	C8	C9	Rarity
Late Classic Box	35	50	75	R7
Plain White Box	50	75	100	R9

3356-150   OPERATING CORRAL WITH HORSES: 1956 - 1957

Lionel gave operators the opportunity to add an extra corral to any section of their layout with the separate-sale listing of the 3356-150. The cost in 1956 was $10.00 and $10.95 a year later.

Each 3356-150 was component boxed with a 3356-42 corral complete, a 3356-77 packed envelope (packed envelope no. 3356-79), 3356-100 horses packed, a 3356-78 instruction sheet dated 5/56 (1956) or 5/57 (1957) and a 3356-80 corrugated insert.

- Box Style Late Classic (1956 - 1957)
  - Tuck Flap Number: 3356-76
  - Box Dimensions: 6" x 12½" x 2½"

Author's Comments: Since nine horses were included with the

The 3356-150 for separate sale is extremely rare due to its Late Classic box.

3356-150, it was a bargain over the earlier 3656-150 Cattle Corral Platform, which didn't include any cattle. In this case, Lionel learned a valuable lesson in marketing, although neither item sold that well.

It's the box, not the contents, that makes the 3356-150 so special. The box is as rare as a black-lettered 3484-25 Operating Santa Fe Box Car, thus accounting for the appropriate rarity level.

3356-150	C7	C8	C9	Rarity
Regular Production Version 1956 - 1957	2,500	3,000	3,500	R10

3366   OPERATING CIRCUS CAR AND CORRAL: 1959 - 1961

The 3366 was an extension of the 3356 in the product line and was offered for separate sale all three years at $17.95. Its operation was the same as that of the 3356 Operating Horse Corral And Car. However, unlike the 3356, which was cataloged for eight years and included in six sets, the 3366 never achieved as much success.

It did, however, make a token appearance in the extremely rare 1960 set 2555W, known as the "Father & Son" or "Over & Under" set. Still, the 3366s included in this set probably were nothing more than leftover inventory from 1959.

The car was molded in white polystyrene, with red heat-stamped lettering, and the catwalk was painted red.

Per Lionel Blueprints dated 3-30-59, the 3366-7 body was molded in white polystyrene color no. 55.

The body was modified, just like the 3356 from 1958, so the brake wheel was to the left when the car was operational. Also changing was the front sliding door, which had a molded stop on its backside. Bar-end trucks with coupler tabs and silver knuckle pins were the norm. The mechanical features were the same as the 1958 - 1960 version of the 3356, and these features stayed the same throughout the 3366's production.

The corral was molded in gray polystyrene, with a red-painted area taking the place of the green area of the 3356. Nine white vinylite horses were included, and the 3366 was well illustrated in the consumer catalog.

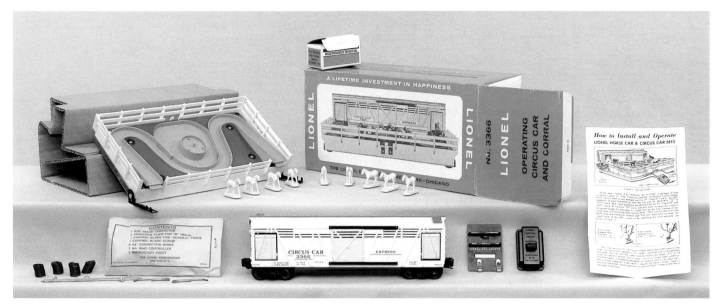

This 3366 has all its peripherals and nine vinylite horses. The 3366-34 packed envelope has the extra control blade. Note that the doors on the car are beginning to yellow.

Per Lionel Blueprints dated 8-14-59, the 3366-20 figures (horses) were 1.203" x 1.218" and changed from white to ivory vinylite.

3366	C7	C8	C9	Rarity
Car Only	125	150	200	
Car & Corral	175	225	300	R8
Boxed	300	600	1,200	

The 3366 was component boxed with a 3366-25 circus car complete, a 3366-21 corral complete, a 3356-72 corrugated liner, a 3366-34 packed envelope (envelope no. 3356-79) and a 3366-33 instruction sheet dated 5/59 (1959 - 1961). See 3356 listing for the contents of 3366-34.

- Box Style Orange Picture (1959 - 1961)
  - Tuck Flap Number: 3366-31
  - Box Dimensions: 6⅛" x 12½" x 4⅞"

Author's Comments: The 3366 wasn't originally a big seller, and those featured in the 1960 and 1961 catalogs were probably leftover inventory from 1959. Consequently this item is very collectible today.

The white plastic car and double doors had a tendency to yellow, sometimes in mixed combinations. Collectors desire pure white versions and will pay accordingly. The C9 pricing is for a pure white version.

3366-100   FIGURES FOR NO. 3366 CIRCUS CAR: 1959 - 1960

The 3366 came packaged with a 3366-100 box of nine white or ivory vinylite horses. The 3366-100 Figures for No. 3366 Circus Car was available for separate sale in 1959 and 1960 for $1.50. However, it wasn't available in 1961, when the 3366 was still offered for separate sale only.

- Box Style Glossy Classic (1959 - 1961)
  - Tuck Flap Number: 3366-27
  - Box Dimensions: 1½" x 3" x 1¼"

Author's Comments: The true value of the 3366-100 depends on it coming complete with its box, and as such, that is the price provided. This is also one of the few examples of a Glossy Classic box that used Late Classic graphics on glossy cardstock.

Rolling Stock w/Access.

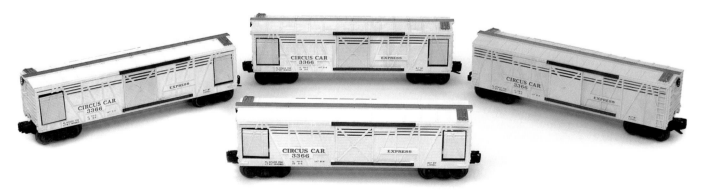

The 3366 was molded in white plastic (front), but over time the color has changed.

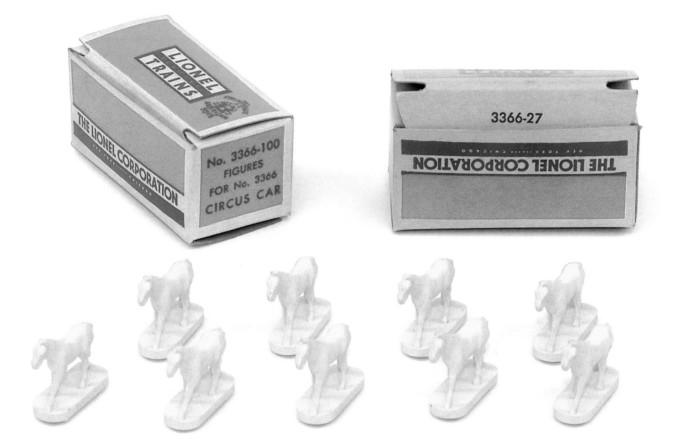

The Circus Car included nine white or ivory vinylite horses.

3356-100	C7	C8	C9	Rarity
Regular Production Version	75	100	150	R8

3456 OPERATING HOPPER CAR: 1950 - 1955

The 3456 black-painted polystyrene car wasn't offered for separate sale until 1952, but first appeared with the 456 Coal Ramp Set introduced in 1950. The car had white heat-stamped Norfolk & Western lettering and not Lehigh Valley as was shown in the catalog. This illustration was corrected in the 1951 consumer catalog. The 3456 modified a 2456 Hopper shell by adding a pair of spring operating black-nylon plastic doors that were beneath the car.

> Per Lionel Blueprints dated 8-1-50, the 2456-3 shell was modified by partially eliminating the girders, providing openings instead of doors and adding bosses.
>
> Per Lionel Production Control Files, the 3456-7 hopper car body was molded using a one-cavity (2456-T-3A-2) mold with an insert for 3456-7. The sprue was cut and a hole drilled. Then the four door openings were milled.

The 3456 combined with the 456 was exciting and easy to operate. The action began by backing up the car to the top of the 456 and coupling it in place. Once in place, the touch of a remote-control button opened the double doors, thus dumping the load into a waiting 456-83 Coal Bin. When combined with a 397 Operating Diesel Type Coal Loader, the hopper car could be refilled and the overall action repeated.

In 1950 and 1951, staple-end trucks with black knuckle pins were the norm; by late 1951, bar-end trucks and couplers were introduced. Also introduced in late 1951 was a new polystyrene shell that had extra rivet detail at the bottom center of the car, along with a new interior design.

In 1952, the 3456 was finally offered for separate sale and the suggested retail price was $5.75. The price remained the same in 1953, and so did the car's features. In 1954, the separate-sale price was still $5.75 and the tops of the knuckle couplers were engraved instead of smooth.

Cars offered for sale in 1955, when the price increased to $6.95, were probably leftover inventory from before. In fact, by 1955 it appears that Lionel was attempting to rid itself of excess inventory as the 456 and 3456 were no longer prominently featured in the catalog.

The 3456 was component boxed with a car and a bag of 207-1 artificial coal. No instruction sheet was included, as operating information was part of the 456 Coal Ramp Set instruction sheet.

- For Each Box:
  - Tuck Flap Number: 3456-26
  - Box Dimensions: 2⅞" x 10¾" x 2⅛"
- Box Style Middle Classic (1950 - 1951 & 1953 - 1955)
  - Other Box Features: Four Dots on one side and Five Dots on other, between New York and Chicago (1950)
  - Other Box Features: Five Dots: (1951 & 1953 - 1955)
- Box Style OPS Classic (1952)

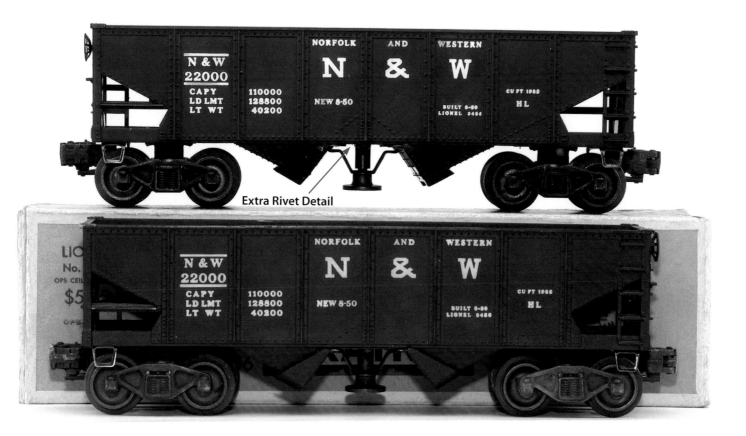

Extra Rivet Detail

The 3456 on top has extra rivet detail.

Author's Comments: The 3456 was part of a multi-year strategy that provided an integrated coaling empire. Lionel began in 1948 by introducing the 397 Coal Loader, which in turn worked in unison with the 456 Coal Ramp Set introduced two years later. This continued when the 3456 was offered for separate sale. This was one of the few times that two accessories were designed to work together. This marketing strategy led to many add-on sales and continued play value.

Also known to exist is a 3456 prototype with Lehigh Valley markings, which may have been used for the illustration in the catalog. It's unfortunate that Lionel didn't issue additional road names.

3456	C7	C8	C9	Rarity
With or Without	40	50	60	R6
Extra Rivet Detail	55	75	100	

3462 OPERATING MILK CAR: 1947 - 1948

In its second full year of production after World War II, Lionel introduced a remarkable item that featured a miniature figure unloading seven milk cans. Thus was born the operating milk car, which has entertained audiences of all ages for over a half century.

The 3462 was activated through the use of a solenoid-type electromagnet that allowed the car's plunger, hidden inside, to activate the mechanism. This caused the milkman to open the aluminum doors, and deliver or drop miniature milk cans onto a waiting platform.

In 1947, the 3462 was included in two cataloged sets and offered for separate sale at $8.95. Although early artwork depicted the car with a brown roof, the car was painted white, with black heat-stamped lettering in the Cheltenham and Gothic fonts. Each car had a circle "L" to the right of the door and "3462" and a built date of "3-47" to the left.

Lionel took advantage of the milk car's instant popularity, and advance orders and other requests must have been staggering as two or more production runs were needed. The result was various shades of white-painted cars, some of which had a high-gloss or semi-gloss finish.

Other 1947 features included staple-end trucks with staked coil wound coupler heads, four aluminum doors, and a brass base plate for the inside mechanism that could be partially viewed by turning the car upside down. Lionel even experimented with the figure as three types were used including:

- Type I - A flat cap, $1^{21}/_{64}$" high and ¾" wide
- Type II - A flat cap, $1^{1}/_{8}$" high and ¾" wide
- Type III - A round cap, $1^{1}/_{4}$" high and $^{9}/_{16}$" wide

They used all three, but Type III is predominant.

> **Per Lionel Blueprints dated 3-4-47, the 3462-40 figure was $1^{21}/_{64}$" and made of white vinylite.**

The platform had a green-painted base, with a white-painted stand, as the consumer catalog suggested, but the steps were painted gray instead of white. Like the milk car, the platforms were painted various shades of white. The earliest platforms had an offset opening in the base (where the uncoupling track section was positioned), and the four tabs (two at each end of the base)

The 3462 on left was painted in a rarer glossy white.

were solid. Later in the production run, the opening was enlarged; soon after, the two tabs closest to the stand were split. This style of platform continued to 1966.

> **Per Lionel Blueprints dated 10-6-47, the opening was enlarged.**

Also, the underside of the platform base had "3462P" and other Lionel data stamped. This information was stamped on all platforms until about 1964 (see 3662).

In 1948, the 3462 was part of three cataloged sets and the separate-sale price jumped to $9.50. The car's outside appearance remained the same, except that glossy paint was no longer used and the circle "L" wasn't red as the catalog suggested. Also, the staple-end coil couplers remained the norm. However, the inside mechanism was redesigned for better performance, as was the new bare metal base plate that attached differently to the frame. Finally, the last figure introduced (Type IV) included a round cap and was 1³⁄₁₆" high and ½" wide. This figure would continue through 1955.

The 3462 was component boxed with a car, a 3462P-1 platform, a 3462-70 box of magnetic milk cans (with seven 3462-69 cans), a corrugated liner and a 3462-67 instruction sheet dated 1/48.

- Box Style Art Deco Toy Logo (1947 - 1948)
  - Tuck Flap Number: None (3462-65 not on box)

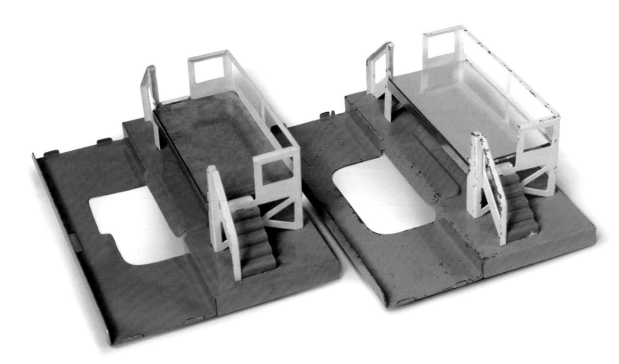

The platform on the left has an offset opening and solid tabs.

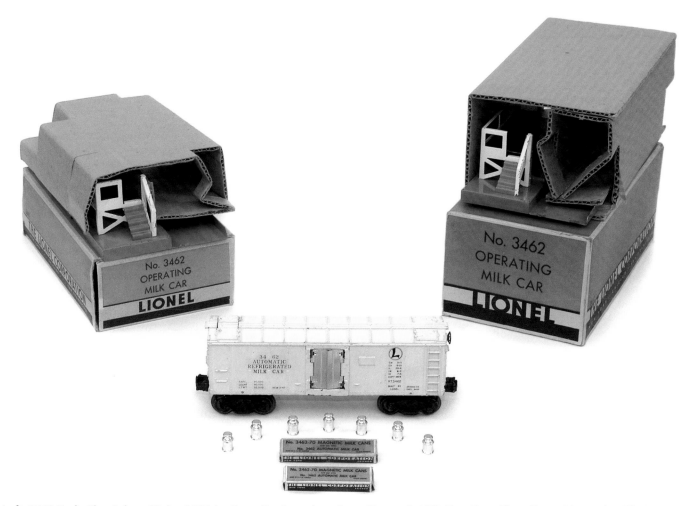

Left: 3462 Early Classic box. Right: 3462 Art Deco Toy Logo box. Rear: Magnetic Milk Cans Type I box. Front: Magnetic Milk Cans Type II box.

- Corrugated Liner: 3462-66
- Box Dimensions: 5⅞" x 11" x 4⅜"
• Box Style Early Classic (1948)
  - Tuck Flap Number: None (3462-90 not on box)
  - Corrugated Liner: 3462-91
  - Box Dimensions: 5¾" x 10" x 2⅞"

Author's Comments: The milk car, along with smoke and magne-traction, jump-started the proud company into the postwar era. Richard G. Smith, who provided the inspiration and idea regarding this popular car, actually came from outside the Lionel family of employees.

For collectors, the semi-gloss cars, as well as the high-gloss cars (often referred to as "super glossy"), are the most desirable, but aren't as rare as often suggested. What's rare, however, is an example that has crisp lettering and unchipped paint.

It appears that Lionel was thinking of making unpainted 3462s, as they changed from clear to white polystyrene, although this experiment didn't pan out initially due to molding flaws.

> Per Lionel Part Card originally dated 12-30-47, Lionel changed the body from clear polystyrene to white opaque Styron™. These bodies were sprayed oyster white S-100 as bodies were rejected because of stains.

3462	C7	C8	C9	Rarity
Super Glossy White Car	225	350	500	
Car & Platform	275	400	550	R9
With Art Deco Toy Logo Box	350	500	800	
Glossy White Car	175	225	300	
Car & Platform	225	275	350	R8
With Art Deco Toy Logo Box	300	375	600	
Regular 1947 - 1948 Car	30	45	60	R2
Car & Platform	55	75	100	
With Art Deco Toy Logo Box	90	125	150	R7
With Early Classic Box	150	200	250	R9

3462P-25 MILK CAR PLATFORM: 1952 - 1955

Lionel offered an individual 3462P-25 Milk Car Platform for separate sale from 1952 through 1955 at the cost of $2.00. The specifications were the same as offered with the 3472 Operating Milk Car from 1952 and 1953, but the bottom of the platform was marked "3462P."

The idea of adding another platform to a layout had possibilities, but the 3462P was probably not a big seller. Those offered in 1954 and 1955 were likely leftover inventory.

A 3462P-25 is a component boxed 3462P-1 with a 3472-80 insert.

• For Each Box:
  - Tuck Flap Number: 3472-79

The 3462P-25 (like the 3356-150) for separate sale is also extremely rare due to its box.

- Box Dimensions: 5¼" x 7⅜" x 2¾"
- Box Style OPS Classic (1952)
- Box Style Middle Classic (1953 - 1955)

Author's Comments: It is the box that commands the value and not the contents. These were likely sold to operators who used them on their layouts and discarded the box. Those boxes that have survived are coveted by collectors.

3462P-25	C7	C8	C9	Rarity
OPS Classic Box	1,500	2,700	3,500	R10
Middle Classic Box	2,000	3,000	4,000	

3462-70 MAGNETIC MILK CANS: 1952 - 1959

A 3462-70 Magnetic Milk Cans box containing seven magnetic milk cans was included with the 3462, 3472 and 3482 Operating Milk Cars, but it wasn't offered for separate sale until 1952. It was cataloged until 1959 at a cost of $1.25.

OPS Classic box version.

The milk cans included with the cars were easily lost or the magnet fell out, so it was natural for Lionel to offer these for separate sale. When the 3662 Operating Milk Car was issued with new non-magnetic style cans, these earlier models became somewhat obsolete. The 3462-70s offered the last three or four years, were probably leftover inventory. The milk cans themselves were updated over the years and included three different part numbers: 3462-59 (1947 - 1948), 3472-13 (1949 - 1952) and 3472-65 (1952 - 1959).

By 1954, 3462-70s packaged with the new 3482 Operating Milk Car have been observed in Type III boxes with fewer than seven milk cans and a small amount of Lionel paper to fill the void. To date, there has been uncertainty whether the box contained five or six cans.

Per the Lionel 3462-70 Part Card, it states that for 1952 use TP-24 3" x 3" tissue paper with five 3472-65 milk cans. For 1954, use TP-24 3" x 3" tissue paper and five 3472-65 milk cans.

3462-70 Magnetic Milk Cans boxes. Left, top to bottom: Type I, Type II, and Type III (all three have seven cans). Right: Type III with five cans and TP-24 3" x 3" tissue paper (1952-1959).

When component boxed the 3462-70 included seven 3462-59 milk cans (1947 - 1948) or 3472-13 milk cans (1949 - 1952). From 1952 forward, it was Lionel's intention to include five 3472-65 (1952 - 1959) milk cans and to fill the gap with TP-24 tissue paper.

- Box Style Art Deco with Middle Classic Design (1947 - 1959)
  - Tuck Flap Number: None (3462-71 not on box)
  - Box Type I - Dimensions: 1¹⁄₁₆" x 3⅛" x ⅜" (3462 on box) (1947)
  - Box Type II - Dimensions: 1¹⁄₁₆" x 2¾" x ⅜" (3462 on box) (1947 - 1949)
  - Box Type III - Dimensions: 1¹⁄₁₆" x 2¾" x ⅜" (3462 and 3472 on box) (1949 - 1959)
- Box Style OPS Classic
  - Tuck Flap Number: None (3462-105 not on box)
  - Box Type IV - Dimensions: 1¹⁄₁₆" x 2¾" x ⅜" (1952)

Author's Comments: The box for the 3462-70 was very delicate and was easily torn upon opening. The longer 1947 box is the most collectible of all the variations.

Thanks to authentic Lionel documentation and the consumer catalog, it is now confirmed that, starting in 1952, it was Lionel's intention to provide only five milk cans. This validates the instruction sheet that suggested to place only five cans in the car at one time.

3462-70		C7	C8	C9	Rarity
Middle Classic Box	Type I	35	60	100	R9
	Type II	20	40	60	R6
	Type III	20	40	60	R6
OPS Classic Box - Type IV		50	75	125	R9

3472 OPERATING MILK CAR: 1949 - 1953

Introduced as a follow-up to the popular 3462 Operating Milk Car, the 3472 now featured staple-end magnetic trucks and couplers and operated in the same manner as its predecessor. In fact, the new trucks and couplers were enough to justify a change in number. As with the 3462, the new car was painted white. However, sometime after the first run, Lionel began molding the shell out of white polystyrene, thus saving money on paint and labor, although there were different shades of white.

The 3472 was included in three cataloged sets and offered for separate sale at $9.50. However, the circle "L" still wasn't red as the 1949 consumer catalog suggested, since the 3472 was heat-stamped in black with the Cheltenham and Gothic fonts. Other features included a flared-end activator rivet, a frame that changed twice (each change included more openings), and a now-standard 1³⁄₁₆" figure.

The platform still had a green-painted base and a white-painted platform with gray steps; it would continue that way through the final run.

In 1950, the 3472 was included in two cataloged sets and the separate-sale price remained the same. Although the shell was still molded in white plastic, the earlier aluminum doors were replaced with plastic doors. For some reason, two different materials were used for the door assembly (eggshell Dupont nylon and pure white Dow Styron™). This led to two different part numbers and variations in door color.

> Per Lionel Blueprints dated 4-6-50, the 3472-42 R.H. and 3472-43 L.H. doors were made of Dupont nylon.

> Per Lionel Parts Card dated 9-1-50, the 3472-57 R.H. and 3472-58 L.H. doors were made of pure white Dow Styron™.

Also in 1950, the shell was redesigned, with a new inside part number 6472-5, from the 6472 Refrigerator Car introduced the same year. A longer white polystyrene roof door (with black instead of silver pins) replaced the previous white painted die-cast one and provided easier loading of milk cans. Two supports were added beneath the catwalk at both ends of the car.

> Per Lionel Blueprints dated 4-17-50, four ribs each 0.04" wide and 0.25" apart were added to support the catwalk.

Also, larger brake-wheel rivets were used in 1950 (see 3464 Operating Box Car and 3656 Cattle Car). The frame also was changed, being notched to accommodate the plastic doors. The inside mechanism was redesigned, probably being introduced during late 1949.

In 1951, the 3472 was part of two cataloged sets and the separate-sale price jumped to $11.50. Because of the Korean War, Lionel issued dealers a packet of pre-priced, gummed OPS labels to place on separate-sale boxes. Although the shell was the same

Left: The 3472 has aluminum doors and shorter roof door. Right: The 3472 has plastic doors and longer roof door.

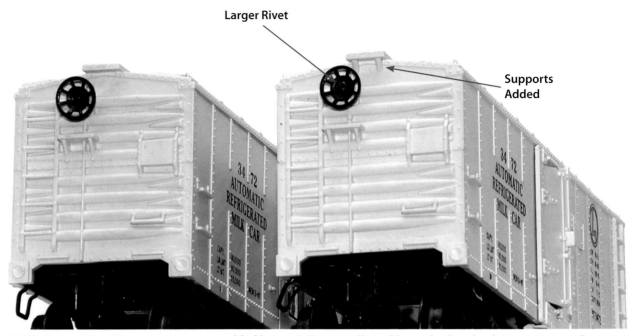

Larger Rivet

Supports Added

Right: The 3472 changed in 1950, as supports were added beneath the catwalk, and larger brake wheel rivets were used.

as before, the frame changed again, as there were fewer openings. Also, an additional washer was used under the horseshoe washer (clip) that attached the truck pivot stud to the inside frame.

The 3472 was part of two cataloged sets in 1952, but only one in 1953; the separate-sale price was $10.50 both years. In 1952, the accessory box had OPS letter-press information (some were also rubber-stamped), but this practice was discontinued in 1953. Although the 3472 was the same as before, examples from 1952 and later can easily be identified by their bar-end trucks.

The 3472 was component boxed with a car, a 3462P-1 platform, a 3462-70 box of magnetic milk cans, a 3462-101 corrugated liner and a 3472-11 instruction sheet. As per the 3462-70 listing, it came in a Type II or Type III style box. Seven milk cans were included until 1952, when it was Lionel's intention to provide five. The instruction sheet included seven versions, dated: 2/49 or 11/49 (1949); 6/50 or 10/50 (1950); 11/51 (1951); 2/52 (1952) and 4/53 (1953).

- For Each Box:
  - Box Dimensions: 6⅛" x 10⅛" x 3"
- Box Style Early Classic (1949)
  - Tuck Flap Number: None (3472-10 not on box)
- Box Style Middle Classic (1949 - 1953)
  - Tuck Flap Number: None (3472-10 not on box) (1949)
  - Tuck Flap Number: 3472-10 (1950 - 1953)
- Box Style OPS Classic (1952)
  - Tuck Flap Number: 3472-10X

Author's Comments: Different hues of white exist for both the shell and the doors, although collectors do not place any premium on the different color combinations.

Even though the 3472 received a new number because of its staple-end magnetic couplers, some cars could have the outdated coil couplers as well as 3462 mechanisms due to transition.

3472	C7	C8	C9	Rarity
Painted Car	35	50	75	
Car & Platform	60	80	115	R8
Boxed	75	100	200	
Unpainted Car With Metal Doors	25	40	55	R5
Car & Platform	50	70	95	
Boxed	65	90	80	R7
Unpainted Car With Plastic Doors	35	50	75	R4
Car & Platform	60	80	115	
Boxed	75	100	200	R6

3482 OPERATING MILK CAR: 1954 - 1955

Introduced in 1954, the 3482 was the last of the smaller 3400-series of operating milk cars. Enough new mechanical changes were in place to signify the new number. The easiest change to notice was how the shell was now attached. The previous milk cars used two "U" shaped frame springs, whereas the 3482 was slotted into the body on one end and screwed on the other. It operated in the same manner as discussed with the 3462 and 3472.

In 1954, the 3482 was included in three cataloged sets and offered for separate sale at $10.50. The car was molded in white polystyrene, with black heat-stamped lettering in the Cheltenham and Gothic fonts. It had a new shell with .015" thinner sidewalls. To compensate for these thinner shells, the door frame had bosses added.

Per the 3472-44 Door Frame Blueprint dated 4-13-53, six .062" diameter by .015" high bosses were added to the back of the frame.

Also, the body door opening had two cutouts (hidden behind the door frame) that provided clearance for the door springs.

Left: This 3482 is harder to find because it has "RT3472" stamped above "Built by Lionel." Right: A 3482 with normal "RT3482" stamping.

Per Lionel Blueprints dated 12-23-53, two .062" by .187" slots were added to each door frame on the body.

Some 3482s (probably the first ones made) still had the "RT3472" number stamped at the bottom right and the correct "3482" number stamped at the top left. This mistake was quickly corrected and is a variation in demand by collectors. Bar-end magnetic trucks were the norm, and the couplers had black knuckle pins.

In 1955, the 3482 was included in only one cataloged set and the separate-sale price remained the same. Those numbers probably represented leftover inventory, especially since the new 3662 Operating Milk Car was now the featured car.

The 3482 was component boxed with a car, a 3462P-1 platform, a 3462-70 box of magnetic milk cans, a 3462-101 corrugated liner and a 3482-36 instruction sheet dated 4/54 or 6/54 (1954 - 1955). As per the 3462-70 listing, it came in a Type III style box with five milk cans and a piece of TP-24 tissue paper.

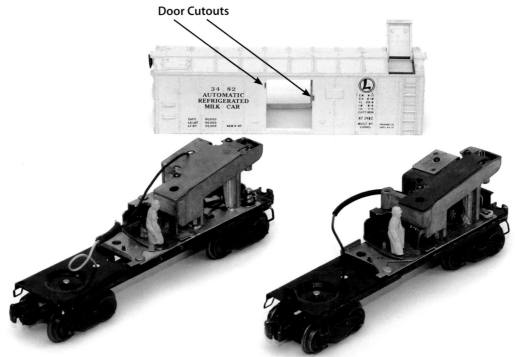

Door Cutouts

Left: The 3400-series frame and inside mechanism from 1948 differs considerably from a 1954 example (right). Top: Note the two door cutouts on the 3482 shell.

| 1949 | 1950 - 1952 | 1952 | 1952 - 1955 | 1956 | 1957 - 1958 |

3656-34 Figures For Cattle Car shown by year.

- Box Style Middle Classic (1954 - 1955)
  - Tuck Flap Number: 3482-35
  - Box Dimensions: 6⅛" x 10" x 3"

Author's Comments: By the time the 3482 came out, the 3400-series of Operating Milk Cars had run its course. Even with an improved mechanical design that allowed it to function much better than its predecessors, the 3482 looked no different than the 3462 and 3472. Lionel would have been better off issuing the 3482 in a new road name or color. Instead they went a different way and issued the longer and near-scale 3662 Operating Milk Car.

Although the 3482 is fairly common, the 3482 with "RT3472" heat-stamped is as rare as a red-lettered 3562-25 Operating Barrel Car. It is also known to appear in set 2231W.

3482	C7	C8	C9	Rarity
Regular Production Car	30	45	75	R6
Car & Platform	55	75	115	
With Middle Classic Box	70	95	200	R7
"3482" & "RT3472" Car	125	160	300	
Car & Platform	165	200	350	R9
With Middle Classic Box	200	250	450	

3656-34 FIGURES FOR CATTLE CAR: 1952 - 1958

The 3656-50 Operating Cattle Car was component boxed with a box of nine black vinylite cattle, but the cattle weren't cataloged for separate sale until 1952 through 1958 at $1.25 each year. From 1949 through 1952, the boxes had "9 No. 3656-9 Figures for Cattle Car" on each end and "3656" on all four sides. Once offered for separate sale later in 1952, "3656-34" began to appear on all four sides. This lasted until 1956, when the Late Classic boxes became the norm and the numbers were omitted. Although the 1949 through 1952 versions were not offered for separate sale, they still show up in the marketplace; therefore, pricing is included.

Of note, the earliest cattle came with a molded ridge along their base that was later removed.

- For Each Box:
  - Box Dimensions: 1¼" x 4¼" x 1⅛"
- Box Style Middle Classic (1949 - 1955)
  - On All Four Sides: 3656 (1949 - 1952)
  - On All Four Sides: 3656-34 (1952 - 1955)
  - Tuck Flap Number: None (1949)
  - Tuck Flap Number: 3656-44 (1950 - 1955)
- Box Style OPS Classic (1952)

Bottom: Early version of cow with a molded ridge on its base.
Top: Later version with the ridge removed.

  - On All Four Sides: 3656-34
  - Tuck Flap Number: 3656-44
- Box Style Late Classic: (1956 - 1958)
  - On All Four Sides: Nothing
  - Tuck Flap Number: 3656-44 (1956)
  - Tuck Flap Number: 3656-34 (1957 - 1958)

Author's Comments: April 1957 and April 1958 internal Lionel sales forecasts reveal that small numbers of 3656-34s were manufactured in 1957. Therefore, the Late Classic with tuck flap number 3656-34 is extremely rare.

Offering cattle for separate sale was a great idea because they would easily get lost or more cattle were desired. The 3656-34 was also necessary as an add-on when purchasing the 3656-150 Corral Platform, as that item did not include any cattle.

The early cattle with a molded ridge are the rarest cattle.

3656-34	C7	C8	C9	Rarity
Molded Ridge Cows (1949) With Middle Classic Box	150	200	250	R9
Middle Classic Box (1949 - 1955)	25	35	50	R5
OPS Classic Box (1952)	50	60	75	R9
Late Classic Box (1956)	50	60	75	R9
Late Classic Box (1957 - 1958)	50	60	75	R10

3656-50 OPERATING CATTLE CAR: 1949 - 1955

New in 1949, the 3656-50 Operating Cattle Car ("-50" not on car or box), along with the Operating Milk Car introduced two years earlier, were among the finest, most creative toy train accessories made during the 20th century. Even better, both were fun to play with.

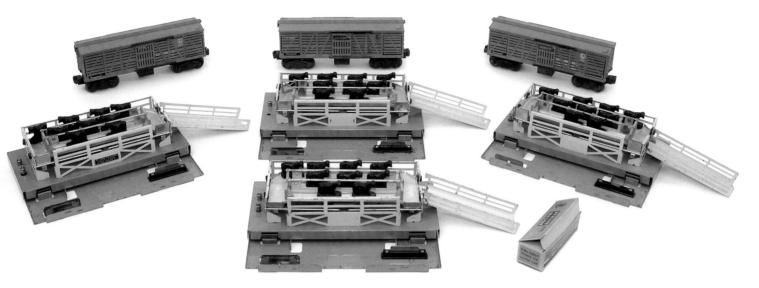

Corrals from 1949. Clockwise from left: Opening with nameplate and chain, opening without nameplate and chain, no opening, and yellow-painted platform floor. Cattle cars from 1949. Left to right: White heat-stamped lettering and no Armour emblem, black heat-stamped lettering and Armour emblem, and white heat-stamped lettering and Armour emblem.

Per Lionel Production Planning Files, two different finished good numbers were used for a Cattle Car Complete and Packed. The first being 3656-200 dated 10-14-49 and the other 3656-50 dated 9-6-50.

The 3656 included both a car and a corral to simulate the loading and unloading of cattle. By placing the car alongside the corral and switching on the enclosed 364 button, solenoids mounted underneath the car and with the corral set the vibration in motion. The black vinylite cattle included with each 3656 moved counterclockwise along the aluminum floating floor of the platform and runway inside the car. A set of nine vinylite cattle was provided with each 3656, each having angled prongs on the underside of its base that allowed it to travel in a forward movement.

The 3656 was cataloged for seven years, thus many differences were present, including the paint (dull and glossy) and the shape of the cattle, of which the earliest ones had a molded ridge running along the base. Also, several changes were attributed to the constant improvement of the product.

In 1949, the 3656 was included in two cataloged sets and offered for separate sale at $14.50. In the full-color consumer catalog, the car was shown with black lettering and an "Armour" emblem, while the corral had a green base with a yellow fence and ramp. The 3656-50 pictured for separate sale also showed a yellow-painted floor, which is known to exist on the earliest corrals. This variation also came with a white heat-stamped car without the "Armour" emblem. Soon afterwards, aluminum platform floors became the norm.

In 1949, the orange-painted 3656 cattle car was made with white or black heat-stamped lettering; both variations had the "Armour" emblem above the top of the center door on both sides. Other features included staple-end magnetic trucks with black knuckle pins and a flared activator flap rivet. The width of the runway where the cattle entered the car was 1⅛" wide on the right-hand side, and some cars didn't have the solenoid housing fully enclosed.

Each year it was offered, the 3656-150 corral had a green-painted base, yellow-painted fence and ramp, and a set of nine black vinylite cattle. However, there were other features to consider. In 1949, the two binding posts (where the wires attached) were on the end opposite the ramp, the four gates were molded in orange polystyrene, and a chain was fastened to the side where the ramp was positioned. However, later in the year, the chain was removed from the design, as Lionel realized its insignificance.

The corral was also equipped with two slots, where a Lionel Corporation name plate was attached. However, two other types also exist. For reasons unknown, some corrals, probably the first made, had the slots omitted from the design, while others had the slots, but the name plates were not attached. To be original, there *must* be no paint chips or scratches that would suggest the name plate had been removed post-factory.

Per Lionel Blueprints dated 9-19-49, name plate slots were added to the 3656-58 front fence.

In 1950, the 3656 was included in two sets, but the separate-sale price dropped to $13.95. The car still had white or black heat-stamped lettering, but to improve operation the width of the runway on the right-hand side of the car was reduced in size. Even the plunger assembly changed inside the car. Other changes included the omission of the "Armour" emblem, the flared rivet process was replaced by the round-end version, and a hole was punched out of the activator flap. Of course, don't forget about transition.

The black-lettered 3656 without the "Armour" emblem is a little-known and rarely documented variation. However, the flat, round-head door guide rivets (see 3464) and the smaller runway authenticate 1950 as the *only* year of production.

Also changing was the corral, as the binding posts were moved to the opposite end, a new magnetic platform covered a simplified and completely redesigned electrical contact system, the gates were molded in yellow polystyrene to match the fence, and rubber sub-base grommets were no longer used.

In 1951, the 3656 was offered for separate sale only at $15.95 and, except for the use of a stubbier door guide rivet, the specifications were the same as before. Lionel was busy with government contracts, so production of the 3656 was probably kept to a minimum and completed early in the year. Dealers were issued a packet, that contained pre-priced ($15.95), gummed OPS labels to place on each accessory box in stock, regardless of the year of production. With a $2.00 increase in the price of the 3656, dealers surely looked forward to getting their labels.

In 1952, the 3656 was part of one cataloged set and the separate-sale price remained the same. The car's specifications were the same as before, except that bar-end trucks became the norm and some models still used the stubbier door guide rivet. The corral remained the same.

Three variations of the component box with OPS data exist. The first two types, which were included with set 2189WS, had smaller OPS lettering and the fifth line of data was either letter-pressed or rubber-stamped. The third variation had larger OPS data and was probably offered for separate sale. Some cardboard liners were rubber-stamped with a 3656-41 stock number.

In 1953, the 3656 was included in a set for the last time and the separate-sale price remained the same. During the year the car's frame bottom was modified, as two openings were made to fasten the connecting wires. The corral also changed, as a different technique of welding the "grommet bracket" to the coil bracket was used.

3656 OPS Classic boxes (1952). Left to right: Five lines of OPS letter-press data, fifth line rubber-stamped and four lines of larger OPS data. Note the two Middle Classic style boxes 1950 - 1952 (left) and 1952 - 1955 (right).

The 3656 was offered for separate sale only in 1954 and 1955, and the price remained the same. Although those offered in 1955 were leftover inventory, three changes identify 1954 production: the top of the knuckle coupler was now engraved, the component box tuck flap number changed, and two additional holes or impressions were made on the corral's platform.

The 3656-50 was component boxed with a 3656-41 corrugated liner, a 3656-1 individually boxed cattle car, a 3656-150 platform complete, a 3656-129 ramp, a 3656-34 box of nine cattle, a 3656-46 packed envelope (envelope no. 3656-47), a TP-20 6" x 6" piece of tissue paper and a 3656-43 instruction sheet. There are at least four variations of the 3656-46 packed envelope. The first three are just changes in styles, whereas the last (1952 - 1955) did not include the instruction sheet.

For The 3656-50:
- For Each Box:
  - Box Dimensions: 8¼" x 10¾" x 3⅜" (1949 - 1955)
- Box Style Middle Classic (1949 - 1951 & 1953 - 1955)
  - Tuck Flap Number: None (3656-40 not on box) (1949)
  - Tuck Flap Number: 3656-40 (1950 - 1955)
- Box Style OPS Classic (1952)
  - Tuck Flap Number: 3656-40

For The 3656-1:
- Box Style Middle Classic (1949 - 1951 & 1953 - 1955)
  - Tuck Flap Number: None (3656-42 not on box) (1949)
  - Tuck Flap Number: 3656-42 (1950 - 1953)
  - Tuck Flap Number: 3656-208 (1954 - 1955)
  - Box Dimensions: 3¼" x 10⅛" x 2¼"

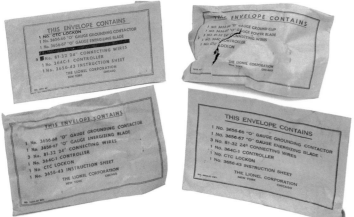

3656 envelope styles (counterclockwise from top left): 1949, 1949 - 1950, 1950 - 1951 and 1952 - 1955 (instruction sheet not in envelope).

The 3656-43 instruction included ten versions, dated: 9/49 or 11/49 (1949); 9/50 (1950); 3/51 or 5/51 (1951); 2/52 or 5/52 (1952); 1/53 (1953); 5/54 (1954) and 2/55 (1955).

The 3656-1 Middle Classic component boxed cattle car included with 3656-50.

Author's Comments: The Lionel Production Planning Files for a component boxed 3656 listed it as both a "-50" (9-6-50) and "-200" (10-14-49). The "-50" was later, thus indicating the 3656's true identity and Lionel's chosen number for the remainder of production.

There has been some debate on whether the white-lettered or black-lettered 3656 was made first. Although the white version often came with the early style of corral without the name plate, this isn't conclusive evidence. However, since both examples were made in 1949, which came first is inconsequential.

The 3656 was an accessory with the car individually boxed within the overall component box, unlike the later 3356 Operating Horse Car And Corral and 3366 Operating Circus Car And Corral, which had the cars unboxed and nested in the liner. This change likely saved Lionel a penny or two.

Some early corrals with chains came without the name plate slots. Add an additional $100 to the price for this variation. Also, early cattle with the molded ridge demand an additional premium (see 3656-34).

3656-50	C7	C8	C9	Rarity
1949 White-Lettered Car Without Armour Emblem	40	50	75	R8
Car, Yellow Corral & Chain	415	500	600	R10
Boxed	465	575	750	
1949 Black-Lettered Car With Armour Emblem	225	350	475	R9
Car, Corral & Chain	300	450	600	
Boxed	350	525	750	
1949 White-Lettered Car With Armour Emblem	40	50	75	R4
Car, Corral & Chain	55	70	125	
Boxed	85	110	275	R6
1950 Black-Lettered Without Armour Emblem	200	325	450	R9
Car, Corral & No Chain	250	375	525	
Boxed	300	450	675	
Regular Production Version	30	40	60	R4
Car & Corral	45	60	100	
Boxed	75	100	250	R6

3656-150 CORRAL PLATFORM: 1952 - 1955

Without having to buy an entire 3656-50, hobbyists could get a boxed corral separately (3656-150) as a replacement accessory starting in 1952. Although the idea had merit, it was probably a sales flop, especially since the platform was priced at $10.00 and didn't include any cattle. The corral's specifications matched those as covered with the 3656-50.

The 3656-150 for separate sale is extremely rare due to its OPS Classic box (OPS data not shown).

The 3656-150 was component boxed with a 3656-202 corrugated liner, a 3656-129 ramp, a 3656-46 packed envelope (envelope no. 3656-47), a TP-20 6" x 6" piece of tissue paper and a 3656-43 instruction sheet.

- For Each Box:
  - Tuck Flap Number: 3656-201
  - Box Dimensions: 7½" x 9⅞" x 2¾"
- Box Style OPS Classic (1952)
- Box Style Middle Classic (1953 - 1955)

The 3656-43 instruction included five versions, dated: 2/52 or 5/52 (1952); 1/53 (1953); 5/54 (1954) and 2/55 (1955).

Author's Comments: It's the box, not the contents, that makes the 3656-150 so special. The box is as rare as a black-lettered 3484-25 Operating Santa Fe Box Car, thus leading to its R10 rating.

The idea of adding another cattle corral to a layout had possibilities. It likely led to additional sales of cattle and cars.

3656-150	C7	C8	C9	Rarity
Regular Production Version	1,800	2,700	3,500	R10

3662 OPERATING MILK CAR: 1955 - 1960 & 1964 - 1966

One by one, longer, near-scale cars, like the 6462-series gondolas and 6464-series box cars, replaced the shorter cars in the Lionel line. So when the 3662 Operating Milk Car was introduced in 1955, it meant that the end was near for the smaller 3400-series milk cars.

Even though the 3662 performed the same basic functions as the earlier cars, it was completely redesigned. Besides being longer, it now used a two-piece shell, with the body section molded in white Styron™ polystyrene, with black heat-stamped lettering in the Cheltenham and Gothic fonts, and the roof section was molded in brown polystyrene. Bar-end trucks, with or without coupler tabs, and black knuckle pins were the norm.

Since the 3662 was included in two 1955 cataloged sets and offered for separate sale at $10.95, more than one production run was necessary. Naturally, differences in the shades of plastic resulted, although it's the variances in the shades of brown, not the white, that collectors have a hard time identifying.

In 1955, the roof section was molded in a reddish brown or a chocolate brown. The doors were intended to match the roof sections, but in reality don't always match.

> Per Lionel Component Parts Index, the doors and roof were all to be molded in "TMD-5151 Styrene Brown #355."

Inside, the 1³⁄₁₆" 3472-36 figure was the same as before, but the seven milk cans (polystyrene tops and cadmium-finished steel

Left to right: 3662 with reddish brown roof and "New 4-55", with chocolate brown roof and "New 4-55", and a richer brown roof and no built date.

bottoms) were non-magnetic, whereas before they were aluminum with an integral magnet. A new can-ejecting mechanism was introduced, and inside the car the black oxide cylinders were screwed to the coil bracket. However, the earliest cylinders were raw steel and held in place by the same cylinder yoke that was used with the brown 352 Ice Depot. The milk platform was still marked "3462P" (see 3462) on the underside and continued without change until 1964.

In 1956, the 3662 was included in four cataloged sets and the separate-sale price remained the same. The chocolate brown roof continued, but was soon joined by a flatter brown version. Also changing during the year were the knuckle pins, as silver examples replaced blackened ones.

On the inside, the figure now had painted face and hands and a copper or whitish-gray colored flexible fiber glass sleeve sometimes replaced the earlier black sleeve. Also, the lower section of the chute was notched for the milk cans to fall into place more effectively.

> **Per Lionel Production Planning Files dated 1-2-57, the 3472-36 vinylite figure was painted to create the 3662-89 figure painted.**

In 1957, the 3662 was part of three cataloged sets and available for separate sale at $10.95. The roof was flatter brown, and the coupler drawbar had a support hole.

In 1958, the Operating Milk Car came in two cataloged outfits and was offered for separate sale, with the price rising to $12.95.

The roof on the car was again the flatter brown; inside, the solenoid coil was red instead of copper.

In 1959 and 1960, the 3672 Bosco joined the 3662 in the product line. The 3662 was cataloged for separate sale only at $10.95 in 1959 and $12.95 in 1960. Those examples offered in 1959 and 1960 probably were leftover inventory.

After a three-year absence, the 3662 returned in 1964 as part of five cataloged and six promotional sets and had a separate-sale price of $14.95. The 3662's stampings were the same as before, except that the previously stamped "New 4-55" was removed.

> **Per Lionel Blueprints dated 11-20-64, "New 4-55" was removed.**

The roof sections were still a flatter brown, and AAR trucks with operating couplers and closed journal boxes were now the norm, with some using a Delrin knuckle with integral copper spring. On the inside, a polyvinyl wire sleeve, which was also used on the axles of a 6405-150 Trailer, replaced the earlier flexible fiber glass sleeve. The 3462P platform also changed, as it no longer had any data stamped on the bottom.

In 1965, the 3662 was part of two cataloged and one promotional set and the price increased to $15.00. The roof was now a richer brown, and AAR trucks with open journal boxes became the norm.

Inside the car the solenoid coil windings were now green in color. The vinylite figure was reworked, with a retainer added to the figure to help keep the milk cans in the correct position.

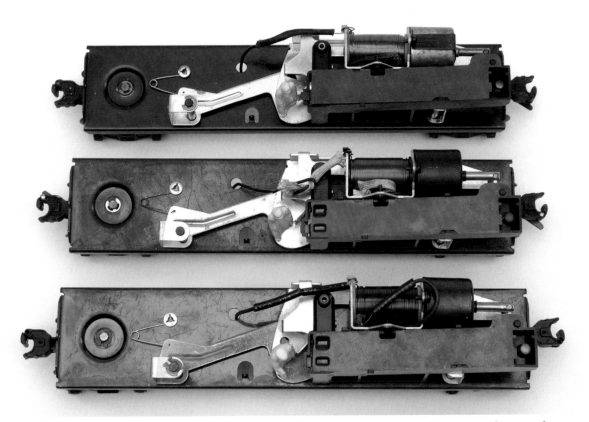

3662 interior design changes, (top to bottom): 1955 features with a raw steel cylinder and separate yoke; 1956 features with one piece blackened cylinder and a notched chute; 1966 features with a notched chute, green solenoid coil and a smaller figure with flat cap and retainer.

3662-79 envelopes (left to right): 1955 - 1956, 1956 - 1960, 1964, 1965, 1966 and 1966.

> Per Lionel Blueprints dated 9-3-65, the 3472-36 figure was modified and an extension was added to the right leg.

Also in late 1965 the figure had a flatter cap, instead of a round one, which made the figure somewhat smaller.

In 1966, the 3662 was included with one promotional and two cataloged sets and the separate-sale price remained the same. These cars had a shinier hue to the plastic, which may just be this way because they are still in C10 condition. The black frame was also shinier. The AAR bottom frame assembly changed as well, as it now had a half-circle cut-out to provide extra room for the coupler disk. Some 1965 style cars also appear in 1966, as Lionel was likely using leftover inventory.

The 3662 was component boxed with a car, a 3462P-1 platform, a 3662-79 packed envelope (envelope no. 3662-80), a 3662-76 corrugated liner, a 1-165 warranty card (1965 - 1966) and a 3662-81 instruction sheet (in packed envelope).

- For Each Box:
  - Tuck Flap Number: 3662-75
  - Box Dimensions: 6¼" x 12⅜" x 3¼"
- Box Style Middle Classic (1955)
- Box Style Late Classic (1956-60)
- Box Style Orange Picture (1964)
  - Other Box Features: Title and Cities Outlined in Blue
- Box Style Orange Picture (1965)
- Box Style Plain White (1966)
  - Tuck Flap Number: None

The instruction sheet included six versions, dated: 4/55 or 12/55 (1955); 2/57 (1957); 6/58 (1958 - 1960); 9/64 (1964) and 6/65 (1965 - 1966).

Author's Comments: This new 3662 Operating Milk Car kept the fun and excitement going by adding the milk mechanism to a larger O gauge car.

Generally speaking, the roof colors are quite subjective, but a semblance of order is needed. The 3672 Bosco car came with a flat brown roof. Using this as a reference, the differences between chocolate and reddish brown can be determined, as the difference between these two colors is easily discernible.

A white-painted version of this car is also known to exist, but its exact year of production is difficult to establish, although it is likely from the first two years of production. Collectors will pay a premium for this variation.

3662	C7	C8	C9	Rarity
1955 "Reddish" Roof Car	75	100	150	R8
Car & Platform	90	125	190	
Boxed	110	150	250	R9
Painted Car Likely 1955 - 1956	75	100	150	R8
Car & Platform	90	125	190	
Boxed	110	150	250	
1955 - 1960 Car	40	60	75	R4
Car & Platform	55	85	115	
Boxed	70	105	150	R6
1964 - 1966 Car	50	70	85	R7
Car & Platform	65	95	125	
Orange Picture Boxed	80	125	250	R8
Plain White Boxed	90	145	275	

3662-79 NON-MAGNETIC MILK CANS: 1955 - 1959

The 3662-79 packed envelope contained seven 3662-60 milk cans and the 3662-81 instruction sheet. It was available for separate sale in 1955 and 1956 for $1.25 and in 1957 through 1959 at $1.00. The cans and instruction sheet came packaged in a 2⅜" x 4⅛" tan envelope, printed with the envelope no. 3662-80.

From 1955 through 1960 and in 1964, the graphics on the envelopes varied slightly, with "The Lionel Corporation" being listed as the company. In 1965, the envelope now listed "The Lionel Toy Corporation." Finally in 1966, the envelope was white and the "3662-79" packed envelope number appeared on the envelope.

Although the 1960 and 1964 through 1966 versions were not offered for separate sale, they still show up in the marketplace and are listed here for completeness.

Author's Comments: The envelope's graphics changed during its nine-year run, with the 1966 white envelope being the rarest. Offering cans for separate sale allowed operators to replace the easily lost cans.

3662-79	C7	C8	C9	Rarity
Regular Production Version	20	25	35	R6
Lionel Toy Version	25	35	50	R8
White Version	50	60	85	R9

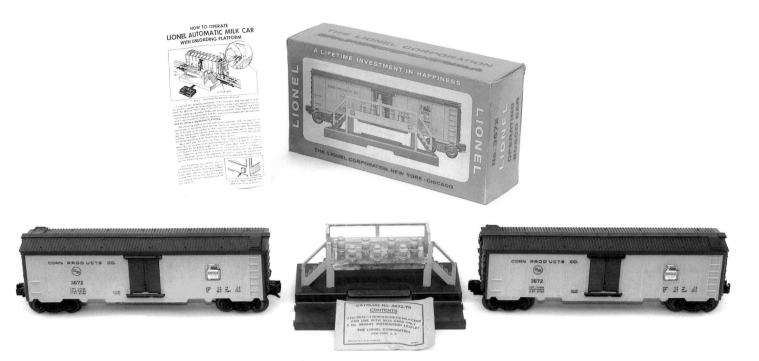

Left: 3672 painted version. Right: Unpainted yellow plastic version.

3672 OPERATING BOSCO CAR: 1959 - 1960

The 3672 was a new road name for the 3600 operating milk car series and operated in the same manner, except now it delivered cans of syrup versus milk. It was included in one cataloged set in both 1959 and 1960 and for separate sale at $12.95. It also made its appearance in two promotional sets for Madison Hardware Co. in 1960.

The Bosco Car used a two-piece shell with a yellow-painted or unpainted polystyrene body and brown heat-stamped lettering, whereas the roof section was molded in the same brown polystyrene as the 3662 from 1957 and 1958.

The car included a Bosco "Nutritious Chocolate Flavored Syrup" decal, and the interior design was the same as the 3662 from 1958, except that a black elastic wire sleeve was the norm. Each 3672 came with seven Bosco Milk Cans. The cans were similar (polystyrene tops and cadmium-finished steel bottoms) to those used with the 3662, except that they were yellow and had "Bosco" rubber-stamped in red. The car's instruction sheet had the front-page heading "Lionel Automatic Milk Car." Bar-end trucks with or without coupler tabs and silver knuckle pins were the norm.

Also changing was the unloading platform. The base was now painted brown, the top structure was painted yellow, and the 3462P and other Lionel data were no longer stamped on the bottom.

> Per Lionel Component Parts Index, each 3672-50, as well as the earlier 3462P-1, platform came with "Scotch Tape (½" wide x 2½")."

The 3672 was component boxed with a car, a 3672-50 platform, a 3672-79 packed envelope (envelope no. 3672-7), a 3662-76 corrugated liner and a 3662-81 instruction sheet, dated 5/59.

- Box Style Orange Picture
  - Tuck Flap Number: 3672-14
  - Box Dimensions: 6¼" x 12⅜" x 3¼"

Author's Comments: After cataloging the milk car with Lionel Lines markings for 12 years, Lionel finally decided to offer a car in a different road name and delivering syrup instead of milk. Unfortunately, by 1959 this was likely too little too late, as the milk car's popularity was waning. Two Madison Hardware Co. promotional sets (actually bulk-packed shipments that Lionel assigned a set number) included a Bosco car. Each set was sold in quantity of 100; as such, these were likely the last 200 Bosco cars sold.

As with the 3662 Operating Milk Car, painted versions are known to exist. These were likely made first, before Lionel decided on unpainted plastic cars for mass production. These rarer, yellow-painted Bosco cars are a known component of 1960 set 2553WS. This fact suggests that painted versions were still in inventory in 1960.

3672	C7	C8	C9	Rarity
Yellow Painted Car	200	250	350	
Car & Platform	250	310	425	R8
Boxed	375	525	700	
Yellow Plastic Car	150	180	225	R7
Car & Platform	200	240	300	
Boxed	325	450	550	R8

3672-79 NON-MAGNETIC MILK CANS: 1959 - 1960

The 3672-79 packed envelope contained seven 3672-11 Bosco cans and the 3662-81 instruction sheet and was available for separate sale in 1959 and 1960 for $1.25. The cans came packaged in a 2⅜" x 4⅛" tan envelope that was printed with the envelope no. 3672-7.

3672-79 packed envelope with seven rubber-stamped Bosco cans.

Author's Comments: Since the Bosco car was cataloged for only two years, finding these packed envelopes in C9 condition is sometimes difficult. As with the separate-sale milk cans, Lionel was smart to offer cans for separate sale as it allowed operators to replace the easily lost cans.

3672-79	C7	C8	C9	Rarity
Regular Production Version	75	100	125	R7

6352-1 REFRIGERATOR CAR (UNBOXED WITH 352 ICE DEPOT): 1955 - 1957
6352-25 ICE CAR (BOXED FOR SEPARATE SALE): 1955 - 1957

Introduced in 1955, a 6352 Refrigerator Car was included with each 352 Ice Depot accessory and protected inside by a corrugated liner. It also came boxed as a 6352-25 for separate sale at $6.95 and was referred to as an Ice Car on the box only. In the consumer catalog it was listed as a replacement accessory in 1955 and 1956 and as an extra accessory in 1957. Otherwise, it was referred to as a "reefer car used in 352 Ice Depot." Examples of the Ice Depot from 1955 came with a brown or red styrene platform structure, and the earliest examples used the same cylinder yoke as a 3662.

> Per Lionel Blueprints, the ice platform changed from "Brown #355 styrene" to "Maroon #215 styrene" on 10-28-55.

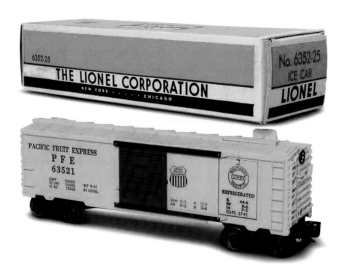

The 6352-25 for separate sale is extremely rare due to its Middle Classic box. Shown with a "4 Line" data car.

The 6352 operated in conjunction with the 352 Ice Depot. Small, clear polystyrene cubes simulating blocks of ice were manually loaded into the ice tower. It was necessary for the car to be correctly positioned next to the depot with the roof hatch next to the "iceman" operator. When the 90 controller was pressed, the figure would glide back and forth, pushing the ice into the car with his paddle. After the car was loaded, the blocks could be delivered to the desired destination, although they would have to be manually removed by opening the ice compartment door.

In 1955, the Ice or Refrigerator Car used bar-end magnetic trucks, with or without the new coupler tab, and a black knuckle pin. However, when the 352 was packaged for sale later in the production year, some 6352s had silver knuckle pins. The car was molded in orange polystyrene, with black rubber-stamped lettering.

> Per Lionel Component Parts Index, the 6352 was originally to be molded in gray and painted. But on 9-6-55 part no. 6352-2 "ice car body painted" was deleted, and the polystyrene color was changed to "Orange-175."

The 6352 used the same Type IIb body as the 6464 box cars, but was modified with an insert to provide the "Ice Hatch" (where cubes were dropped) opening on the roof, and the side "Ice Compartment Door" (where cubes were removed). Other box cars made after this modification (see 3424 and 3484-25) now had a visible line on the roof and sides. The modification for the ice hatch was actually the genesis of the Type IIb body.

The swinging side door had four lines of black, rubber-stamped data. The sliding door, one on each side of the car, was molded in reddish-brown polystyrene and had the large, four-block 1955 design (known as multi-block).

By the time the separate-sale 6352-25 was made available a few changes had been made, notably, the sliding doors came in a brownish-gray polystyrene, while the others were painted or unpainted chocolate brown. The swinging side door changed, as

Left: A 6352 with four lines of rubber-stamped data on the ice compartment door. Right: A 6352 with three lines of heat-stamped data. Note that the sliding doors are different shades of brown.

a rarer variation had three lines of heat-stamped data. Also, the inside of the shell body was modified, as the bracing was moved left of the gusset, whereas before it was to the right. These variations can show up with the later red 352 ice stations, but should not show up with the brown one.

> Per Lionel Component Parts Index, the 6352-17 brown door changed from styrene Brown No. 35 to Brown No. 355 on 10-20-55 and then again to Brown No. 104 on 3-15-56.
>
> Per Lionel Blueprints dated 2-3-56, "Cu. Ft. 2742" was deleted from ice compartment door.

In 1956, production followed the same pattern as late 1955. Also, those 6352-25s offered for separate sale were leftover inventory from 1955. The same was true in 1957.

The 6352-25 was component boxed with a car only. No instruction sheet was included because operating information was part of the 352 Ice Depot (352-44) instruction sheet.

- Box Style Middle Classic (1955 - 1957)
  - Tuck Flap Number: 6352-26
  - Box Dimensions: 3⅜" x 11¾" x 2⅜"

Author's Comments: It's the 6352-25 box that makes this item so special, and it is as rare as a black-lettered 3484-25 Operating Santa Fe Box Car.

Lionel also issued the 3356-2 Horse Car for separate sale. Although both cars boxed for separate sale are highly collectable, the 3356-2 was available from Madison Hardware Co. well into the early 1990s, whereas the 6352-25 was not. Therefore, the only 6325-25s that exist are likely from original purchases made in the 1950s. The box was likely discarded when the item was purchased.

To date, only rubber-stamped 6352s are known to exist.

6352	C7	C8	C9	Rarity
6352-1 4 Lines of Data	60	80	100	R7
6352-1 3 Lines of Data	200	250	300	R9
6352-25	2,000	2,750	3,500	R10

CHAPTER SEVEN

Novelty & Cranks

Lionel issued many novelty and crank cars. The assortment rapidly grew in the late 1950s and early 1960s.

3370-1 ANIMATED SHERIFF AND OUTLAW CAR (BOXED VERSION): 1961 - 1965

3370-25 ANIMATED SHERIFF AND OUTLAW CAR (UNBOXED VERSION): 1961 - 1963

Besides manufacturing Space and Military items, Lionel hit the Western scene in 1961 when it introduced the 3370 Animated Sheriff And Outlaw Car. The 3370-1 was the *boxed* version of this car, whereas the *unboxed* version was referred to as a 3370-25.

The operation for the 3370 depended on the work of a ratchet wheel that caused a pair of lift bars carrying the figures of a sheriff and an outlaw to rise and descend alternately through roof openings on the car. A cam on one of the wheels provided the operation as the car moved along the rails. The action simulated a shootout between the good guys and the bad.

> Per Lionel Blueprints dated 1-31-61, the sheriff and bandit are to be molded in "flesh color vinyl." "Note! Figure to be painted by Lionel."

The Animated Sheriff And Outlaw Car used the same shell (3656-4) as the Operating Giraffe Car, but the roof was modified to provide an opening for the sheriff and the outlaw. Once modified, the outline from the openings was visible on the inside of cars that used the same mold (see 3376, 3376-160 and 6473), and the inside bracing moved as well.

The shell was molded in green polystyrene, like the 3376-160, and had yellow heat-stamped lettering. AAR trucks with a three-piece metal knuckle were the norm; however, the 3370-25 packaged with set 1644 used the same Archbar style trucks as the General Passenger Cars.

Left: The 3370 with AAR trucks. Right: With Archbar trucks.

Per Lionel Production Planning Files, normal production for a 3370 was Archbar trucks but changed to AAR. On 7-18-61, it detailed that for 1961 production (4,000 units), use coupler truck complete 566-1 (AAR) in place of coupler truck complete 560-50 (Archbar).

In 1961, the 3370-1 was offered for separate sale at $7.95 and included in several promotional sets (see also the *Authoritative Guide to Lionel Promotional Outfits*, by Project Roar Publishing). The *unboxed* 3370-25 version was included in two cataloged and eight promotional sets.

In 1962, the 3370-1 was included in two promotional sets and offered for separate sale at $7.95. The 3370-25 was included in one cataloged and two promotional sets. The trucks changed for the 3370, as the one-piece Delrin operating coupler was now used.

In 1963 and 1964, the 3370-1 was offered in the consumer catalog for separate sale; although the price remained the same, those offered were most likely leftover inventory. The 3370-1 was also included in several 1963 promotional sets, whereas the 3370-25 was featured in three promotional sets in 1963 and then not heard from again.

In 1965, the Lionel Factory Order for Sears promotional set 19433 included the substitution of 106 units of 3370-1 for 3376-160, which was probably Lionel's remaining inventory of boxed Sheriff And Outlaw Cars.

The 3370-1 was component boxed with a car and a 3370-17 instruction sheet, dated 6/61 (one version has an advertisement for 110 Trestles on the back).

The 3370-25 Archbar version as it was included in "Western" Gift Pack 1809 from 1961.

- Box Style Orange Picture (1961 - 1965)
  - Tuck Flap Number: 3370-21
  - Box Manufacturer: Shuttleworth
  - Box Dimensions: 3¼" x 9½" x 2¼"

Author's Comments: The full-action shootout of the sheriff and outlaw has entertained audiences of all ages. Although this is an easy car to add to a collection, the mock-up, which featured stationary figures, is a collector's dream to own. It was painted green over a modified 3376 giraffe car body, but was non-operational because of the stationary figures (see Chapter 8).

The 3370-25 was the unboxed version of the 3370. It was included in two 1961 cataloged sets: 1644 General Passenger and 1809 "Western" Gift Pack. The model included in both sets is truly special, because it had two Archbar trucks with operating couplers instead of AAR trucks which were the norm. This is the most difficult version to find.

3370		C7	C8	C9	Rarity
3370 Archbar Trucks	-25	100	125	150	R8
3370 AAR Trucks		45	55	75	R5
and Couplers	-1	85	100	125	R6

3376-1 OPERATING GIRAFFE CAR (BOXED VERSION): 1960 - 1965 & 1969
3376-25 OPERATING GIRAFFE CAR (UNBOXED VERSION): 1960 - 1962 & 1969

The 3376-1 was the *boxed* version of the Operating Giraffe Car, whereas the 3376-25 was the *unboxed* version. The car depicted a giraffe being transported in a box car with its head protruding from a hole in the roof. The car's operation depended on the counterweighted giraffe head to bob up and down while avoiding certain clearances (a tell-tale pole was included) along the rails. This movement of the giraffe's head was accomplished through the use of a cam assembly located beneath the car. The assembly was activated by a cam plate assembly positioned along a straight section of track. This operation was purely mechanical in that no electricity was needed.

The 3376 used a completely modified 3656 (Cattle Car) mold with the 3656-4 part number still shown on the inside of the shell. The shell was molded in blue polystyrene with white heat-stamped lettering. Because of the large quantities made, the shell colors varied from light, to medium, to dark blue plastic.

The giraffe was molded in yellow polystyrene with spots on its face and neck to generate realism (even the drawing in the *Lionel Service Manual* depicted spots), although some apparently came assembled without the spots (*unintended production*). Some of the giraffes were shinier than others.

AAR trucks with three-piece metal knuckle couplers were used, and some included notches on top of the side frame.

The 3376-1 wasn't included in any 1960 cataloged sets, but it was included in several promotional ones, of which sets for Channel Master are collector favorites. Lionel must have thought the 3376-1 would be a hit with junior engineers because it flooded the market with this unique novelty item priced separately at $6.95. This car was highlighted in the 1960 feature film, "The Wonderful World of Trains."

When boxed, a 3376-118 packed envelope, containing the necessary peripherals to operate the car, was included. The tell-tale pole was molded in darker orange polystyrene than was used with the 3424 Operating Brakeman Car (see 3424).

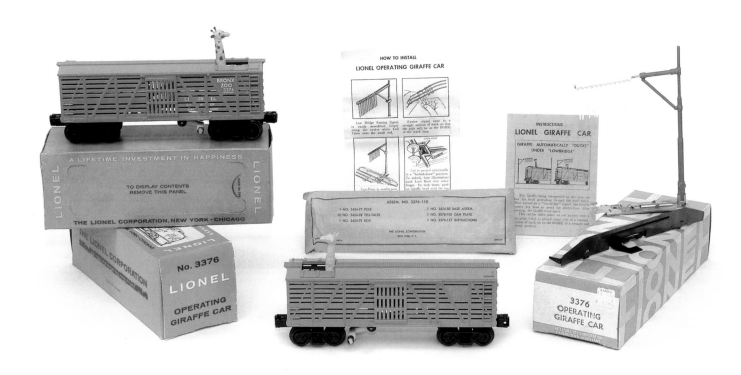

Left: 3376-1 with white heat-stamped lettering and an Orange Perforated or Orange Picture box. Middle: 3376-1 with yellow lettering, a giraffe with no spots (1969). Right: A Hagerstown Checkerboard box (1969).

The 3376-25 was included in one promotional set in 1960. When included with a set, the 3376-118 packed envelope was placed loose in the set box.

In 1961, the 3376-1 was included in several promotional sets and the separate-sale price remained the same. The first giraffe cars made in 1961 were the same as before; however, when Lionel brought out the 3370 the shell changed. The 3370 required an opening at each end of the roof, and when the mold was used again for the 3376, an outline from this modification appeared as a faint impression left on the inside roofline and as extra flashing on the outside. The 3376-25 was included in three promotional and two cataloged sets.

In 1962, the 3376-1 was offered for separate sale only and the price remained the same. Although AAR trucks were still the norm, the Delrin one-piece coupler replaced the earlier three-piece design and had closed journal boxes. The 3376-25 came in one cataloged set, 12502.

In 1963 and 1964, only leftover inventory remained; those items were offered for separate sale with the same suggested retail price of $6.95. To help reduce inventory, Lionel also included 23 units of 3376-1s (as a substitute for 3376-160) in 1965 Sears promotional set 19433.

In 1969, the Operating Giraffe Car was reissued and numbered 3376-150 in the consumer catalog for separate sale at $8.00, but in reality it could be green (3376-160), blue with white lettering (3376-1), or blue with yellow lettering (3376-1). Lionel was just filling up generic 3376 Checkerboard boxes with whatever was on hand.

The Operating Giraffe Car was part of one cataloged set 11760 and numbered 3376 (shown in green) in the consumer catalog. But it most often came as the blue polystyrene version. Some blue cars even had rarer yellow heat-stamped lettering instead of white.

In 1969, the features of the 3376s distinguished them from earlier versions. These included giraffes without spots (*intended production*), open journal boxes, and some armature pins being brass, with or without a rounder disk.

The 3376-1 was component boxed with a car, a 3376-118 packed envelope (envelope no. 3376-119), a 6809-12 coupler protection tube and a 3376-117 instruction sheet (in the envelope) dated 6/60 (1960) or 1/61 (1961 - 1965 and 1969).

- For Each Box (1960 - 1965):
  - Tuck Flap Number: 3376-120
  - Box Dimensions: 3¼" x 9¼" x 3¼"
- Box Style Orange Perforated (1960)
- Box Style Orange Picture (1961 - 1965)
- Box Style Hagerstown or Hillside Checkerboard (1969)
  - Tuck Flap Number: 12-278
  - Box Dimensions: 3½" x 10½" x 3¼"

The 3376-118 packed envelope (envelope no. 3376-119) included a dark orange polystyrene 3424-77 tell-tale pole, 12 white 3424-78 tell-tales, a 3424-79 tale support rod, a zinc-plated 3424-80 support base assembly, a 3376-105 cam plate assembly and the 3376-117 instruction sheet.

Author's Comments: In 1969, Lionel was in the process of licensing the Toy Train Division to General Mills Inc., so exactly which color Giraffe Car was included in set 11760 or for separate sale was not of importance to Lionel. However, those cars assembled in 1969 should still have 1969 features.

Lionel's mock-up for the 3376 was non-operational, and the car was painted over a modified 6646 stock car shell. That shell was molded in orange plastic, and when the mock-up's blue paint starts to chip, the orange plastic is revealed (see Chapter 8).

The 1969 version with yellow lettering is the one that collectors relish.

3376		C7	C8	C9	Rarity
Regular Production	-25	35	50	65	R4
Version	-1	60	100	150	R6
1969 Yellow	-25	250	300	350	R9
Heat-Stamped	-1	325	400	500	

3376-150 OPERATING GIRAFFE CAR (UNBOXED VERSION): 1962 - 1963, 1965 & 1969
3376-160 OPERATING GIRAFFE CAR (BOXED VERSION): 1962 - 1965 & 1969

Introduced in 1962, the 3376-150 and "-160" were nothing more than a 3376 molded in green polystyrene with yellow heat-stamped lettering. It even operated in the same manner as before.

The plans for the green Operating Giraffe Car began in late 1961.

In 1962, the 3376-160 was included in Sears promotional set 9657, where 3,200 sets were targeted for production. The 3376-1 was shown as blue in the consumer catalog for separate sale at $6.95, but it was likely that the 3376-160 was also available for separate sale, especially since it had its own box. The 3376-150 was the *unboxed* version of the "-160" green Operating Giraffe Car. It was included in cataloged set 12502, but Lionel Factory Orders allowed for the substitution of the 3376-25.

The 3376-160 included a 3376-118 packed envelope containing the peripherals needed to operate the car. However, the 3376-150 was placed *unboxed* within a set box and the 3376-118 packed envelope was placed loose inside the set box. Interestingly, the unboxed example (3376-150) had a lower suffix number than did its boxed counterpart (3376-160).

Since the 3376-160 was made after the 3370 was introduced, the inside roof had the impressions left by the 3370's modification. However, the green Giraffe Car was also made after the modification for the 6473 introduced in 1962 and lacked the four molded door

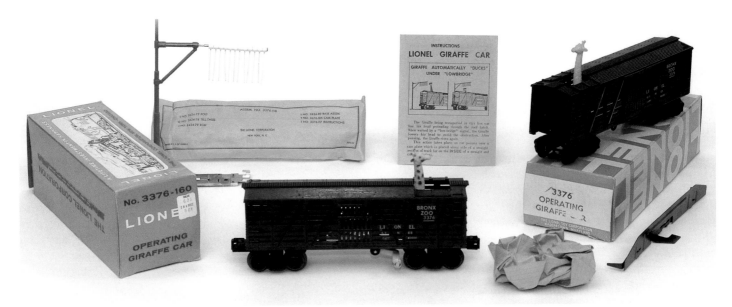

Left: 3376-160 and Orange Picture box with separate-sale price tag. Right: 3376-160 and giraffe with no spots and a Hagerstown Checkerboard box (1969).

guide rivets (two each on the right side of the car door).

The 3376-160 had two AAR operating trucks that were equipped with the new Delrin one-piece coupler. Of course, don't forget about transition.

Because the 1963 and 1964 catalogs were printed in black and white, it's likely Lionel was offering both the blue and green cars for separate sale at the same price. These models were probably leftover inventory.

To further deplete inventory, Lionel used both the 3376-150 and "-160" in several 1963 promotional sets and finally in 1965 promotional set 19433. Keep in mind that a short run of green cars could have been made in 1963 to provide the cars needed to fill these sets.

The green Giraffe Car returned in 1969. Although it was shown as part of cataloged set 11760, the blue Giraffe Car, with yellow or white lettering, was often substituted (see 3376-25).

Also, the green Giraffe Car was offered for separate sale at $8.00. However, instead of using the correct 3376-160 number, the full-color consumer catalog pictured the blue Giraffe Car for separate sale with a 3376-150 number, which was reserved for the *unboxed* green Giraffe Car. The net of all this is that Lionel was just filling up the boxes with whatever they had,

The shell for the green Giraffe Car was the same as produced in 1962, but the frame had the same 1969 features as the 3376. It is likely that Lionel used up old stock of green shells and assembled them with the new frames until they were totally depleted.

The 3376-160 was component boxed with a car, a 3376-118 packed envelope (envelope no. 3376-119), a 6809-12 coupler protection tube and a 3376-117 instruction sheet (in the envelope) dated 1/61.

- Box Style Orange Picture (1962 - 1965)
  - Tuck Flap Number: 3376-161
  - Box Dimensions: 3¼" x 9¼" x 3¼"
- Box Style Hagerstown or Hillside Checkerboard (1969)
  - Tuck Flap Number: 12-278
  - Box Dimensions: 3½" x 10½" x 2½"

The 3376-118 packed envelope (envelope no. 3376-119) included a dark orange polystyrene 3424-77 tell-tale pole, 12 white 3424-78 tell-tales, a 3424-79 tale support rod, a zinc-plated 3424-80 support base assembly, a 3376-105 cam plate assembly and the 3376-117 instruction sheet.

Author's Comments: The 3376-150 and "-160" were nothing more than the 3376-1 or "-25" (blue) now molded in green. A new color alone was not enough to drive additional sales of this car. See 3376-1 and "-25" for additional comments.

The 1969 version paired with the correct Checkerboard box is tougher to find than the Orange Picture box version.

3376-150 / 3376-160		C7	C8	C9	Rarity
Regular Production Version	-150	60	75	100	R6
	-160	90	115	150	R7
1969 Version	-150	60	75	100	R8
	-160	135	175	250	R9

3386-1 OPERATING GIRAFFE CAR (BOXED VERSION): 1960
3386-10 OPERATING GIRAFFE CAR (BOXED VERSION): 1960
3386-25 OPERATING GIRAFFE CAR (UNBOXED VERSION): 1960

The 3386 Operating Giraffe Car was the same as a 3376, but was fitted with two dummy Archbar trucks instead of operating AAR trucks. The 3386 operated in the same manner as did the other giraffe cars (see 3376-1).

The shell for a 3386 was molded in several shades of blue polystyrene with white heat-stamped lettering and had the same modifications as the 3376-1 from 1960.

The 3386-1 was the *boxed* version of the Operating Giraffe Car, but the "-1" suffix was not printed on the car or the box. This version was included in three 1960 promotional sets that totaled 4,200 units.

The 3386-10 was also *boxed*, but this version was offered for

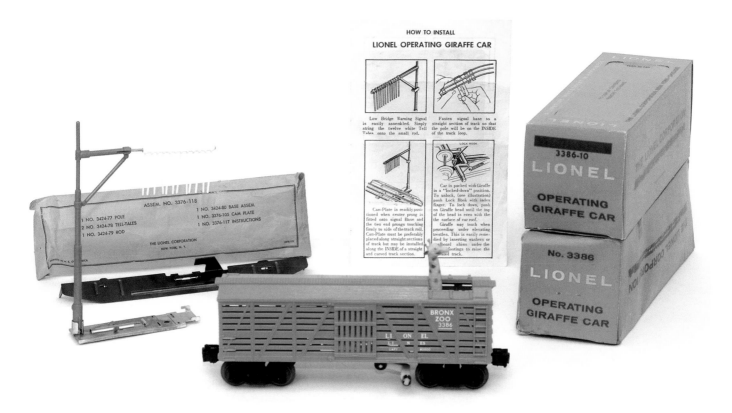

3386-1 shown with its separate-sale, rarity R10, 3386-10 Orange Perforated (3376 over-stamp) box as well as Orange Perforated (non over-stamp) box.

separate sale at the same $6.95 price as a 3376-1. The "-10" suffix was not printed on the car, but was printed on the box. In this instance, a box for a 3376 was used, but the number was blackened out and the 3386-10 number was stamped below.

The 3386-25 was the *unboxed* version and was introduced to the product line as part of 1960 advance catalog set 1109. It was also included with several other promotional sets. As with the other two 3386 examples, the "-25" suffix was not printed on the car. Per Lionel Factory Orders, just over 60,000 cars were produced; this quantity is reflected in its rarity (see also the *Authoritative Guide to Lionel Promotional Outfits*, by Project Roar Publishing).

> Per Lionel Factory Orders, the 3386-1 came in promotional sets X-526NA, X-565NA and X-574NA and unboxed as 3386-25 in sets 1109, 1111, 1117, X-549NA, X-567NA, X-568NA and X-575.

The 3386-1 and "-10" were component boxed with a car, a 3376-118 packed envelope (envelope no. 3376-119), a 6809-12 coupler protection tube and a 3376-117 instruction sheet (in the envelope) dated 1/60.

- For Each Box:
  - Box Dimensions: 3¼" x 9¼" x 3¼"
- Box Style Orange Perforated (1960)
  - Tuck Flap Number: 3386-10
- Box Style Orange Perforated Over-stamped 3376 (1960)
  - Tuck Flap Number: 3376-120

The 3376-118 packed envelope (envelope no. 3376-119) included a dark orange polystyrene 3424-77 tell-tale pole, 12 white 3424-78 tell-tales, a 3424-79 tale support rod, a zinc-plated 3424-80 support base assembly, a 3376-105 cam plate assembly and the 3376-117 instruction sheet.

Author's Comments: Although the 3386 is a common car, the 3386-1 box is as rare as a red-lettered 3562-25 Operating Barrel Car. However the 3386-10 version ranks as an R10 with quantities believed to be fewer than 25.

Even though the 3386 used two dummy couplers, it found its way into being a separate-sale item. Apparently Lionel had too many unboxed 3386s remaining in stock, so they took advantage of the car's cute style of operation, over-stamped some 3376 boxes, and reduced their inventory accordingly.

3386		C7	C8	C9	Rarity
Regular Production Version	-25	30	40	50	R4
With Orange Perforated Box	-1	45	100	200	R9
With Orange Perforated Over-Stamped Box	-10	150	250	400	R10

3512 OPERATING FIREMAN AND LADDER CAR: 1959 - 1961

Introduced in 1959, the 3512 came equipped with a telescoping extension ladder that could be raised and lowered by hand. The car included a flashing light caused by the turning motion of a lamp

3512 with black extension ladder (left) and silver (right). Note the original no. 4-6 elastic band in front used to hold down the ladder.

shade concealed inside the red plastic lens. This motion was the work of the drive gear located beneath the 3512-37 red polystyrene superstructure. The 3512 introduced a special 566-100 AAR truck and operating coupler with a polyurethane rubber drive belt (which deteriorates over time) driven by the axles. The vinylite fireman oscillated from side to side through the motion of the return arm. However, the arm was incorrectly illustrated as turned around in the *Lionel Service Manual*.

In 1959, the 3512 was included with five cataloged sets and offered for separate sale at $9.95. The flat car was molded in red polystyrene (mold 6424-11) with white heat-stamped lettering in the Cheltenham Bold font. AAR trucks with three-piece knuckle couplers were the norm, including one with a pickup.

A red polystyrene turret held the extension ladder in place. Although the full-color consumer catalog illustrated the ladder as silver (bright nickel plate), a more common black oxidized example was also made.

> **Per Lionel Blueprints, the bright nickel-plated extension ladder was replaced by a black oxidized one and the material changed from "1/4 hard" cold rolled steel to "soft" cold rolled steel.**

Also included were a white figure seat; a vinylite figure with painted face, hands and hat; three spare nickel-plated brass nozzles; an ornamental bell; and a red plastic lens.

In 1960, the separate-sale price remained at $9.95. It was included in two cataloged sets, 2551W and 2549W. Six promotional sets also featured the 3512.

> **Per Lionel Factory Orders for set 2549W, the 3512 was substituted for the 3540; quantity 800.**

By 1961, the 3512 was offered for separate sale only at $9.95. Those were leftover inventory from the previous two years.

The 3512 was component boxed with a car, a 4-6 elastic band and a 3512-60 instruction sheet dated 9/59.

- Box Style Orange Perforated (1959 - 1961)
  - Tuck Flap Number: 3512-61
  - Box Manufacturer: CCA
  - Box Dimensions: 4" x 11⅛" x 2¼"

Author's Comments: This car introduced at least 55 new parts, all of which included numerous tooling changes. The blueprint for the 3512-37 superstructure included 26 changes alone. Lionel tried to address this issue by consolidating tooling for many of the new small parts, and an eight-cavity mold was produced. This is one of the few times so many parts were consolidated in a family tool.

> **Per Lionel Production Control Files, an eight-cavity mold was used to mold the 3512-56, 3512-7, two 3512-23s, 3512-30, 3512-44, 3512-55 and 3512-63 in black Cycolac® (GE Plastics' ABS plastic).**

Collectors enjoy owning both the silver and black extension ladder variations of the 3512, and operators enjoyed the action the car provided. Kids, however, just liked playing with this car, especially raising and lowering the extension ladder.

The silver extension ladder variation is the rarer model. However, what is really hard to find is an example that still has all its original peripherals, including the three nozzles, the side ladders and the figure, and no broken plastic parts.

3512	C7	C8	C9	Rarity
Silver Ladder Version	125	175	225	R8
	185	300	400	
Black Ladder Version	75	150	175	R6
	125	250	300	R7

6473-1 RODEO CAR (BOXED VERSION): 1962 - 1966
6473-25 RODEO CAR (UNBOXED VERSION): 1962 - 1967
6473-50 RODEO CAR (UNBOXED VERSION): 1969
6473-60 RODEO CAR (BOXED VERSION): 1969

The 6473 Rodeo Car simulated the carrying of horses in a stock car and provided openings in the car for them to enjoy the scenery. The operation for a 6473 was smooth and easy, as the movement along the rails caused the horses to swivel back and forth with their heads popping in and out of the car. The car came with four different suffixes, each indicating some sort of change in the trucks and couplers or the boxes. Also, this car spanned eight years, and many different shades of yellow can be accurately dated.

Introduced in 1962, the Rodeo Cars were molded in yellow polystyrene, with red heat-stamped lettering. The cars used the same shell as the 3376 and 3370, except the shell was modified with four openings, two on each side, for the swivel action of the horses. The location of those openings caused a change in the car's design, as the top and bottom molded door guide rivets on the right side of the car door on both sides of the car were removed. This change also affected the production of the 3376-160, and both cars were missing the 3656-4 mold number on the inside of the shell.

The 6473s used two operating AAR trucks with the new early Delrin one-piece coupler, but most examples still included the lancing technique near the spring-mounting hole. The lancing was phased out during the 1962 production year (late Delrin).

> **Per Lionel Production Control Files, the 6473 was originally intended to have 560-50 operating (Archbar) trucks and couplers.**

The 6473-1 was the *boxed* example of the Rodeo Car, but the suffix "-1" was not printed on the car or the box. In 1962, the car was packaged with cataloged set 11278 and two promotional sets, and offered for separate sale at $5.95. Inside the car, a center balance unit (6473-6 pivot) and a beam (6473-7 pivot arm) were molded in white or brown polystyrene; they often were assembled in mixed combinations. Attached to the beam were two pairs of polystyrene horses: one white and one brown. The 6473-25 was the *unboxed* version of the Rodeo Car, and in 1962 it was part of several promotional sets. Lionel Factory Orders also mentioned that the car was targeted for cataloged set 12502 as a substitution for the 1877-25 Flat Car With Horses.

> **Per Lionel Blueprints dated 1-15-62, the 6473-8 horse team brown #9654 (Lionel code 69141) and 6473-9 horse team white #9310 (Lionel code #69137) were molded with Dow medium-impact styrene. Per Production Control Files, for each car, one team of horses is brown and the other is white.**

In 1963, the 6473-1 was offered for separate sale only and the price remained the same. The 6473-25 was part of one cataloged and several promotional sets. The bright lemon yellow version was introduced, but a partially filled horizontal slot to the right of the door was caused by a break in the mold (broken tool variation). A polystyrene shell was also molded in yellow-orange (cadmium) that made the heat-stamped lettering appear a darker red than before.

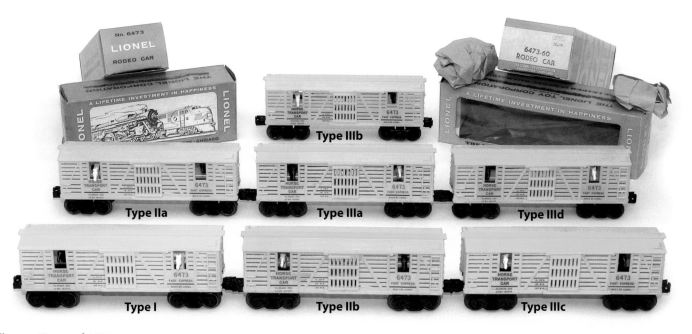

All seven Types of 6473s.

The year 1963 could be called the "year of the dummy coupler", because many of the cars included in O27 cataloged and promotional sets had one of their operating couplers replaced by a dummy coupler. The 6473-25 was no different, as one operating and one dummy coupler soon became the norm. Also, the 6473-1s packaged later in the year could have one operating and one dummy coupler.

In 1964, the 6473-1 was offered for separate sale only and the price remained the same. Those cars were probably leftover inventory, and the illustration in the consumer catalog changed, no longer showing the molded brake wheel. The car's specifications were the same as before, but at the end of the run the dummy couplers had open journal boxes. So, if any 6473-1s were assembled and packaged late in the year, they would exhibit this feature.

The 6473-25 was part of two cataloged and several promotional sets. The car's specifications were the same as before, except some of the cadmium shells were a shade more yellow. At the end of the

run, the dummy couplers came with open journal boxes.

In 1965, the 6473-25 was part of three cataloged and several promotional sets. As the first sets were packaged, the car's specifications were the same as before, but now the journal boxes were open on both trucks.

As production for both cataloged and promotional sets continued, the shell was changed. The mold was repaired, but a tiny mark remained. Also, the cadmium yellow shells with red heat-stamped lettering were joined by ones that had maroon heat-stamped lettering.

Lionel made another change when promotional set 19440 was packaged. Some of the 6473-25s were molded in lighter lemon yellow polystyrene, with maroon heat-stamped lettering. This variation is much harder to find.

In 1965, the 6473-1 was offered for separate sale only and the price increased to $6.00. The illustration in the consumer catalog was basically the same as 1964, and the cars offered were undoubtedly leftover inventory. However, if any cars were assembled and packaged, they had the same features as the 6473-25 from 1965.

In 1966, the 6473-1 was packaged for separate sale only and came in the new Cellophane Window box. The price remained the same. The cadmium yellow shell with maroon heat-stamped lettering was the norm, and both trucks had open journal boxes. Starting in 1966, some cars had a washer placed under the leaf spring rivet, possibly for better tension.

The 6473-25 was included in three cataloged and several promotional sets. The maroon-lettered version continued, but the shell again was molded in cadmium yellow.

In 1967, Lionel didn't manufacture any 6473s. However, they still were included in promotional sets, such as 19706 sold by Sears, to further reduce leftover inventory.

After a two-year absence, the 6473-1 returned as 6473-60 *boxed* for the last time as part of one cataloged set 11750 in 1969. It also was offered for separate sale at $7.00.

Even so, the specifications were the same as 1966, except the car had two operating couplers, which was probably the reason for the "-60" suffix. Also, as with many 1969 cars, some used brass armature pins. When packaged within its 6473-60 box, a scrunched up piece of bogus paper (instead of coupler protection flaps) was placed at both ends of the car to keep it in place. In summary:

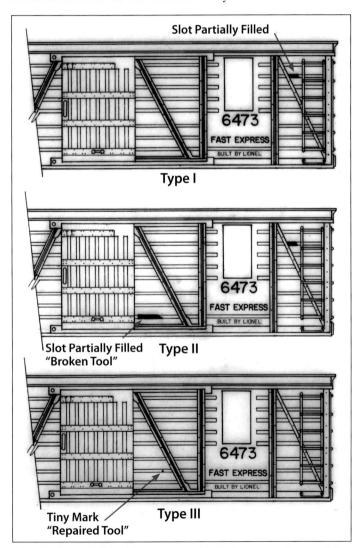

6473 body variations. Top: Type I - Original tool has slot partially filled (same as 3376-160 and 3370). Middle: Type II - Additional filled slot due to break in the mold. Bottom: Type III - Mold repaired but tiny mark remained.

6473 Types					
Body Type	Tool	Yr.	Color	Heat-Stamp	Trucks & Couplers
I	Original Tool	1962	Yellow	Red	2OC
IIa	Broken Tool	1963	Bright Lemon Yellow	Red	2OC or 1OC & 1NOC
IIb	Broken Tool	1963 1964	Cadmium-Yellow	Red	2OC or 1OC & 1NOC
IIIa	Repaired Tool	1965	Cadmium-Yellow	Red	1OC & 1NOC
IIIb	Repaired Tool	1965	Lighter Lemon Yellow	Maroon	1OC & 1NOC
IIIc	Repaired Tool	1965 1966	Cadmium-Yellow	Maroon	1OC & 1NOC
IIId	Repaired Tool	1969	Cadmium-Yellow	Red	2OC

Legend:
- 2OC - Two operating couplers
- 1OC - One operating coupler
- NOC - Non-operating couplers

For 6473-1:
- Box Style Orange Picture (1962 - 1965)
  - Tuck Flap Number: 6473-12
  - Box Manufacturer: None (1962 - 1965)
  - Manufacturer Logo: "Die" in a "C" (1962 - 1963)
  - Box Dimensions: 3¼" x 8½" x 2¼"
- Box Style Cellophane Window (1966)
  - Tuck Flap Number: 12-234 (6473-13 not on box)
  - Box Dimensions: 3¼" x 10½" x 2½"

For 6473-60:
- Box Style Hillside or Hagerstown Checkerboard (1969)
  - Tuck Flap Number: 12-278
  - Box Dimensions: 3⅝" x 10½" x 2½"

Author's Comments: The 6473 was produced in very large numbers, and because of the numbers made the color of the shell and heat-stamped lettering can vary from light to dark, thus making the choice of how many different shades to recognize quite subjective.

When Lionel finally closed shop, they still had many 6473 shells left in stock. These shells were sold through regular channels. In fact, quite a few Lionel Service Stations, especially along the Eastern Seaboard, had these shells for sale during the 1970s (the cost was usually less than $2.00 each).

The 6473-60 boxes are the rarest and are accounted for in their rarity ratings. The 1965 lemon yellow with maroon lettering is the most difficult of the variations to find. Also, many of the variations only came unboxed; therefore, no box is listed in the pricing table.

6473		C7	C8	C9	Rarity
Type I - Yellow	-25	20	25	35	R7
With Orange Picture Box	-1	40	50	75	
Type IIa Bright Lemon Yellow	-25	75	100	125	R8
With Orange Picture Box	-1	95	125	175	
Type IIb or IIIa Cadmium-Yellow	-25	20	25	35	R3
Type IIIb Lighter Lemon Yellow	-25	75	100	125	R9
Type IIIc Cad-Yellow (With Maroon)	-25	20	25	35	R6
With 1965 Orange Picture Box With 1966 Cellophane Window Box	-1	40	50	75	
		50	75	100	R8
1969 Type IIId Cad-Yellow (With Red)	-50	25	30	40	R8
With Checkerboard Box	-60	50	100	150	R9

6501-1 JET MOTOR BOAT TRANSPORT CAR (BOXED VERSION): 1962 - 1964
6501-25 JET MOTOR BOAT TRANSPORT CAR (UNBOXED VERSION): 1962 - 1963

Trying to recapture some of the diminishing toy train market, Lionel introduced novelty items like the 6501 in 1962. The 6501-1 was the *boxed* version and the 6501-25 was *unboxed*.

The 6501's operation was separate from the flat car, as the boat is what provided the fun. Placing four or five of the included sodium bicarbonate "fuel" pellets into the boat, filling the chamber with warm tap water, and shaking the boat caused pressure to build up. Then replacing the jet nozzle and placing the boat in water released pressure that caused the boat to travel about 10 feet.

In 1962 the 6501-1 was included in two cataloged sets and offered for separate sale at $6.95. The 6501-25 was included in several promotional sets. The flat car was incorrectly illustrated in the full-color consumer catalog as a black flat car in set 11268, but was corrected to a red flat car in set 13008.

The 6501 used a red polystyrene flat car (mold 6511-2) with white heat-stamped "Lionel" in the Cheltenham Bold font. However, the "6501" was on the box only and not the car. The 6501 used two operating AAR trucks with the new Delrin one-piece coupler with closed journal boxes. The 6501-2 polystyrene boat had a brown deck over a white hull and a clear polystyrene window. It sat atop a gray polystyrene cradle that was held in place by a 6418-9 elastic band. Also included was a silver packet of 40 fuel pellets.

Per Lionel Blueprints dated 5-28-62, the fuel pellets had two variations. One was manufactured by Azo Products and measured .31" in diameter and .18" thick. The other was manufactured by Leeds-Dixon Lab, Inc. and measured .31" in diameter and .12" thick. Also on the blueprint was the note "Pellets must not lose their effectiveness for a minimum of one year after packaging." The 6501-17 packet was made of a poly-foil/poly-cell combination as packed by Ivers Lee, Co.

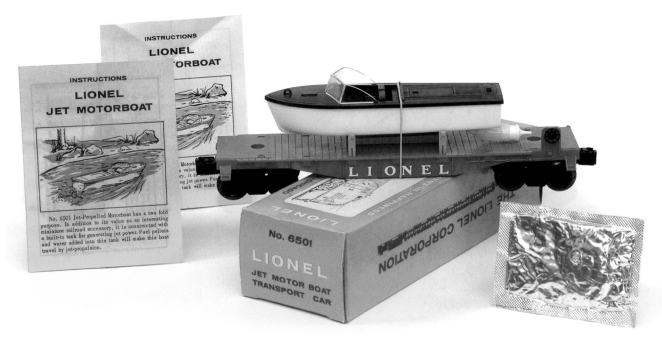

The 6501 (note the number is not on the flat car) came with a foil packet containing 40 fuel pellets.

When the 6501-25 was placed unboxed within a set box, the instruction sheet and the fuel pellet packet were handled as "loose goods."

> Per Lionel Production Control Files dated 6-5-62, a 6501-2 boat assembly and 6501-17 "fuel pellets packed" are additional parts required for packing in the Outfit Packing Department.

In 1963, the 6501-1 was offered for separate sale at the same price as before and included in several promotional sets. The 6501-25 was included in three promotional sets.

In 1964, the 6501-1 made its last appearance in several promotional sets as Lionel was burying the last 305 units that they had in inventory.

The 6501-1 was component boxed with a flat car, a 6501-2 boat assembly, a 6501-17 packet of fuel pellets, a 6418-9 elastic band and a 6501-14 instruction sheet (on white or yellow paper) dated 7/62.

- Box Style Orange Picture (1962 - 1964)
  - Tuck Flap Number: 6501-15 (6501-15 printed both ends)
  - Box Date: 6-62
  - Box Dimensions: 3⅜" x 10⅛" x 2⅜"

Author's Comments: The 6501 apparently wasn't a hit with consumers after all, as dealers had plenty in stock during the early 1970s. The instruction sheets pointed out that the "pellets are a compound of Sodium Bicarbonate and are harmless."

6501		C7	C8	C9	Rarity
Regular Production	-25	90	125	150	R6
Version	-1	140	200	250	R7

6660 BOOM CRANE CAR: 1958

Designed to lift and lower freight with the greatest of ease, the 6660 was introduced in 1958 as part of two cataloged sets and a separate-sale item at $6.95.

The hand-operated Boom Car was a useful part of any layout. The boom could be raised or lowered to the desired angle by one of the cranks. The block and hook were controlled by the other crank. Using these two cranks, the crane could be used to simulate maintenance or cleanup of a train wreck.

The 6660 used either a 6511-2 or 6424-11 flat car mold, which was molded in red polystyrene with white heat-stamped lettering in the Cheltenham Bold font. The number was stamped to the left of "Lionel", but the illustration in the full-color consumer catalog was to the right. Also, production of the 6660 paralleled the 6805, so the 6424-11 mold used an insert that left two raised rectangular insert marks on each end of the top of the flat car where the rail stops were on the 6805.

The 6660 used AAR trucks with three-piece metal couplers, with the boom (which was the same as used with the 3360 Burro Crane introduced in 1956) and mast molded in yellow Cycolac® ABS. The fine detail of the outriggers and winches completed the design and operation.

> Per Lionel Component Parts Index dated 4-27-59, the length of the 6660-4 cord changed from 19" to 21" 12-pound test braided spinning line Airex 455 or equal.

The 6660 was component boxed with a car, two 6660-56 corrugated inserts and a 6660-58 instruction sheet dated 6/58.

- For Each Box:
  - Tuck Flap Number: 6660-55
  - Box Dimensions: 3⅜" x 12" x 2⅜"
- Box Style Late Classic (1958)

Top: A 6660 with Bold Classic box. Bottom: The 6660's Late Classic box.

- Box Style Bold Classic (1958)
  - Box Manufacturer: Berles Carton Co.
  - Box Date: BC583

Author's Comments: The 6660 was a realistic addition to the line, especially when the non-train oriented Space and Military items were beginning to appear.

A complete C9, 6660 Boom Crane Car includes two corrugated 6660-56 inserts used to protect the couplers and the boom.

6660	C7	C8	C9	Rarity
Regular Production Version	50	75	100	R6
	100	150	200	R7

6670 BOOM CRANE CAR: 1959 - 1961

The 6670 Boom Crane Car was basically a 6660 without the outriggers, although it also had a different style hook. It operated in the same manner as the 6660.

> Per Lionel Blueprints, the 6660 had a 6560-13 hook and pulley assembly whereas the 6670 came with a 6670-4 block and hook.

In 1959, the 6670 was part of one cataloged set and offered for separate sale at $5.95. It even underwent a personality change, when it became a "Derrick Car" in the consumer catalog. AAR trucks with three-piece metal knuckle couplers were the norm for the entire run.

In 1960, the 6670 was offered in the consumer catalog for the same separate-sale price, although leftover inventory was probably used in several promotional sets. In 1961, the 6670 was offered for $6.95 in the advance catalog *only*. However, not enough were left in stock by the time the consumer catalog was printed; consequently, 1,862 units of the remaining cars were substituted for the 6519 Allis-Chalmers Car in set 1648, as indicated by Lionel Factory Orders for 1961.

Like the 6660, the 6670 used a red polystyrene flat car (mold 6424-11 or 6511-2), with white heat-stamped lettering in the Cheltenham Bold. However, the 6511-2 mold was being used for the 1959 production of the 3419 helicopter cars, so the 6424-11 mold dominated production. The polystyrene used on the 6670 was usually more translucent than that used on the 6660.

The 6424-11 mold was the same as with the 6660 and had two raised rectangular insert marks on each end of the top of the flat car. Like the 6660, the number for the 6670 was stamped to the left of "Lionel", but a rarer example had the number heat-stamped to the right. Regardless of the mold or placement of the number, a hole was punched in all the flatcars to secure the rivet that held the mast and hook's base in place.

6670 left to right: Number left of "Lionel", number right of "Lionel", and factory error with no stamping.

> Per Lionel Blueprints dated 4-2-59, the 6670-4 block and hook was made of Zamak #5 and was black oxidized.

The 6670 was component boxed with a car, a 6670-9 corrugated insert and a 6670-5 instruction sheet dated 4/59.

- Box Style Orange Perforated (1959 - 1961)
  - Tuck Flap Number: 6670-6
  - Box Manufacturer: Berles Carton Co.
  - Box Date: BC594
  - Box Dimensions: 2⅞" x 12" x 2⅜"
- Note: The 6670 also used over-stamped 6660 boxes.

Author's Comments: Although the 1959 box explained that a Boom Crane Car was packaged inside, the 6670 shown in both the advance and consumer catalogs was referred to *only* as a Derrick Car.

The 6670 was probably a harder sell than a 6660, but the yellow mast and boom, together with a modified base, were used again with the 462 Derrick Platform Set introduced in 1961. These sat on dealer shelves into the early 1970s.

The 6670 in an Orange Perforated box came with one 6670-9 insert whereas when packaged in an over-stamped 6660 box, it included two 6660-56 inserts. The 6670-9 insert is more difficult to find and is reflected in the C9 price below.

6670		C7	C8	C9	Rarity
Reg. Prod.	Regular Production	50	75	100	R6
	Orange Perforated Box	100	150	200	R7
	"6660" Over-Stamp	100	150	175	R8
"6670" Right	Regular Production	150	200	250	R9
	Orange Perforated Box	200	275	375	
	"6660" Over-Stamp	200	275	350	

6812-1 TRACK MAINTENANCE CAR (BOXED VERSION): 1959 - 1962
6812-25 TRACK MAINTENANCE CAR (UNBOXED VERSION): 1960 - 1961

The 6812 Track Maintenance Car came *boxed* (6812-1) and *unboxed* (6812-25). It was designed to simulate the raising of a platform to allow maintenance access to bridges, signals and other elevated railroad structures. The operation for a 6812 depended on careful turning of the fragile crank projecting from the platform floor. This raised the platform to a height designated for maintenance work. Two inspectors (figures) were included, one to simulate the operation of the platform and the other to do the work.

In 1959, the 6812-1 was expected to be a hot item, since Lionel included it in six cataloged sets and offered it for separate sale at $5.95. The 6812 used a red polystyrene flat car (mold 6424-11 or 6511-2) with white heat-stamped lettering in the Cheltenham Bold font. Production for 1959 primarily used the 6424-11 mold, as it likely paralleled the production of the 3419 Operating Helicopter Car (which used the 6511-2). AAR trucks with a three-piece knuckle coupler were the norm and followed the normal progression.

The 6812 came equipped with a polystyrene base and top platform. To meet the demand of 1959 production, both parts were color-coded in various shades of yellow plastic: light yellow (cream), medium yellow (lemon) and dark yellow (mustard). The crank was also color-coded to match the various shades, but sometimes that color is slightly off. The full-color consumer catalog illustrated the 6812 with a yellow base and yellow platform. Two exceptions are found: page 16 (gray base and yellow platform) and page 23 (orange base and orange platform). Regardless of the shade of yellow, the base was heat-stamped with black lettering.

Also included with the 6812 were two blue vinylite figures with painted face and hands. One figure was positioned on the

The five color variations of 6812-1, (left to right on boxes): lemon, mustard, cream, gray over black and black over gray. Front: When in sets, the 6812-25 came unboxed with a 6812-40 packed envelope.

base, while the one to be placed on the top platform was packaged loosely in the box. The base of each figure should have been T-shaped to fit T-shaped areas on both the bottom and top platforms. However, in 1959, closer inspection reveals that these 3562-62 figures weren't originally T-shaped. Apparently, the 3562-62, whose original design had only a single slot on its base, was never modified, and Lionel may have used a hot iron or some other instrument to open up the hole in its base. Lionel corrected this problem in 1960, as the figures were molded with a T-shaped base and were a darker shade of blue (see 6822).

Left: The base of the 1959 figure for the 6812 was opened up by a hot instrument (Type IIP Altered). Right: Figure with "T" shaped opening and a brighter blue (Type IIPT) vinylite.

Of further interest, most of the illustrations in the consumer catalog included arrows pointing up and down. This allowed the reader to understand that the top platform moved up and down.

In 1960, the 6812's busy schedule continued as the 6812-1 was part of two cataloged and several promotional sets and was also offered at the same $5.95 separate-sale price. It also came *unboxed* as a 6812-25 in set 1631WS and promotional set 9745

and retained the same features as 6812-1. With each set a 6812-40 packed envelope was enclosed that included one T-shaped figure and two 81-32 connecting wires. In fact, Lionel Factory Orders for cataloged set 1631WS revealed that 30,000 units were projected for both the boxed set and the envelope.

> **Lionel Production Control Files dated 1-4-60 stated:** "additional parts (6812-40 envelope packed) required to be packed by Outfit Packing Department."

Most importantly, in 1960, the colors of the base and platforms changed. Gray plastic bases with black plastic platforms, or black bases with gray platforms, replaced the all-yellow examples. Regardless of color, the crank that raised or lowered the top platform was color-coded to match that platform. Although the full-color consumer catalog illustrated only the black-over-gray variation, the gray-over-black one was made in 1960. The gray base had black heat-stamped lettering, whereas the black had white lettering.

> **Per Lionel Changes Affecting Future Production dated 5-10-60:**
>
> "Note 1: One half of production to be assembled with black base & nut assembly, gray platform and gray crank handle & screw assembly and the other half with gray base & nut assembly, black platform and black crank handle & screw assembly.
>
> Note 2: For the first 3,000 units only, use a yellow base & nut assembly, yellow platform and yellow crank handle & screw assembly until all inventories are used."

When in set 1631WS, the 6812-25 included a 6812-40 packed envelope with a 3562-62 figure and two wires.

The 6812-1 got a breather in 1961, when it appeared in only one cataloged set and eight promotional sets and the separate-sale price remained the same. The 6812-25 was included only in two promotional sets. Gray platforms over black bases as well as black platforms over gray bases continued to be offered in 1961.

In 1962, left-over inventory of 6812-1s was included with promotional set 19172 for Maritz as well as 254 units as a substitution in cataloged set 13068.

When placed unboxed in a set, the 6812-25 included a 6812-40 packed envelope (envelope no. 6812-41) and a 6821-22 instruction sheet dated 8/59 loose in the set box.

The 6812-1 was component boxed with a car, a 3562-62 figure for the top platform loose in the box, and a 6812-22 instruction sheet dated 8/59.

- For Each Box:
  - Box Dimensions: 3⅜" x 10⅛" x 2⅜"
- Box Style Orange Perforated (1959 - 1960)
  - Tuck Flap Number: 6812-23
  - Box Manufacturer: CCA
- Box Style Orange Picture (1961 - 1962)
  - Tuck Flap Number: 6812-23

The 6812-40 packed envelope (envelope no. 6812-41) included a 3562-62 painted figure and two 81-32 24" RC wires, all in a 4½"x 2½" tan envelope.

Author's Comments: Collectors, dealers and operators have often replaced the 1959 figures (with the *hot iron* modification) because they felt this was not an original Lionel figure. They likely replaced them with T-shaped based figures from the 1960s.

Based on internal Lionel documentation, the true color combinations and the years of their production for the 6812 are now known. Lionel *never* intended any other color combinations than the ones listed in the pricing table. The yellow (cream) platform over the yellow (cream) base is the one that collectors covet.

These cars are very fragile and finding them original in complete, unbroken condition is becoming difficult. The 6812-40 packed envelope is required to complete sets that included 6812-25 and is not included with 6812-1s.

6812		C7	C8	C9	Rarity
Cream Colored Version	-25	200	250	325	R8
	-1	225	300	400	
Lemon Colored Version	-25	125	150	175	R7
	-1	150	200	250	
Mustard Colored Version	-25	100	125	150	R7
	-1	125	175	225	
Black Over Gray Version	-25	100	125	150	R6
	-1	125	175	225	R7
Gray Over Black Version	-25	100	125	150	R6
	-1	125	175	225	R7
6812-40 Envelope		75	100	150	R8

CHAPTER EIGHT

Prototypes, Mock-ups & Factory Errors

In the field of collecting toy trains, nothing excites collectors more than being able to acquire an authentic, preproduction sample of an item that a manufacturer was about to mass produce. At different stages of the life of an item, Lionel would create early, and most often one-of-a-kind, prototypes or mock-ups. These preproduction items were sometimes marked with a sticker stating: "This is a mock-up, not a production line item."

If an item were approved for manufacturing, pilot runs were conducted to ensure that this item was ready for the assembly line.

> A 1960 Lionel Factory Procedures and Bulletins document states, "After approval by Production Engineering, six units are to be given to Quality Inspector for Pilot Run Test."

Finding a preproduction sample is one problem, authenticating it is another. The authors have observed hundreds of preproduction samples, as well as production samples in the Lionel archives. This research allows them to validate many preproduction examples. Other validation techniques include finding a picture of a preproduction item in a publication, such as a magazine, newspaper, or catalog (Lionel or other).

Prototypes, mock-ups, and factory errors provide insights into Lionel's manufacturing processes. Clockwise from left front: 3370 mock-up, 3672 decorating concept test, 6473 factory error not printed on one side, 3435 test shot, and 3361 rubber-stamped upside down.

Left: 3545 mock-up originally on display at Lionel's showroom at the Merchandise Mart in Chicago (notice Lionel "mock-up" label).
Right: 3376 mock-up. Front: A production-run sample of the frame for a 6805 Atomic Energy Disposal Car.

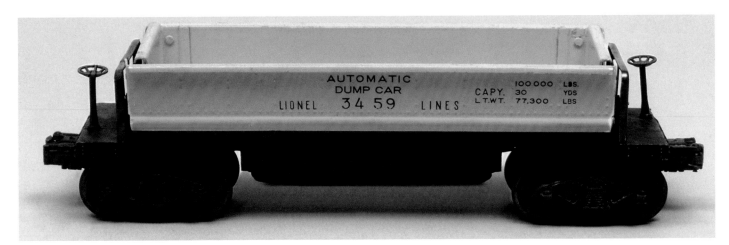

A yellow-painted 3459 Automatic Dumping Ore Car.

The internal Lionel documentation used in compiling this volume also assists in authenticating preproduction samples. Almost everything that Lionel did was recorded on Blueprints, Factory Orders, Production Control Files, Engineering Change Documents, Engineering Projects Progress Reports and the like. Preproduction and decorating samples were often recorded in great detail.

The cover of the December 1948 issue of *Science Illustrated* magazine helps to authenticate the yellow-painted 3459.

The 2089 led a double life: It was the prototype for the 6464 State of Maine Box Car and the mock-up for the 3424 Brakeman Car.

The 1955 advance and accessory catalogs help to authenticate the 2089 State of Maine mock-up. Note the "and" on the door as well as the "2089" number.

Using this information has allowed the authors to further authenticate previously undocumented items. Finding a preproduction item discussed in Lionel documentation often becomes the issue. Still, if you already have the item and the supporting Lionel documentation, this validates its existence.

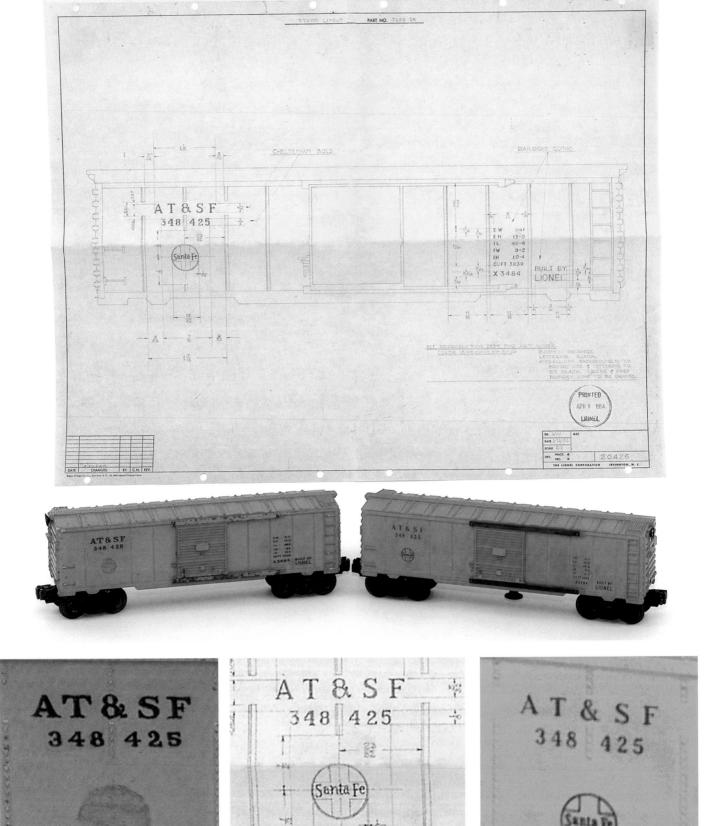

The car on the left is the mock-up of the 3484-25 as authenticated by the original Lionel blueprint. The "AT&SF" printing matches the blueprint, versus the early production 3484-25 (right). Pay particular attention to the "&."

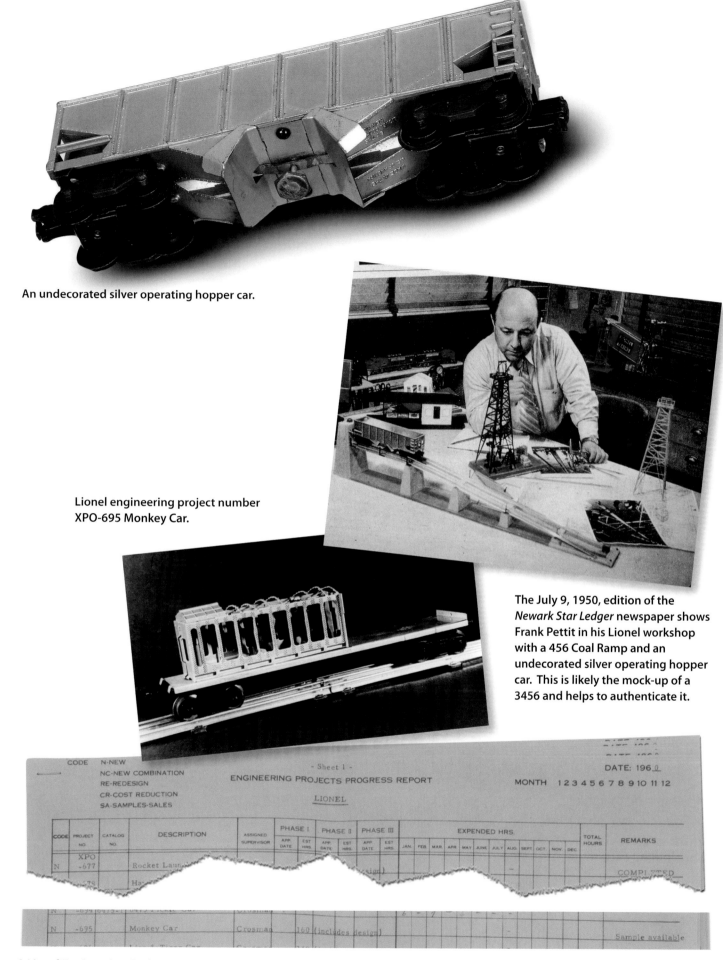

An undecorated silver operating hopper car.

Lionel engineering project number XPO-695 Monkey Car.

The July 9, 1950, edition of the *Newark Star Ledger* newspaper shows Frank Pettit in his Lionel workshop with a 456 Coal Ramp and an undecorated silver operating hopper car. This is likely the mock-up of a 3456 and helps to authenticate it.

A Lionel Engineering Projects Progress Report reveals that a sample of the Monkey Car was made and the "sample available."

3454-series box car paint sample (orange-painted), decorated with Baby Ruth graphics and "X2454" number.

3454-series box car paint sample (silver-painted), decorated with Baby Ruth graphics and "X2454" number.

Two silver-painted 3454-series box car paint samples, with red heat-stamped lettering. The car on the left is decorated with Pennsylvania graphics. The one on the right has "Automatic Merchandise Car." Notice the clear plastic roof hatch on the Pennsylvania car.

Lionel would also take existing production line items and test other color and decorating possibilities. Many of these preproduction items, which never made it into regular production, served their original purpose at Lionel and were destroyed or discarded per Lionel's normal operating procedures. Others survived and were placed in the company's archives. Still others found their way into the collector community, some of which are shown here.

The 3454 Merchandise Car was the first 9¼-inch operating boxcar made during the postwar era. Although a 3454 with red heat-stamped lettering is very rare, Lionel also considered a few other ideas before deciding on mass-producing the silver-painted 3454.

Gray-painted 3562-25 Operating Barrel Car stamped with the black barrel car's "35621" number.

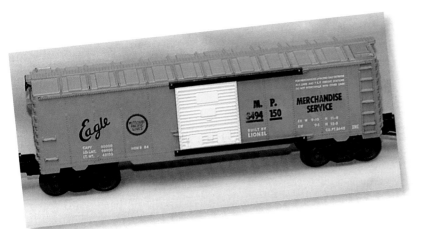

3494-150 paint sample on a non-operating frame.

Other rare or unique paint and decorating samples include a "35621" gray (not black) Operating Barrel Car, a 3494-150 Box Car in blue "on a non-operating frame," and a red 3650 Searchlight Extension Car, which may have been used for the illustration in the 1959 consumer catalog.

The 3650 Searchlight Extension Car with a red-painted frame matches the illustration on page 31 of the 1959 full-color consumer catalog.

Front to back: Undecorated shells, factory-error shells with printing on one side only (note the printing is on the back of cars and not shown), and regular production.

Clockwise from bottom left: 3494-275 with multiple stamping on right, 3562-50 with no printing on one side, 3545 with no stamping on its frame, and 3456 with one clear molded hatch door.

Left side shows preproduction test samples, right side regular production. Front: A 3662 with a gray roof and black plastic door. Middle: A Gray molded shell for 3434. Rear: A Partially decorated 3494-550 Monon Box Car on non-operating frame.

Without a doubt, there are hundreds, if not thousands of legitimate factory-error cars. These have all or part of their printing missing, or were double- or even triple-stamped. Other odd ball cars include undecorated or partially decorated shells. The majority of these left the Lionel factory without a frame or assembly. Included on this and the previous page are a few as a sampling of the many that exist.

Postwar Box Car Types

The 10½-inch 3484-series, 3494-series, 3424 Operating Brakeman Car, 3428 Operating Mail Car and 6352-25 Ice Car all used the same polystyrene plastic box car body as the popular 6464-series of box cars, which Lionel introduced in 1953. During the postwar years, Lionel made many modifications to the tooling used to mold these body shells, both inside and outside the body. Some changes added support, while others helped reduce molding cycles, increasing production efficiency.

A few cars required major changes, such as the roof hatch and ice compartment door on the 6352-25 Ice Car. By far the easiest change to observe is the number of rivets on the exterior sides of the car. Lionel removed or added rivets, thus allowing for more intricate decorating. The doors also underwent at least one change, as the number of "blocks" on the door sides increased.

The 8½-inch plug door box car body shells also underwent similar changes. The 3357 Cop and Hobo Car was the only *operating car* to use these shells. It also had rivets removed and other modifications to the tooling used to mold these shells.

Most of these changes can be dated thus providing an understanding of when specific operating cars were manufactured. Collectors have assigned "Types" to these changes, which are detailed in this Appendix. Lionel Blueprints record the exact dates when these changes occurred and are used in compiling this Appendix.

APPENDIX A
10½ - INCH BOX CAR BODY AND DOOR TYPES

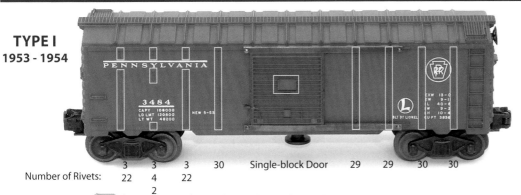

TYPE I
1953 - 1954

Number of Rivets:	3 22	3 4 2	3 22	30	Single-block Door	29	29	30	30

A Type I body shell has four complete rows of rivets to the right of its single-block door. On the left, it has three incomplete and one complete row of rivets.

A Type I door has one large block in the middle of the door and is known as a "single-block" door. These doors were used from 1953 to 1955.

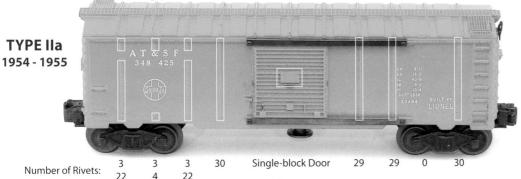

TYPE IIa
1954 - 1955

Number of Rivets:	3 22	3 4	3 22	30	Single-block Door	29	29	0	30

A Type IIa body shell has three complete and one non-existent (removed) row of rivets to the right of its single- or multi-block door. On the left, it has three incomplete and one complete row of rivets. Per Lionel Blueprints, the Type II change occurred on 4-6-54.

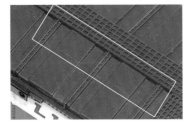

TYPE IIb
1955 - 1958

A Type IIb body shell used the same rivet layout as a Type IIa; the only change relates to the roof. The 6464 mold was modified to provide a roof hatch opening for the 6352-25 Ice Car. Subsequent use of this mold left an outline where the roof hatch insert was placed. Per Lionel Blueprints, the Type IIb change occurred on 3-25-55.

The quickest way to "Type" a 10½-inch operating box car is to look at the number of rivets to the right-hand side of the door. Type I, Type II and Type III/Type IV all differ. The rivets on the left-hand side are relevant in determining the difference between Type III and Type IV.

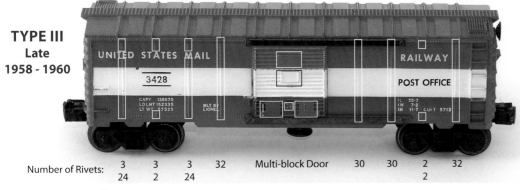

TYPE III
Late
1958 - 1960

Number of Rivets:	3 24	3 2	3 24	32	Multi-block Door	30	30	2 2	32

A Type III body shell has three complete and one incomplete row of rivets to the right of its multi-block door. On the left, it has three incomplete and one complete row of rivets.

A Type II door has four large and one small block on the side of the door and is known as a "multi-block" door. Per Lionel Blueprints, the change occurred on 6-7-55. This door was used until 1969.

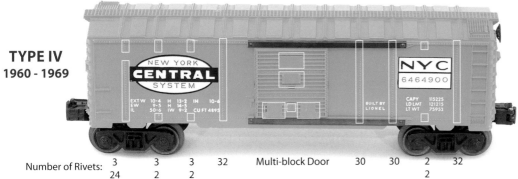

TYPE IV
1960 - 1969

Number of Rivets:	3 24	3 2	3 2	32	Multi-block Door	30	30	2 2	32

A Type IV body shell has three complete and one incomplete row of rivets (same as Type III) to the right of its multi-block door. On the left, it has three incomplete and one complete row of rivets. Per Lionel Blueprints, the Type IV change occurred on 4-4-60.

APPENDIX A
8½ - INCH BOX CAR BODY TYPES

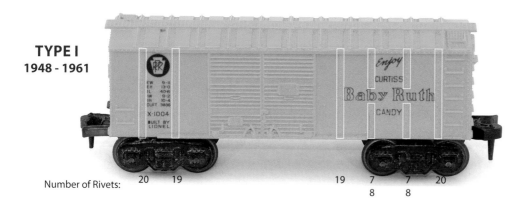

TYPE I
1948 - 1961

Number of Rivets: 20 19   19 7 7 20
                          8 8

A Type I body shell has two complete rows of rivets to the left of its door. On the right, it has two complete and two incomplete rows of rivets.

TYPE IIa
1962

Number of Rivets: 20 19   19 1 1 20
                          2 2

A Type IIa body shell has two complete rows of rivets to the left of its door. On the right, it has two complete and two incomplete (each with 12 less rivets than Type I) rows of rivets. Per Lionel Blueprints, the Type IIa change occurred on 8-22-61.

Holes added for 3357

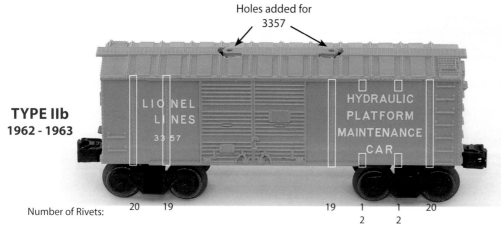

TYPE IIb
1962 - 1963

Number of Rivets: 20 19   19 1 1 20
                          2 2

A Type IIb body shell used the same rivet layout as Type IIa; the only change relates to the roof. The 1004-3 mold was modified to accommodate the gray plastic platform of the 3357 Cop and Hobo Car. Subsequent use of this mold for cars other than the 3357 had plug marks instead of holes. Per Lionel Blueprints, the Type IIb change occurred on 4-10-62.

TYPE III
1963 - 1969

Number of Rivets: 1 1   19 1 1 20
          2 1   2 2

A Type III body shell has two incomplete rows of rivets to the left of its door. On the right, it has two complete and two incomplete rows of rivets (same as Type IIa and IIb). Per Lionel Blueprints, the Type III change occurred on 8-8-63.

Postwar Lionel Boxes

APPENDIX B
DATING POSTWAR INDIVIDUAL ITEM BOXES

ART DECO	ART DECO TOY LOGO	EARLY CLASSIC

ART DECO
1945 - 1946

ART DECO TOY LOGO
VARIATION OF ART DECO
1947 - 1948

EARLY CLASSIC
Early 1948 - 1949

From 1945 - 1946 Art Deco orange and blue boxes were used to package Lionel trains. The term Art Deco was used because the Lionel font resembled the one used on Radio City Music Hall and surrounding building's Art Deco motif.

The most distinguishable feature was that the bold blue lettered Lionel on both sides and end flaps touched the blue border above and below. The company was listed as The Lionel Corporation in New York, Chicago and San Francisco. Item numbers were listed on both sides, the top and bottom. The overall cardboard had a heavier textured feel.

In 1947 and 1948 Lionel used an Art Deco Toy Logo box. This was an exact copy of the Art Deco box except it included the Toy Manufacturers Association Logo on top of the box.

In early 1948 and 1949 Lionel used the Early Classic orange and blue box. This style of box and subsequent variations were in use for over ten years, making it one of the most recognizable boxes of the Postwar era. The most distinguishable feature from previous boxes is that the blue lettered Lionel on both sides and end flaps no longer touched the blue border above and below. All other features remained the same. The company was still listed as The Lionel Corporation in New York, Chicago and San Francisco. Item numbers were listed on both sides, the top and bottom of the boxes.

The Lionel Corporation touches the blue borders.
Item number on both sides, top and bottom.
New York, Chicago and San Francisco.

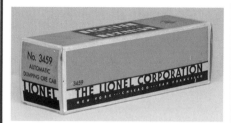

The Lionel Corporation touches the blue borders.
Item number on both sides, top and bottom.
New York, Chicago and San Francisco.

The Lionel Corporation does not touch the blue borders.
Item number on both sides, top and bottom.
New York, Chicago and San Francisco.

Item number on top and bottom (above) and sides (below).

Toy Manufacturers Association Logo on top.

Item number on bottom (above) and sides (below).

Toy Manufacturers Association Logo on top.

Item number on bottom (above) and sides (below).

Toy Manufacturers Association Logo on top.

Changes from previous style shown in red.

APPENDIX B
DATING POSTWAR INDIVIDUAL ITEM BOXES

1949	1955	1956	1958

MIDDLE CLASSIC
Late 1949 - 1955

From Late 1949 - 1955 Lionel used a Middle Classic style box. This box was the same as the Early Classic, except San Francisco was eliminated from the box sides due to Lionel closing their San Francisco sales office.

In 1950 the box part number (previously not shown) began to appear on the tuck flap. In 1955 individual item boxes were redesigned to eliminate or simplify individual inserts and liners. This cheapening of the packaging process led to both smaller item boxes and different box variations.

The Lionel Corporation does not touch the blue borders.
Item number on both sides, top and bottom.
New York and Chicago (No San Francisco).

Toy Manufacturers Association Logo and item number on top.

Item number on bottom (above) and sides (below).

LATE CLASSIC
Late 1955 - 1958

From late 1955 - 1958 Lionel used a Late Classic style box. This box was the same as the Middle Classic except the item number was eliminated from the box sides, top and bottom.

There is also a Late Classic Generic (not shown) a box used in Late 1955 - 1956. These boxes were purchased blank and rubber-stamped as needed. No. 6464-275 (box part no. 12-6) is one notable example.

The Lionel Corporation does not touch the blue borders.
Item number eliminated from both sides, top and bottom.
New York and Chicago (No San Francisco)

Toy Manufacturers Association Logo and no item number on top.

No Item number on bottom (above) and sides (below).

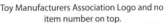

OPS CLASSIC
VARIATION OF MIDDLE CLASSIC
1952

In 1952 Lionel used an OPS Classic style box. This box was the same as the Middle Classic, except it was printed with an Office of Price Stabilization (OPS) price. These "retail ceiling" prices were required due to high inflation during the Korean War. OPS stickers first appeared in 1951 and were used internally and also provided to dealers for items already in the channel.

OPS Logo and price on top.
The Lionel Corporation does not touch the blue borders.
Item number on both sides, top and bottom.
New York and Chicago (No San Francisco)

OPS Logo and price on top.

BOLD CLASSIC
VARIATION OF LATE CLASSIC
1958

In 1958 Lionel used a Bold Classic style box for part of the product line. This box had the same graphics as Late Classic, except the item number and description were printed in dark bold blue lettering on the end flaps.

Dark blue bold font on end flaps.

Lionel Corporation does not touch the blue borders.
Item number eliminated from both sides, top and bottom.
New York and Chicago (No San Francisco).

GLOSSY CLASSIC
VARIATION OF LATE CLASSIC
1959 - 1961

From 1958 - 1961 Lionel used a Glossy Classic style box. This box had the same graphics as Late Classic, except it was printed on a glossy coated cardboard versus the textured cardboard used in the past. This box was only used for a few items, two examples include the no. 55 Tie-Jector (1959) and no. 3366-100 Figures for Circus Car (1959).

Glossy coated card stock.

The Lionel Corporation does not touch the blue borders.
Item number eliminated from both sides, top and bottom.
New York and Chicago (No San Francisco).

| 1959 | 1960 | | 1961 | 1962 | | 1963 |

ORANGE PERFORATED
1959 - 1960

From 1959 - 1960 Lionel used an Orange Perforated style box. This new design coincided with the introduction of individually boxed display pack outfits. The perforated top allowed dealers to punch out the top perforated panel and display items individually or within a display outfit. The graphics were printed on glossy coated stock. The company was listed as The Lionel Corporation in New York and Chicago on the box top and sides. The bottom included a Lionel Lion graphic.

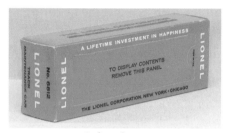

Perforated top.
The Lionel Corporation New York and Chicago.

Lion graphic on bottom.

The Lionel Corporation New York and Chicago on sides.
Made in USA on one side.

ORANGE PICTURE
1961 - 1965

From 1961 - 1965 Lionel used an Orange Picture style box. This box was the same as Orange Perforated but eliminated the punch out and in its place included new top panel graphics. It was also a lighter shade of orange. The graphics were of a 4-6-4 Steamer and F3 and were also used for a new version of hinged display pack outfits. The company was listed as The Lionel Corporation in New York and Chicago on the top and sides. The bottom included a Lionel Lion graphic.

Solid (no perforations) top.
4-6-4 Steamer and F3 graphic.
The Lionel Corporation New York and Chicago.

Lion graphic on bottom.

ORANGE PERFORATED PICTURE
VARIATION OF ORANGE PICTURE
1961 - 1962

From 1961 - 1962 Lionel used an Orange Perforated Picture style box for some items. It used the same graphics as Orange Picture except it was printed on leftover Orange Perforated cardboard. It has been observed on some rolling stock items, but most often can be found with 2500 series presidential passenger cars.

Perforated top.
Same graphics as Orange Picture.
The Lionel Corporation New York and Chicago.

Lion graphic on bottom.

The Lionel Corporation New York and Chicago on sides.
Made in USA on one side.

ORANGE NON PERFORATED
VARIATION OF ORANGE PERFORATED
1963

In 1963 Lionel used an Orange Non Perforated style box. It was the same as the Orange Perforated except without the perforations. It has only been observed on the no. 6827 Harnischfeger power shovel car.

Orange Perforated graphics but no perforations.
The Lionel Corporation New York and Chicago.

HILLSIDE ORANGE PICTURE
VARIATION OF ORANGE PICTURE
1963 - 1965

From 1963 - 1965 Lionel used a Hillside Orange Picture style box. This box was the same as Orange Picture, except the company was now listed as The Lionel Toy Corporation on the top and sides. This reflected the change in corporate structure that took place in 1963. New York and Chicago were replaced with the location of the factory, Hillside, N.J. on the top of box only, not the sides. Only one 1963 item the no. 6429 work caboose used this new box. Over time, as old boxes were depleted, new boxes were printed with this new artwork.

APPENDIX B
DATING POSTWAR INDIVIDUAL ITEM BOXES

1963	**1964**	**1965**

The Lionel Corporation New York and Chicago on sides.
Made in USA on one side.

In 1964 a variation of the Orange Picture box exists where the top panel white corners are more rounded than normal.

From 1964 - 1965 the texture of the cardboard changed for some items. The cardboard felt stiffer and more brittle than in the past. Some items also have a lighter shade of orange.

DARK ORANGE PICTURE
VARIATION ORANGE PICTURE
1963

In 1963 Lionel used a Dark Orange Picture style box. This box was the same as the Orange Picture except it was printed using a darker shade of orange. New and repeat item boxes printed in 1963 were all this color. Most boxes were dated on the inside flap as being manufactured in 1963.

From 1961 - 1965 if an item came in a longer Orange Picture box, this led to a full or partial repeat of the 4-6-4 and F3 graphic.

From 1964 - 1965 the new Lionel double arrow oval logo which was introduced in 1963 replaced the Lionel lion on the bottom of some Hillside Orange Picture boxes.

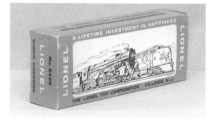

Solid (no perforations) top.
4-6-4 Steamer and F3 graphic.
The Lionel Toy Corporation, Hillside, N.J.

Lion graphic on bottom.

The Lionel Toy Corporation.
No mention of location.
Made in USA on one side.

New Lionel double arrow oval logo on bottom.

145

APPENDIX B
DATING POSTWAR INDIVIDUAL ITEM BOXES

1966 | 1967

CELLOPHANE WINDOW
1966

In 1966 Lionel used a Cellophane Window style box. This redesigned box provided a window in which the item could be viewed without removing it from the box. The window was cut into the top of the box and covered with flimsy cellophane. Following a practice that began with outfit boxes in 1961, these boxes were generic in that the item number was not preprinted by the box manufacturer, but rubber-stamped by Lionel.

The graphics now included the phrase The Leader in Model Railroading on the top and sides. The company name remained The Lionel Toy Corporation, Hillside, N.J. and appeared on the sides. The bottom had the Lionel double arrow oval logo.

**Viewing window covered with cellophane.
The Leader in Model Railroading.
Generic rubber-stamped box.**

Lionel double arrow oval logo on bottom.

The Lionel Toy Corporation, **Hillside, N.J.**
Made in USA on one side.
The Leader in Model Railroading.

PLAIN WHITE
LATE 1960's

During the late 1960's Lionel used a Plain White style box. These boxes were undecorated with rubber-stamped or occasionally preprinted item numbers. They were most likely used when stock regularly decorated boxes were depleted.

Plain white cardboard box.
Rubber-stamped number.

NO BOXED PRODUCTION
1967

During 1967, there was no cataloged train production and all promotional train outfits assembled came with unboxed items. There were no new box designs in 1967.

APPENDIX B
DATING POSTWAR INDIVIDUAL ITEM BOXES

1968	1969

HAGERSTOWN CHECKERBOARD
1968 - 1969

In 1968 and 1969 Lionel used a Hagerstown Checkerboard style box. This was the final new Postwar design that accompanied Lionel's move of production to the Lionel Porter factory in Hagerstown, Maryland.

The orange box had Lionel printed in a "checkerboard" pattern that wrapped around the top, bottom and both sides. The majority of these boxes were generic with the item number rubber-stamped on the side. Many items shared the same size box and were padded using what Lionel called bogus paper (Kraft paper). A few items had their own preprinted boxes. The company name was listed as The Lionel Toy Corporation, Hagerstown, Maryland on the end flaps.

HILLSIDE CHECKERBOARD
1969

In 1969 Lionel used a Hillside Checkerboard style box. This box was exactly the same as Hagerstown Checkerboard except the company location was changed from Hagerstown, Maryland to Hillside, New Jersey on the end flaps. This reflected the move back to the Hillside location. Lionel had to leave Hagerstown because Porter's Chemistry line was sold in January 1969 and by March, the entire Porter company sold. Even though the Hillside building was for sale, it was not sold until September 1969.

Checkerboard Lionel pattern.
Rubber-stamped item number.

Checkerboard Lionel pattern.
Rubber-stamped item number.

Checkerboard Lionel pattern wraps around bottom and sides.

Checkerboard Lionel pattern wraps around bottom and sides.

The Lionel Toy Corporation, Hagerstown, Maryland on both ends.

The Lionel Toy Corporation, Hillside, New Jersey on both ends.

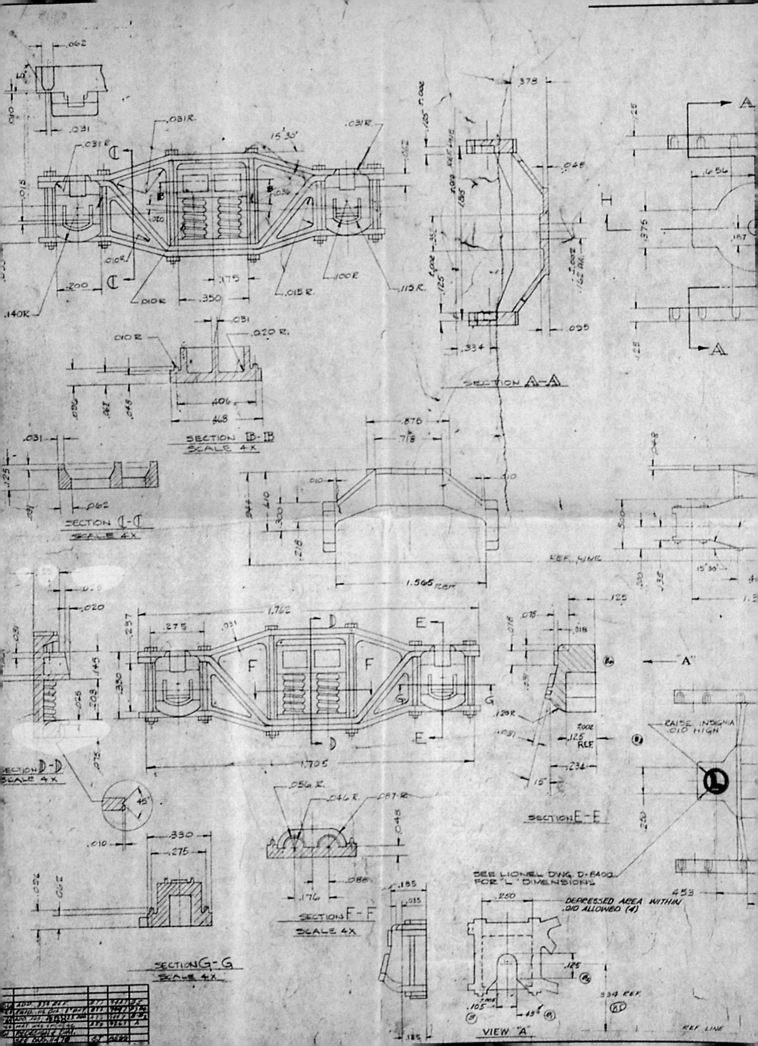

Postwar
Trucks & Couplers

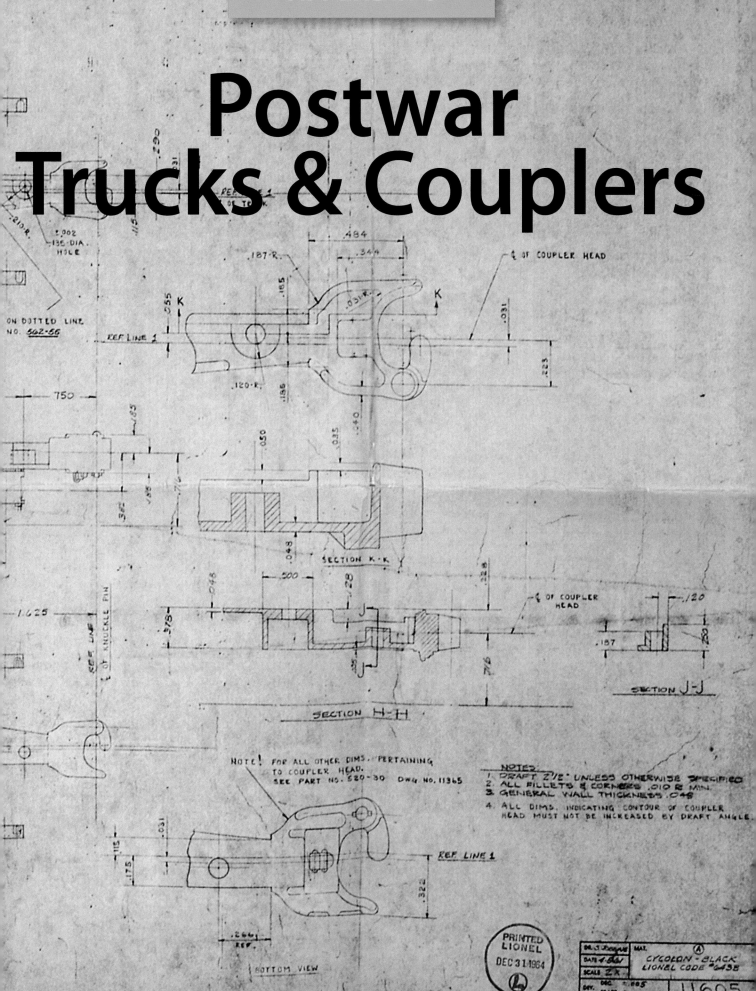

APPENDIX C
DATING POSTWAR TRUCKS AND COUPLERS
STAPLE END AND SCOUT TRUCKS

| 1945 | 1946 | 1947 | 1948 | 1949 | 1950 | 1951 | 1952 | - | 1955 |

STAPLE END TRUCKS

STAPLE END TRUCKS

STAPLE END TRUCKS

METAL FRAME TRUCKS
WITH DIE CAST "STAPLE" ATTACHED SIDES

From 1945 - 1951 metal frame trucks with die cast sides were used for rolling stock. The die cast sides were attached to the truck's metal frame so that when viewed from the side, it appeared that they were stapled together. Staple end trucks first appeared with coil couplers and later with magnetic couplers.

STAPLE END TRUCKS WITH COIL COUPLERS

Two versions of staple end coil couplers exist. They are categorized by the way the coupler was attached to the truck.

Swedging - An operation to attach the base plate to the coupler. Used on all metal trucks

Staking - First appeared in late 1946

STAPLE END
COIL COUPLERS

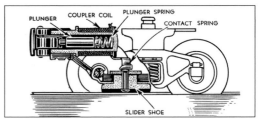

PLUNGER   COUPLER COIL   PLUNGER SPRING   CONTACT SPRING

SLIDER SHOE

From 1945 - 1948 couplers were opened by an electromagnet whose coil was integrated on the coupler, hence the name "Coil" coupler. Electricity passes from the track to the slider shoe. When activated, the plunger spring contracts pulling the plunger back, thus releasing the knuckle.

From 1945 - mid 1946 the coil coupler was attached to the metal coupler bracket.

From mid 1946 - 1948 the coil coupler was attached to a bottom frame assembly which was then attached to the trucks.

STAPLE END TRUCKS WITH MAGNETIC COUPLERS

STAPLE END
MAGNETIC COUPLERS

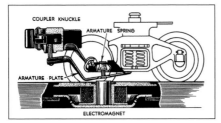

COUPLER KNUCKLE

ARMATURE SPRING

ARMATURE PLATE

ELECTROMAGNET

From 1948 - 1951 couplers were opened by an electromagnet in the uncoupling track section. When the track section was activated, the trucks metal armature plate was pulled down, thus releasing the knuckle.

Flared end of rivet is visible. This feature appeared from 1948 into 1950.

From 1948 - 1951 staple end trucks used magnetic couplers.

SCOUT TRUCKS

SCOUT TRUCKS

METAL FRAME TRUCKS
WITH PLASTIC SIDES

From 1948 - 1952 metal frame trucks with plastic sides were used for low end starter outfits known as "Scout" outfits. The coupler on these trucks were not compatible with regular postwar knuckle couplers. Scout couplers can be converted to magnetic knuckle couplers by adding a no. 480-25 magnetic coupler conversion kit.

SEMI SCOUT TRUCKS
METAL FRAME TRUCKS
WITH PLASTIC SIDES
NOT SHOWN

From 1952 - 1955 metal frame trucks with plastic sides and a "coupler frame complete" attached to the trucks were used in a few low end starter outfits. This allowed Scout style truck frames to be compatible with regular postwar knuckle couplers.

1951	1952	1953	1954	1955	1956	1957	1958	1959	1960	1961	-	1969

BAR END TRUCKS
METAL FRAME TRUCKS
WITH DIE CAST "BAR" ATTACHED SIDES

BAR END
MAGNETIC COUPLERS

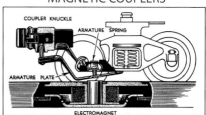

From late 1951 - 1961 and 1969 metal frame trucks with die cast sides were used for rolling stock. The die cast sides were attached to the metal frame via a process that resembled a bar sticking through the side of the truck. Bar end trucks always came with magnetic couplers. Two major variations exist based on how the truck was attached to the frame; either by a pivot stud or mounting clip.

From 1957 through 1961 Bar End trucks were being replaced with plastic AAR trucks. Only a few newly issued items appear with bar end trucks in 1958. From 1959 through 1961, Bar End trucks are used for newly issued operating cars requiring sliding pickup shoes and some items requiring roller pickup shoes. This occurred because the AAR pickup shoe replacement was not yet available and the roller pickup version was in transition.

All bar end couplers were opened by an electromagnet in the uncoupling track section. When the track section was activated, the trucks metal armature plate was pulled down, thus releasing the knuckle.

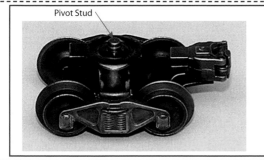

Pivot Stud

From late 1951 - 1961 bar end trucks were attached to the frame using a pivot stud. The pivot stud was held in place by a horseshoe shaped retaining washer.

MOUNTING CLIP

CAR FRAME

From 1955 - 1958 and 1969 bar end trucks were attached to the trains frame using a mounting clip. The mounting clip came in different sizes based on the frame thickness.

Truck Mounting Clips are made in three sizes to fit different car frames. For easy identification they are colored as shown

PART NO.	COLOR	"A"
6257-10	GREEN	.085
600-15	ALUMINUM	.100
1002-6	BLACK	.145

In 1953 couplers had a smooth knuckle top versus engraving.

In 1957 a support hole was added to the coupler drawbar.

In 1955 the armature assembly was changed adding a small tab to ease in manual uncoupling.

During late 1955, the knuckle pin changed from black to silver.

BAR END TRUCKS & Couplers

BAR END TRUCKS

BAR END WITH PIVOT STUD

BAR END WITH MOUNTING CLIP

BAR END OTHER FEATURES

APPENDIX C
DATING POSTWAR TRUCKS AND COUPLERS
AAR (TIMKEN) TRUCKS

1957	1958	1959	1960	1961	1962	1963	1964	1965	1966 - 1969

AAR (TIMKEN) TRUCKS
PLASTIC FRAME TRUCKS

From 1957 - 1969 one piece molded plastic trucks modeled after AAR (Association of American Railroads) trucks with Timken bearings were used. The trucks had Timken molded into the side and are also sometimes called Timken trucks.

AAR couplers were opened by an electromagnet uncoupling track section. When activated, a small metal disk shaped armature attached to the truck frame via an armature pin is pulled down along with the spring assembly, thus releasing the knuckle. This disk has also led to the name disk operating coupler. AAR trucks included operating and dummy (fixed) couplers.

AAR TRUCKS

Early AAR 1957 - 1961	Middle AAR 1961 - 1963/64	Late AAR 1964/1965 -1969
Die Cast Knuckle and Closed Journal Boxes	Delrin (Early or Late) Knuckle and Closed Journal Boxes	Late Delrin Knuckle and Open Journal Boxes

AAR JOURNAL BOXES

In 1963 dummy (fixed) couplers, Journal Boxes were closed.

From 1964 - 1969 for dummy (fixed) couplers and 1965 - 1969 for operating couplers, Journal Boxes were open.

From 1957 - 1964 operating couplers Journal Boxes were closed.

AAR KNUCKLES

From 1957 - 1961 a die cast knuckle with knuckle spring mounted by a knuckle pin or rivet was the norm.

Integrated pivot points   Notice shape of cam

Integrated leaf spring

"Early Delrin Knuckle"

In 1961 - 1962 a one piece Delrin plastic knuckle (Part no. 566-27) with integrated leaf spring and pivot points replaced the die cast knuckle. This was most often used with the metal Leaf Spring Assembly with Lancing. Although it has also been observed with the metal Leaf Spring with no Lancing.

"Late Knuckle"

From 1962 - 1969 another version of one piece Delrin plastic knuckle (Part no. 566-54) with integrated leaf spring was used. The shape of cam changed for the new metal Leaf Spring Assembly with no lancing. It was most often used with this Leaf Spring Assembly, although it has also been observed with the Leaf Spring with lancing.

In 1963 and 1964, some rolling stock had Delrin knuckle with an integral copper spring. This design improvement did not last more than a year.

AAR LEAF SPRING ASSEMBLY

From 1957 - 1962 the leaf spring assembly had lancing and a smaller rivet hole.

LANCING

LARGER RIVET HOLE
NO LANCING

From 1962 - 1969 the leaf spring assembly had no lancing and a larger rivet hole. This redesign improved the locking and release of the coupler knuckles.

AAR WHEELS

From 1957 - 1961 the wheel hubs were flush with the wheel surface. These were used with truck frames that had pads on the sides.

WHEEL HUB PROJECTS ABOVE WHEEL SURFACE

From 1962 the wheel hubs were raised above the wheel surface. These were used with truck frames that had smooth sides.

AAR PLASTIC SIDE FRAME

From 1957 - 1961 AAR trucks had pads on inner surfaces of truck side frames, Part no. 560-1.

From 1962 - 1969 AAR trucks had smooth inner surfaces on the truck side frames. This helped improve the molding process, Part no. 560-50.

AAR OTHER FEATURES

In 1960 notches appeared on top of some side frames. The inner pads also changed accordingly.

From 1961 - 1969 Delrin couplers show different levels of reddish tint instead of black.

In 1966 some trucks had a washer above or below the leaf spring rivet.

1959	1960	1961	1962	1963

ARCHBAR COIL SPRING TRUCKS
PLASTIC FRAME TRUCKS

From 1959 - 1963 plastic trucks were styled after old fashioned archbar coil spring trucks. Originally designed for the General Outfits, they emulate trains of the Civil War period. They follow the same progression of changes as AAR trucks. Archbar trucks included operating, dummy (fixed) and plain (no coupler) couplers, although most cars come with dummy couplers. Operating coupler examples include nos. 3370, 1872T and 1877. The operating couplers on nos. 1875, 1875W and 1876 were actually plain archbar trucks with an entirely separate coupler assembly. All Archbar couplers had closed journal boxes.

Archbar operating coupler side view.

From 1959 - 1962 Archbar operating couplers were used. Bottom view with die cast knuckle and knuckle spring both mounted by a knuckle pin. This also included a metal leaf spring assembly with lancing.

From 1959 - 1963 Archbar dummy couplers were used.

Postwar Trucks & Couplers

ARCHBAR TRUCKS

APPENDIX C
DATING POSTWAR TRUCKS AND COUPLERS
SIX WHEEL, 2400 SERIES AND 2500 SERIES TRUCKS

1946	1947	1948	1949	1950	1951	1952	1953	1954	1955-1966

SIX WHEEL TRUCKS

SIX WHEEL TRUCKS
METAL FRAME TRUCKS
WITH PLASTIC SIDES

From 1946 - 1951 six wheel metal frame trucks with plastic sides were used for Madison Pullman "2625" series cars along with the no. 2460 crane car and nos. 2571W and 2426W tenders. All versions include coil couplers.

2400 SERIES TRUCKS

2400 SERIES TRUCKS
METAL FRAME TRUCKS
WITH DIE CAST SIDES

From 1948 - 1966 metal trucks with detailed die cast side frames were used for 2400 series passenger cars and the no. 6517 caboose. 2400 series trucks first appeared with coil couplers and later with magnetic couplers.

From 1948 - 1953 coil couplers were used.

From 1954 - 1966 magnetic couplers were used.

2500 SERIES TRUCKS

2500 SERIES TRUCKS
METAL FRAME TRUCKS
WITH DIE CAST SIDES

From 1952 - 1966 metal trucks with die cast side frames were used for 2500 series passenger cars. 2500 series trucks always utilized magnetic style couplers.

From 1952 - 1966 magnetic couplers were used.

Operating Car Peripherals

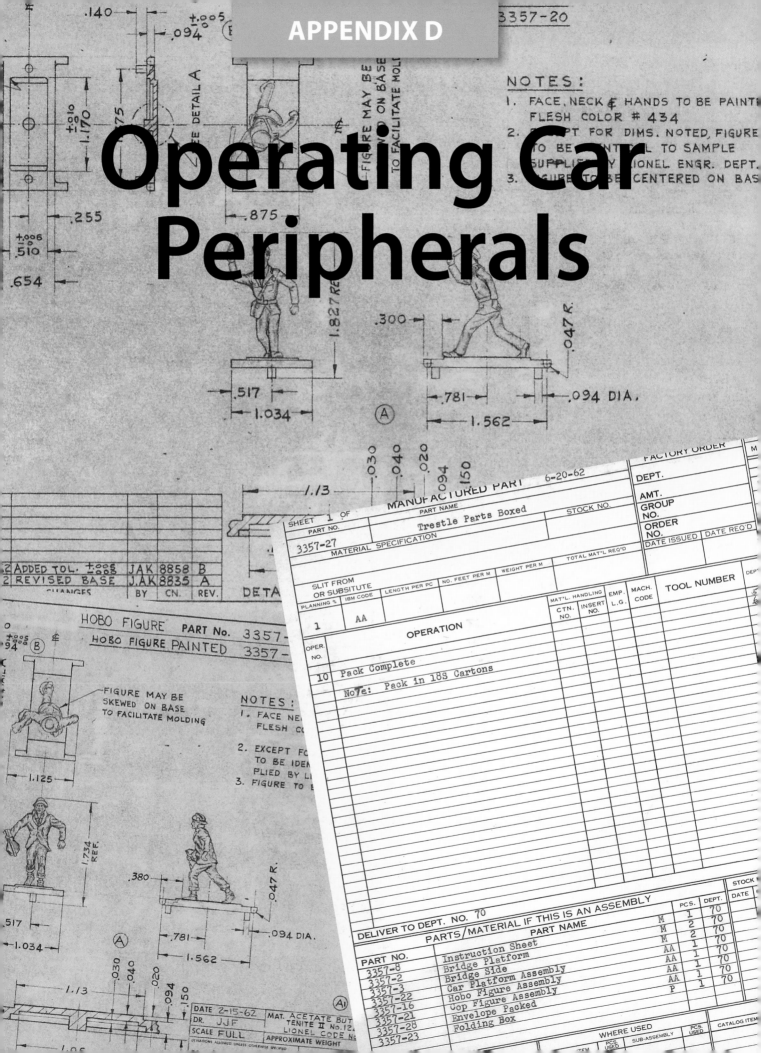

APPENDIX D
OPERATING CAR PERIPHERALS

Catalog Number	Years Offered for Sale	Instruction Sheet	Date	Packed Envelope Number	Envelope Number	Packed Boxes and Other Peripherals	Insert / Liner	Comments
3356-1	56 - 58	3356-78	9/56 5/57	3356-77	3356-79	3356-100	Liner 3356-72	Service Station leaflet 927-56 included in component box (56 only)
3356-1	59 - 60	3366-33	5/59	3366-34	3356-79	3356-100	Liner 3356-72	Envelope number same, but contents changed (see description in volume)
3356-1	64 - 66	3356-78	6/64 6/65	3356-77	3356-79	3356-100	Liner 3356-72	3356-100 in white box
3356-1	66	3356-78	6/65	3356-77	3356-79	3356-100	Liner 3356-72	Includes corral adjustment flyer 3356-112 dated 10/66; 3356-100 in white box
3356-2	56 - 57	none	None	none	none	none	none	
3356-100	56 - 59	none	None	none	none	none	none	
3356-110	66	3356-111	8/66	3356-77	3356-79	3356-100	Liner 3356-72	Includes corral adjustment flyer 3356-112 dated 10/66; 3356-100 in white box
3356-150	56 - 57	none	None	none	none	3356-100	Insert 3356-80	
3357-1	62 and 65	3357-8	9/62 (1-Year Warranty)	3357-28	3357-29	3357-27	none	Instruction sheet in peripheral box
3357-1	63 - 64	3357-8	9/62 (90-Day Warranty)	3357-28	3357-29	3357-27	none	Instruction sheet in peripheral box
3357-25	62 and 65	3357-8	9/62 (1-Year Warranty)	3357-28	3357-29	3357-27	none	Operating peripherals included loose in sets
3357-25	63 - 65	3357-8	9/62 (90-Day Warranty)	3357-28	3357-29	3357-27	none	Operating peripherals included loose in sets
3359	55 - 58	3359-79	9/55 12/55	3359-80	3359-78	160-2 Long Bin; 207-1 Artificial Coal	Insert 3359-76	
3361	55 - 61	3361-29	9/55 2/56 3/56 6/57 6/58	none	none	160-2 Long Bin	Insert 3361-26; Insert 3361-35	Five 3361-21 5" long x ⁷⁄₁₆" diameter stained logs included
3361X	55 - 61	3361-29	9/55 2/56 3/56 6/57 6/58	none	none	none	none	Five 3361-21 5" long x ⁷⁄₁₆" diameter stained logs included; 160-2 Long Bin included loose in sets
3362-1	61 - 63 and 65	3362-15	6/61	none	none	none	none	Three 3362-14 silver helium tanks included
3362-25	61 - 62	3362-15	6/61	none	none	none	none	Three 3362-14 silver helium tanks included; Instruction sheet included loose in sets
3362 / 3364	69	3364-10	4/65	none	none	none	none	Three 3362-14 helium tanks or three 3364-8 stained logs included
3364-1	65 - 66 and 68	3364-10	4/65	none	none	none	none	Three 3364-8 6" long x ⅝" diameter stained logs included
3364-25	64 - 67	3364-10	6/64 4/65	none	none	none	none	Three 3364-8 6" long x ⅝" diameter stained logs included; Instruction sheet included loose in sets
3366	59 - 61	3366-33	5/59	3366-34	3356-79	3366-100	Liner 3356-72	See 3356 listing for packed envelope information
3366-100	59 - 60	none	none	none	none	none	none	
3370-1	61 - 65	3370-17	6/61	none	none	none	none	Instruction sheet variation; (see description in volume)
3370-25	61 - 63	3370-17	6/61	none	none	none	none	Instruction sheet included loose in set
3376-1	60 - 65 and 69	3376-117	6/60 1/61	3376-118	3376-119	none	Tube 6809-12	3376-117 included in 3376-118 packed envelope
3376-25	60 - 62	3376-117	6/60 1/61	3376-118	3376-119	none	none	3376-117 included in 3376-118 packed envelope and included loose in sets
3376-150	62 - 63 and 65	3376-117	1/61	3376-118	3376-119	none	none	3376-117 included in 3376-118 packed envelope and included loose in sets
3376-160	62 - 65 and 69	3376-117	1/61	3376-118	3376-119	none	Tube 6809-12	3376-117 included in 3376-118 packed envelope
3386-1	60	3376-117	6/60	3376-118	3376-119	none	none	3376-117 included in 3376-118 packed envelope
3386-10	60	3376-117	6/60	3376-118	3376-119	none	Tube 6809-12	3376-117 included in 3376-118 packed envelope
3386-25	60	3376-117	6/60	3376-118	3376-119	none	none	3376-117 included in 3376-118 packed envelope and included loose in sets

APPENDIX D
OPERATING CAR PERIPHERALS

Catalog Number	Years Offered for Sale	Instruction Sheet	Date	Packed Envelope Number	Envelope Number	Packed Boxes and Other Peripherals	Insert / Liner	Comments
3424	56 - 58	3424-95	8/56 5/57	3424-93	3424-94	3424-100	Insert 3424-90	Service Station leaflet 927 dated 55 or 56 included in the component box
3424-75	56 - 57	3424-95	8/56 5/57	3424-96	3424-97	none	none	Single pole accessory only for separate sale
3424-100	56 - 58	3424-95	8/56 5/57	3424-93	3424-94	none	none	Two pole accessory comes with car or for separate sale
3428	59 - 60	3428-23	8/59	none	none	none	none	Mailbag included inside box car
3434	59 - 60 and 64 - 65	3434-21	8/59	none	none	none	none	64 instruction sheet has 90-day warranty and Lionel Toy Corporation but is dated 8/59.
3434	66	3434-21	5/66	none	none	none	none	
3434-50	n/a	n/a	n/a	none	none	none	none	Not manufactured
3435	59 - 62	3435-33	8/59	none	none	none	none	
3444	57 - 60	3444-33	5/57 5/59	none	none	none	none	Yellow instruction sheet in 57 and white in 58 (both dated 5/57)
3451	46 - 48	3451-27	5/46 5/47 2/48 4/48	none	none	160-1 Short Bin	Liner 3541-40	Five 164-64 4⅝" long x ⁷⁄₁₆" diameter unstained logs included
3454	46	3454-57	5/46	Unknown	3454-51	none	Liner Number Unknown	Car wrapped in brown tissue paper
3454	47	3454-57	5/47	Unknown	3454-51	none	Liner Number Unknown	Car wrapped in brown tissue paper
3456	50 - 55	none	none	none	none	none	none	Operating instructions included only with 456 Coal Ramp Set
3459	46	3459-28	5/46 7/46	none	none	160-1 Short Bin; 207-1 Artificial Coal	Liner 3459-26	May also come with metal bin
3459	47 - 48	3451-27	5/47 2/48 4/48	none	none	160-1 Short Bin; 207-1 Artificial Coal	Liner 3459-26	
3461	49 - 53	3461-11	2/49 11/49 2/50 3/50 4/50 9/50 10/51 2/52 2/53	none	none	160-1 Short Bin	Liner 3541-40	Five 164-64 4⅝" long x ⁷⁄₁₆" diameter unstained (until 49) and stained logs afterwards included
3461X	49 - 53	3461-11	2/49 11/49 2/50 3/50 4/50 9/50 10/51 2/52 2/53	none	none	none	none	Five 164-64 4⅝" long x ⁷⁄₁₆" diameter unstained (until '49) and stained logs afterwards included; 160-1 Short Bin included looses in sets
3461-25	54 - 55	3461-11	1/54	none	none	160-1 Short Bin	Liner 3461-20	Five 164-64 4⅝" long x ⁷⁄₁₆" diameter stained logs included; May also come with 160-2 Long Bin
3461X-25	54 - 55	3461-11	1/54	none	none	none	none	Five 164-64 4⅝" long x ⁷⁄₁₆" diameter stained logs included; 160-1 Short or 160-2 Long Bin included loose in sets
3462	47	3462-67	No Date	none	none	3462-70 Type I or Type II	Liner 3462-66	
3462	48	3462-67	No Date and 1/48	none	none	3462-70 Type I or Type II	Insert 3462-91	1/48 instruction sheet is white or blue
3462P-25	52 - 55	none	none	none	none	none	Insert 3472-80	
3462-70	52 - 59	none	none	none	none	none	TP24 Tissue Paper	Lionel intended production was five milk cans and TP24 - 3" x 3" tissue paper to fill gap in box (52 - 59)
3464-1 NYC	49	3464-28	3/49	none	none	none	Insert 3464-29	3464-29 is a truck alignment corrugated insert 8" long x 1" wide
3464-1 NYC	50 - 51	3464-28	1/50 9/50 4/5 10/51	none	none	none	Insert 3464-29	3464-29 is a truck alignment corrugated insert 8" long x 1" wide
3464-1 NYC	52	3474-14	5/52	none	none	none	Insert 3464-29	3464-29 is a truck alignment corrugated insert 8" long x 1" wide
3464-50 SF	49	3464-28	3/49	none	none	none	Insert 3464-29	3464-29 is a truck alignment corrugated insert 8" long x 1" wide
3464-50 SF	50 - 51	3464-28	1/50 9/50 4/5 10/51	none	none	none	Insert 3464-29	3464-29 is a truck alignment corrugated insert 8" long x 1" wide

Operating Car Peripherals

Catalog Number	Years Offered for Sale	Instruction Sheet	Date	Packed Envelope Number	Envelope Number	Packed Boxes and Other Peripherals	Insert / Liner	Comments
3464-50 SF	52	3474-14	5/52	none	none	none	Insert 3464-29	3464-29 is a truck alignment corrugated insert 8" long x 1" wide
3469	49 - 53	3461-11	2/49 11/49 2/50 3/50 4/50 9/50 10/51 2/52 2/53	none	none	160-1 Short Bin; 207-1 Artificial Coal	Liner 3459-26	
3469	54 - 55	3461-11	1/54	none	none	160-1 Short Bin; 207-1 Artificial Coal	Liner 3469-20	May also come with 160-2 Long Bin
3469X	49 - 53	3461-11	2/49 11/49 2/50 3/50 4/50 9/50 10/51 2/52 2/53	none	none	207-1 Artificial Coal	none	160-1 Short Bin included loose in sets
3469X	54 - 55	3461-11	1/54	none	none	207-1 Artificial Coal	none	160-1 Short or 160-2 Long Bin included loose in sets
3472	49 - 53	3472-11	2/49 11/49 6/50 10/50 11/51 2/52 4/53	none	none	3462-70 Type II or Type III	Liner 3462-101	
3474	52 - 53	3474-14	5/52 6/53	none	none	none	Insert 3464-29	3464-29 is a truck alignment corrugated insert 8" long x 1" wide
3482	54 - 55	3482-36	4/54 6/54	none	none	3462-70 Type III	Liner 3462-101	
3484-1	53	3474-14	6/53	none	none	none	none	
3484-25	54 - 56	3474-14	11/54 12/55 2/56	none	none	none	none	
3494-1	55	3474-14	12/55	none	none	none	none	
3494-150	56	3474-14	2/56	none	none	none	none	
3494-275	56 - 58	3474-14	2/56 5/57	none	none	none	none	
3494-550	57 - 58	3474-14	5/57 8/57	none	none	none	none	
3494-625	57 - 58	3474-14	5/57 8/57	none	none	none	none	
3512	59 - 61	3512-60	9/59	none	none	none	none	A 4-6 elastic band included
3520	52 - 53	3520-33	5/52 2/53 6/53	none	none	none	Insert 3520-38	
3530	56 - 58	3530-45	11/56	none	none	none	Insert 3530-40; TP-6 Tissue Paper	Yellow instruction sheet in 57 and 58 (dated 11/56); TP-6 - 9"x 9" striped logo paper used to nest transformer pole & light
3530-50	56 - 57	none	none	none	none	none	none	
3540	59 - 60	3540-38	9/59	none	none	none	Insert 3540-36	
3545	61 - 63 and 65	none	none	none	none	none	none	
3559	46	3559-4	1/46 5/46	none	none	160-1 Short Bin; 207-1 Artificial Coal	Liner Number Unknown	
3559	47	3451-27	5/47	none	none	160-1 Short Bin; 207-1 Artificial Coal	Liner Number Unknown	
3559	48	3451-27	2/48 4/48	none	none	160-1 Short Bin; 207-1 Artificial Coal	Liner 3559-21	
3562-1	54	3562-54	6/54	3562-52	3562-53	362-100 Middle Classic; 160-2 Long Bin	Insert 3562-61	#96C controller included in packed envelope
3562-25	54	3562-54	6/54	3562-52	3562-53	362-100 Barrel Set; 160-2 Long Bin	Insert 3562-61	#96C controller included in packed envelope
3562-25	55	3562-54	8/54 8/55	3562-52	3562-73	362-100 Barrel Set; 160-2 Long Bin	Insert 3562-61	#90-1 controller in component box
3562-50	55 - 57	3562-54	8/54 8/55 4/56	3562-52	3562-73	362-100 Barrel Set; 160-2 Long Bin	Insert 3562-61	#90-1 controller in component box
3562-75	57 - 58	3562-54	5/57	3562-52	3562-73	362-100 Late Classic; 160-2 Long Bin	Insert 3562-61	#90-1 controller in component box

APPENDIX D
OPERATING CAR PERIPHERALS

Catalog Number	Years Offered for Sale	Instruction Sheet	Date	Packed Envelope Number	Envelope Number	Packed Boxes and Other Peripherals	Insert / Liner	Comments
3620	54 - 56	3620-14	4/54 4/55	none	none	none	Insert 3520-38	
3650	56 - 59	3650-38	7/56 2/57 7/57	none	none	none	Insert 3520-38	Form 1629 (white or yellow) is included with 7/56 instruction sheet
3656-34	52 - 58	none	none	none	none	none	none	
3656-50	49 - 55	3656-43	9/49 11/49 9/50 3/51 5/51 2/52 5/52 1/53 5/54 2/55	3656-46	3656-47	3656-34	Line 3656-41	TP-20 - 6"x 6" logo paper included to protect ramp
3656-150	52 - 55	3656-43	5/52 1/53 5/54 2/55	3656-46	3656-47	none	Liner 3656-202	TP-20 - 6"x 6" logo paper included to protect ramp
3662	55 - 60 and 64 - 66	3662-81	4/55 12/55 2/57 6/58 & 9/64 6/65	3662-79	3662-80	none	Liner 3662-76	Instruction sheet in included in packed envelope
3662-79	55 - 59	3662-81	4/55 12/55 2/57 6/58	none	none	none	none	See description in volume
3672	59 - 60	3662-81	5/59	3672-79	3672-7	none	Liner 3662-76	Instruction sheet in included in packed envelope
3672-79	59 - 60	3662-81	5/59	none	none	none	none	Instruction sheet in included in packed envelope
3854	46 - 47	3454-47	5/46 5/47	Unknown	3454-51	none	Liner Number Unknown; Kimpak	Car wrapped in Kimpak brown cotton wadding paper
5459	46 - 49	Included as part of ECU-50		none	none	160-1 Short Bin; 207-1 Artificial Coal	Liner 3459-26	
6352-1	55 - 57	none	none	none	none	none	none	Operating instructions included only with 352 Ice Depot
6352-25	55 - 57	none	none	none	none	none	none	
6434	58 - 59	none	none	none	none	none	none	
6473-1	62 - 66	none	none	none	none	none	none	
6473-25	62 - 67	none	none	none	none	none	none	
6473-50	69	none	none	none	none	none	none	
6473-60	69	none	none	none	none	none	none	
6501-1	62 - 64	6501-14	7/62	6501-17	none	none	none	A 6418-9 elastic band included
6501-25	62 - 63	6501-14	7/62	6501-17	none	none	none	Operating peripherals included loose in sets
6520	49 - 50	6520-23	5/49 5/50	none	none	none	Insert 6520-21	Uses 2" cloth tape to close ends of insert
6520	51	6520-23	5/50	none	none	none	Insert 6520-40	Uses 2" cloth tape to close ends of insert
6660	58	6660-58	6/58	none	none	none	Two 6660-56 Inserts	
6670	59 - 61	6670-5	4/59	none	none	none	Insert 6670-9	Insert for Orange Perforated box only; Over-stamped 6660 box uses two 6660-56 Inserts
6805	58 - 59	6805-22	8/58	none	none	none	none	
6812-1	59 - 62	6812-22	8/59	none	none	none	none	
6812-25	60 - 61	6812-22	8/59	6812-40	6812-41	none	none	6812-40 packed envelope and instruction sheet included loose in sets
6822-1	61 - 66 and 68 - 69	none	none	none	none	none	none	
6822-25	63	none	none	none	none	none	none	
6822-50	63 - 66	none	none	none	none	none	none	

Operating Car Peripherals

INDEX